THE GLUTEN-FREE GUIDE TO ITALY

Maria Ann Roglieri, Ph.D.

Published by Mari Productions, LLC
63 Fremont Rd
Sleepy Hollow, NY 10591

Visit www.gfguideitaly.com for updates and additional publications.

1.Health 2.Travel 3.Gluten intolerance 4.Italy 5.Tuscany 6.Celiac Disease 7.Gluten-Free 8.GF 9.Senza Glutine 10.Celiac 11.Venice 12.Rome 13. Florence14. Sicily15. Sardinia

ISBN 978-0-9835409-1-5

Mari Productions, LLC gratefully acknowledges the Italian Celiac Association, known as Associazione Italiana Celiachia (AIC) for having granted permission to use and reformat information presented on the website www.celiachia.it. The efforts of the AIC to promote awareness of celiac disease and to help and organize restaurants to provide gluten-free food to their celiac customers are extraordinary and serve as a model for other celiac groups around the world.

We would also like to thank our friends who contributed photos: Susan Amatangelo, Amy Smith, Daniel Frost, David Impastato, Anna Komorowski, Elvira DiFabio, Sarah Wolozin, Luca Riccò, John Lubin, Gerald Friedman, John Roglieri, David Kraushaar, Julie Kelly, Ulla Benninger, Carly Caneparo, and Joe Coyne.

Maria Roglieri is a professor of Italian at St. Thomas Aquinas College in New York. She got her MA and Ph.D. in Italian from Harvard University, and her BA in Italian from Columbia University. She and her daughter, Sara, have both been gluten-free for years. In addition to authoring *The Gluten-Free Guides* series, she has authored *Dante and Music: Musical Adaptations of the Commedia from the 16th Century to the Present* (Ashgate Publishing, 2001) and numerous articles and chapters on Dante and music, and Dante and Ovid.

The Gluten-Free Guides

The Gluten-Free Guide to Italy
www.gfguideitaly.com

is part of the series which also includes:

The Gluten-Free Guide to France
www.gfguidefrance.com

The Gluten-Free Guide to Spain
www.gfguidespain.com

The Gluten-Free Guide to New York
www.gfguideny.com

The Gluten-Free Guide to Washington, D.C.
www.gfguidedc.com

To purchase these guides or to find out
about upcoming publications, see

www.theglutenfreeguides.com

TABLE OF CONTENTS

This book is dedicated with love
to my wonderful family,
Daniel, Sara, David and Julia Friedman

INTRODUCTION

As an Italian professor, a musician and an Italian-American, I have traveled all over Italy; I have even been lucky enough to occasionally spend long periods of time in my favorite Italian city, Rome. The country, the people, the art, the history, and the culture are fantastic. The food in Italy is a delight, a feast of the senses.

Ah, l'Italia: il paese della pasta (the land of pasta) . . . Most people imagine it to be a daunting destination for gluten-free tourists. To my surprise, as I have learned through extensive research, **Italy is a GF (gluten-free) paradise!**

Anyone on a GF diet can get GF croissants (known as *cornetti senza glutine*) in the local hotels and bakeries for breakfast; GF pizza for a mid-morning snack; GF lasagna with fresh-made GF bread for lunch; gelato with a GF cone in the afternoon; and if you still have room for dinner, three or four courses of anything you want GF for dinner. (Save room for the GF tiramisu for dessert!) Your biggest problem in Italy is going to be deciding what to eat first and trying not to gain 30 pounds from eating all the *delizioso cibo italiano* (delicious Italian food)!

Everyone in Italy knows about celiac disease. When you ask restaurant staff about GF food, they automatically respond, *Lei è celiaca?* (You have celiac disease?) This is because all Italians are tested for celiac disease at an early age. The many who test positive receive great services: a monthly stipend from the government for GF food as well as extra vacation time to shop for and prepare GF food. In addition, the Italian Celiac Association (AIC), the Italian government and a few major Italian companies that sell GF products have all worked to promote awareness and understanding of celiac disease. As a result, restaurant owners, managers, chefs, and waiters are well-informed.

While writing this book, I contacted the Italian Celiac Association and spoke to hundreds of restaurant owners, managers, and customers in Italy. Sometimes, restaurant owners said that they could not provide me a GF meal. But much more often, they said things like "Of course, Madame, with pleasure. Would you like gnocchi or tagliatelle? They are both GF and were homemade this morning.)"; and even "I am also a celiac and so I prepare everything here GF." Music to my ears!!!!

This book is presented as a service to the gluten-intolerant community, in the spirit of "celiacs helping celiacs." It offers lists of hotels, inns, B&B's, restaurants, caterers, pizza places, ice cream stores, bakeries, health food stores, and pharmacies that serve the GF community all over Italy. It lists all of the above by region. The establishments that are participating in the Italian Celiac Association program (more information about this in the opening pages of the book) are marked with AIC.

Let the reader be forewarned that *these lists are fluid*: restaurants come and go. It is a good idea to call first; for virtually all restaurants in this guide, phone numbers are listed. The list of restaurants *does not represent a guarantee* that food served at any restaurant is GF. Remember that it is always important to communicate with the chefs as to your own special dietary needs. For help with this, check out the Gluten-Free Italian 101 section which includes "Questions for the chef", food vocabulary, as well an extensive multilingual glossary section.

Enjoy your trip to Italy, and especially enjoy the food! Revel in your new-found gluten-free paradise.

Buon viaggio e buon appetito!

HOW TO USE THIS BOOK

The first part of the book offers information that is useful before you go to Italy. The second part of the book offers extensive vocabulary help for ordering gluten-free (GF) food in Italy. The third part of the book presents 4000 GF venues all over Italy. The venues are those that have been either personally contacted by the author of this book, recommended by fellow celiacs, sponsored by the Associazione Italiana Celiachia (AIC), trained and supplied by DS Food, or those listed by Dr. Schaar (a leading gluten-free food product company in Italy) as selling gluten-free food products.

The book is divided into **chapters** that represent each **region of Italy**, i.e. Sicily, Veneto and Tuscany. The chapters are divided into **provinces** and then into **cities and towns** within each province. The provinces are identified in bold print.

The following venues are identified in each chapter in this order:

- hotels and B&B's
- pizza places
- supermarkets and pharmacies that carry GF food products
- restaurants
- gelato places

The following information on each venue is provided:

Name   type of venue   price range
address   phone number   website (if any)
specialized notes such as days closed, etc, and, for the major cities, neighborhood location.

EXAMPLE:
Cammillo   trattoria   €€*, AIC **
Borgo S. Jacopo, 57   tel. 055.212427***   www.cammillo.it
Notes: closed Tuesdays and Wednesdays. GF pasta available.****

*price points are provided when possible for a main course for one including tax and service and are categorized as follows:

price range	symbol
Under €17	€
€18-€24	€€
€25-€32	€€€
Over €32	€€€€

** AIC = sponsored by AIC (Italian celiac society)
*** phone numbers provided are from *within* Italy and do not include codes to dial out of the country of residence or the country code for Italy (which is 39).
****GF= gluten-free

WHAT YOU NEED TO KNOW

BEFORE YOU GO

GETTING TO ITALY:THE FLIGHT
There are a number of airlines that will provde a gluten-free meal on the flight to Italy (see list below). It is very important to notify the staff that you need such a meal well in advance. You can do so via their website or in person on the phone.

Air Canada	Air France
Alitalia	American Airlines
Austrian Airlines	British Airways
Cathay Pacific	Continental Airlines
Delta Airlines	El Al
Eurowings	Finnair
Iberia	Iceland Air
LAN Airlines	Lufthansa
Luxair	Malev
Olympic Airlines	Qantas
SAS	SATA
Swiss International Airlines	TAP Air Portugal
Turkish Airlines	United Airlines
US Air	Virgin Atlantic

GETTING TO AND AROUND ITALY: THE CRUISE

Many of the major cruise lines are able to serve customers gluten-free meals with advance notice:

- Carnival Cruise Lines (tel. 800 438- 6744, www.carnival.com)
- Celebrity Cruises (tel. 800 647-2251, www.celebritycruises.com)
- Costa (tel. 800 288-6006, www.cruises.com/promotion/costa-cruises.do)
- Disney Cruise lines (tel. 800 951-3532, http://disneycruise.disney.go.com)
- Norwegian Cruise lines (tel. 866 234-7350, www2.ncl.com/)
- Princess Cruise lines (tel. 800 774-6237, www.princess.com)
- Thompson Cruise Lines (England: tel. 08712314691, www.thomson.co.uk/cruise.html)
- MSC Cruises (www.msccruises.com)

Your best bet is to book on one of two major cruise lines: Costa Cruises and MSC Cruises. The Italian Celiac Society (AIC) works directly with these two cruise lines to ensure a careful choice of GF food products, and a special GF menu.

WHEN YOU'RE THERE: FOOD OPTIONS

BREAKFAST

When you stay in a hotel, make sure to phone ahead and asked them if they can serve you a **gluten-free breakfast** ("colazione senza glutine"). Most hotels and B&B's serve a complimentary continental breakfast; with advance notice, they can order gluten-free food for you from a pharmacy or make it themselves. You can have, as I did, warm gluten-free croissants (called "cornetti senza glutine"), breads and little cakes for breakfast.

If your hotel says they cannot provide you a gluten-free breakfast, you can go to any pharmacy and buy some GF products to bring to the hotel breakfast. You can also buy gluten-free bread there and use it for lunch with some fresh cheese and cold cuts (when you walk into any food store in Italy, they will tell you which cold cuts are gluten-free and most of them are).

WHERE TO FIND PREPACKAGED GF PRODUCTS:

You will find gluten-free products in pharmacies, *farmacia* and in supermarket chains such as Carrefour and Conad. We have listed the biggest of these venues alongside our list of restaurants for each region (see the section "Italy by Region".)

AN ITALIAN STAPLE: PIZZA

If you're looking for gluten-free pizza ("pizza senza glutine"), you're better off looking for it at *night* instead of during the day because Italians tend to have a bigger lunch and a smaller dinner. A lot of places don't even make gluten-free pizza during the day. In addition to the restaurants and pizzerias that participate in the Italian Celiac Society program (see next page), there are a number of restaurants and pizzerias that offer gluten-free pizza under the tutelage of a commercial venture, DS. This is a brand of the Dr. Schär group that provides restaurants with all the right cooking tools, gluten-free foods and ingredients and the training operators need to prepare meals safely. The restaurants that participate in this program are called DS Pizza Points. The "DS Pizza Points" are clearly indicated in this book

ANOTHER ITALIAN STAPLE: GELATO (ICE CREAM)

You can't go to Italy without sampling the delicious ice cream but be careful. Just as in the US, gluten is thrown into things you wouldn't expect, in Italy it is thrown in as well.

Obviously you need to stay away from flavors that have cookies in them, but additionally, to be absolutely certain there is no cross contamination; you should go to the designated ice cream stores that serve GF ice cream. There you can often get a gluten-free ice cream cone ("cono senza glutine"). All *gelaterie* that are indicated in this book have guaranteed GF gelato, since they are sponsored by the Italian Celiac Society.

You can also get pre-prepared ice cream in bars or restaurants just about anywhere if you look for this poster:

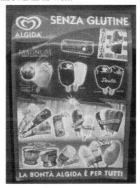

A NOTE ABOUT CALLING AHEAD

Some restaurants close in winter, and those that are open in winter will often have different hours from the summer hours. Also, restaurants open for dinner much later than in other countries; 9 pm is a typical dinner hour. Finally, restaurants can go out of business very quickly. Make sure to call ahead before you go to any of the recommended restaurants.

ASKING FOR GLUTEN-FREE FOOD IN RESTAURANTS

Keep in mind that when you inquire about getting gluten-free food in a restaurant, the first response might be "no". In this case, ask again in a different way! Here's the deal: the Italians have a national, very well-coordinated celiac society (AIC) that works closely with restaurants to serve GF food that has been prepared in a completely uncontaminated environment. The restaurants are equipped with a separate "laboratory" with a separate oven, stove, utensils, and cookware to prepare GF food. The restaurants' special labs are inspected every six months. If there are any violations of the food preparation rules, the restaurants are taken off the GF restaurant list until the violations have been remedied. This keeps restaurant owners hyper-vigilant about the GF food they prepare and serve.

So if you go to a restaurant that is not working directly with the Italian Celiac Society, the owners/managers may automatically say that they are "not prepared" or "not set up" to serve you a GF meal. This is just a way to indicate to you that they don't participate in the program. You can still get an excellent meal at this restaurant because odds are they have GF pasta stashed away for their regular clients, and they're already well familiar with celiac disease and gluten-free food. Even if they don't have GF pasta stashed away, they can still easily prepare you a "second piatto," that is, a meat, chicken, rabbit, veal, or fish dish that is gluten-free. So you should let them know that you understand they don't participate in the Italian Celiac Society program, but that you would love to have a GF "secondo" at their restaurant.

GLUTEN-FREE ITALIAN 101:

REQUESTING A
GLUTEN-FREE MEAL
in italiano

CELIAC IDENTIFICATION CARD
FOR THE CHEF AND WAITER

Sono celiaca e devo mangaiare cibo SENZA GLUTINE. **Posso mangiare** il cibo che ha riso, mais, patate, ortaggi e qualsiasi frutta, uova, formaggio, latte, carne, pesce, purchè non sia stato preparato con farina, pangrattato, o salsa che contiene frumento o glutine. **Non posso mangiare** il cibo che contiene farine di grano o di cereali (kamut, spelta, duram, semola, e bulgar), segale, orzo, o glutine. Grazie per il Suo aiuto.

TRANSLATIONS:

(E) I have celiac disease and I have to eat food WITHOUT GLUTEN. I can eat food that has rice, corn, potatoes, vegetables and any fruit, eggs, cheese, milk, meat, fish, as long as it has not been prepared with flour, breadcrumbs or sauce containing wheat or gluten. I can not eat food containing wheat flour or cereal (kamut, spelt, duram, semolina, and bulgar), rye, barley, or gluten. Thank you for your help.

(D) Ich habe Zöliakie und ich muss Lebensmittel OHNE GLUTEN essen. Ich kann Reis, Mais, Kartoffeln, Gemüse und Obst, Eier, Käse, Milch, Fleisch, Fisch essen, solange sie noch nicht mit Mehl, Paniermehl oder Sauce mit Weizen oder Gluten zu bereitet sind. Ich kann nicht Lebensmittel mit Weizen Mehl oder Getreide (Kamut, Dinkel, langsamer, Grieß und Bulgarisch), Roggen, Gerste, oder Gluten essen. Vielen Dank für Ihre Hilfe.

(S) Tengo la enfermedad que se llama celiaca y tengo que comer alimentos SIN GLUTEN. Puedo comer alimentos que contienen arroz, maíz, papas, vegetales y cualquier tipo de fruta. También, puedo comer alimentos que contienen huevos, queso, leche, carne, y pescado, siempre que no hayan sido preparados con harina, pan, salsa o que contengan gluten de trigo. No puedo comer alimentos que contengan harina de trigo o cereales (kamut, escanda, duram, sémola, y bulgar), centeno, cebada, o gluten. Gracias por su ayuda.

(F) J'ai la maladie coeliaque et je dois manger des aliments SANS GLUTEN. Je peux manger la nourriture qui a le riz, le maïs, les pommes de terre, de légumes et de fruits tout, des oeufs, du fromage, du lait, la viande, le poisson, tant qu'elle n'a pas été préparée avec la farine, la chapelure ou de la sauce contenant du blé ou du gluten. Je ne peux pas manger des aliments contenant de la farine de blé ou de céréales (kamut, épeautre, duram, semoule, et bulgar), le seigle, l'orge ou du gluten. Merci pour votre aide.

QUESTIONS FOR THE CHEF OR WAITER

D=Deutsch
Sp=Spanish, Fr=French
Italian in bold

Is this dish breaded or dusted in wheat flour before it is cooked?

(D) Ist das Gericht paniert mit Weizenmehl, bevor es gekocht wird?
(Sp) ¿Está este plato preparado con pan rallado o harina de trigo?
(Fr) Est-ce que ce plat est pané ou préparé avec de la farine avant sa cuisson?

È questo piatto impanato di farina di frumento o molliche di pane prima che sia cotto?

Is this dish preseasoned or cooked in broth or bouillon?

(D) Ist das Gericht gewürizt oder gekocht in Brühe oder Bouillon?
(Sp) ¿Está sazonado o cocinado el plato con caldo?
(Fr) Est-ce que ce plat est cuit ou préparé avec du bouillon?

È questo piatto condito o cotto in brodo o bouillion?

(E) If it is preseasoned or cooked with boullion is there any wheat, rye, barley, or gluten in the mix or in the boullion?

(D) Wenn Sie verpackt Gewürze oder Brühe oder vorgefertigten bouillion, gebrauchen gibt es eine Weizen, Roggen, Gerste, oder Gluten Mischung?
(Sp) Si utilizó condimentos envasados o caldo, ¿ contienen trigo, centeno, cebada, gluten o una mezcla de estos ingredientes ?
(Fr) Si vous utilisez des assaisonnements emballés ou préemballés avec du bouillon, y at-il de blé, du seigle, de l'orge ou du gluten dans le mélange?

Se si utilizzano condimenti confezionati in imballaggi o brodo o bouillion, non vi è alcun grano, segale, orzo, o glutine nel miscuglio?

Is this dish fried in the same fryer where wheat dishes are fried?

(D) Ist das Gericht gebraten in der gleichen Friteuse, wie die speisehaus Weizer?
(Sp) ¿Se frió este plato en la misma sartén en que se fríen platos que contienen trigo?
(Fr) Est-ce que ce plat frit dans la même friteuse que des plats frits avec la farine?

È questo piatto fritto nella stessa friggitrice dove i piatti di grano sono fritti?

Is this dish thickened with flour?

(D) Ist das Gericht mit Mehl verdickt?
(Sp) ¿Se ha espesado el plato con harina?
(Fr)   Ce plat est-il épaissi à la farine?

Questo piatto è ispessito con farina?

Do you have gluten-free pasta?

(D) Haben Sie glutenfreie Nudeln?
(Sp) ¿Tiene usted pasta sin gluten?
(Fr)   Avez-vous des pâtes sans gluten?

Avete la pasta senza glutine?

Could I please get this dish without the pasta?

(D) Könnte ich bitte dieses Gericht bekommen ohne die Nudeln?
(Sp) ¿Podría usted servirme este plato sin pasta?
(Fr)   Pourrais-je obtenir s'il vous plaît ce plat de pâtes sans accompaniment?

Posso ottenere questo piatto senza la pasta?

Could you please substitute rice for pasta in this dish?

(D) Könnte ich bitte Reis anstatt Pasta für dieses Gericht haben?
(Sp) ¿Podría usted traerme arroz en vez de pasta?
(Fr)   Pourriez-vous s'il vous plaît echanger le riz pour les pâtes dans ce plat?

Potrebbe sostituire il riso per questo piatto?

ESSENTIAL ITALIAN FOOD VOCABULARY

Senza glutine (gluten-free)	Posso parlare con il cuoco, per favore? (May I please speak to the chef?)

MEALS AND COURSES IN ITALY

antipasti	appetizers	
primo piatto	first course (pasta or risotto)	breakfast **colazione**
secondo piatto	second course (poultry, meat, fish)	lunch **pranzo**
contorno	side dish, such as vegetables	dinner **cena**
dolce	dessert	

TYPES OF RESTAURANTS IN ITALY

ristorante—trattoria—osteria Traditionally, ristoranti are more expensive and more upscale, while trattorie and osterie tend to be more homestyle and family- oriented.

pizzeria---pizza a taglio--ristorante-pizzeria The pizzeria are similar to pizza places we have here. The pizza a taglio places sell pizza by weight, where you determine how big a slice you would like. The restaurant pizzerias are more like restaurants that also serve pizza.

tavola calda is a kind of fast food place where all dishes are preprepared. Celiacs are advised to stay away from these types of establishments.

gelateria --caffé—bar A gelateria is strictly an ice cream parlor, while a café or bar serves just about everything including ice cream and alcohol. People go to cafés or bars for breakfast and lunch and anytime for a drink (alcoholic or coffee) or ice cream.

enoteche—bacari (wine bar) is a place to go for wine and cheese. They often offer elaborate menus that describe which cheeses would complement particular wine.

agriturismo agricultural tourism has become increasingly popular in Italy. Accommodations vary quite widely from luxury apartments to farmhouses, but they are all generally on a working farm or a vineyard.

Italian	English	Spanish	French	German
pesce	fish	pescado	poisson	fisch
carne	meat	carne	viande	fleisch
legumi	beans	frijol	haricots	bohnen
verdura	vegetables	vegetales	legumes	gemüse
frutta	fruit	frutas	fruits	obst

SAFE AND UNSAFE INGREDIENTS

UNSAFE INGREDIENTS

Italian	English	Spanish	French	German
farina	flour	harina	farine	mehl
frumento	wheat	trigo	blé	weizen
amido di frumento	wheat starch	fecula de trigo	amidon de blé	weizenstärke
farina di frumento	wheat flour	harina de trigo	farine de blé	weizenmehl
orzo	barley	cebada	orge	gerste
segale	rye	centeno	froment	roggen
pane	bread	pan	pain	brot
pane grattugiato	breadcrumbs	pan rallado	chapelure	paniermehl
semolina	semolina	sémola	semoule	grieb

SAFE INGREDIENTS

Italian	English	Spanish	French	German
avena	oats	avena	avoine	hafer
riso	rice	arroz	riz	reis
amido di riso	rice starch	fecula de arroz	l'amidon de riz	reisstärke
farina di riso	rice flour	harina de arroz	farine de riz	reismehl
patate	potatoes	papa	pomme de terre	kartoffel
fecola di patate	potato flour	harina de papa	farine de pommes	kartoffel- mehl
mais	corn	maiz dulce	maïs dous	mais
amido di mais	cornstarch	de maicena	fécule de maïs	maisstärke
farina di tapioca	tapioca	harina de tapioca	farine de tapioca	tapioca mehl
farina di castagne	chestnut flour	harina de castaña	farine de châtaigne	kastanienmehl
farina di mandorle	almond flour	harina de almendra	farine d'almande	mandel-mehl
farina di soia	soy flour	haina de soja	farine de soja	soja-mehl

ICE CREAM IN ITALY

Italians love *gelato* (ice cream)! Their ice cream is relatively low in fat, often fruit or nut-based and is sold in *gelaterie* and bars. You can eat it in a cone or cup and enjoy whipped cream on top! All *gelaterie* that are indicated in this book have gluten-free ice cream and many have gluten-free ice cream cones. Be sure to be clear and ask for a *cono senza glutine* when ordering.

How to Order

cono – cone

cono senza glutine – GF cone

coppa (or *coppetta*)- cup

gusto - scoop, flavor

granita -a flavored iced drink

frappe -a milkshake

panna - whipped cream (*con* = with, *senza* = without)

piccolo (small)   *medio* (medium)   *grande* (big)

Sample of Gelato Flavors *(gusti)*

bacio - double chocolate and hazelnuts   *cioccolato* - chocolate

caffè - coffee   *limone* - lemon

fragola - strawberry   *giunduia* - chocolate hazelnut

melone - cantaloupe   *nocciola* - hazelnut

panna - cream   *vaniglia* - vanilla

risotto - cream with honey, rice, cinnamon and chocolate.

Spumoni - a blend of 3 flavors (e.g. zuppa inglese, pistachio and gianduia)

stracciatella – chocolate chip   *mora* - blackberry

tiramisu - Mascarpone cheese, lady fingers, Kahlua

lampone - raspberry

zabaione - Egg yolks, marsala, and fresh cream

pesca - peach

zuppa inglese - fruits and marsala, and cream

COFFEE IN ITALY

Italians love their coffee! They drink **espresso**, and in many variations:

caffé ristretto is extra-concentrated espresso.

caffé lungo is espresso with extra water.

caffé corretto is espresso "corrected" by a shot of liquor (i.e. Sambuca or Amaretto).

caffé macchiato is coffee "spotted" with milk.

cappuccino (or **cappuccio** for short) is a good morning drink, consisting of espresso with a "hood" of steamed milk. This drink was named for the Cappuccine monks who invented it; their hoods were "cappucci."

doppio is a double serving of espresso.

zucchero is sugar.

FOOD WORDS DICTIONARY IN MULTIPLE LANGUAGES

- **ITALIAN TO ENGLISH AND GERMAN**
- **ITALIAN TO SPANISH AND FRENCH**

ITALIAN	ENGLISH	GERMAN
abbacchio	lamb	lamm
aceto	vinegar	Essig
acqua	water	Wasser
acqua minerale	mineral water	Mineralwasser
affumicato	smoked	geräucherte
aglio	garlic	Knoblauch
agnello	lamb	Lamm
al forno	baked	gebacken
al sangue	very rare	sehr selten
albicocca	apricot	Aprikose
alla griglia	grilled	gegrillt
alla milanese	battered with eggs and bread crumbs and fried	mit Eiern und Semmelbrösel und gebratene panierte
alla parmigiana	with Parmesan cheese and tomatoes	mit Parmesan-Käse und Tomaten
alla tartara	raw with lemon and egg	Roh mit Zitrone und Ei
alla valdostana	with ham and cheese	mit Schinken und Käse
amido di frumento	wheat starch	Weizenstärke
amido di mais	cornstarch	Maisstärke
amido di riso	rice starch	Reisstärke
ananas	pineapple	Ananas
anatra	duck	Ente
anguria	watermelon	Wassermelone
aragosta	lobster	Hummer
arancia	orange	Orange
aringa	herring	Hering
arista	pork roast	gebratenes schweinefleisch
arrosto	roasted	geröstet, geschmort, gebraten

ITALIAN	ENGLISH	GERMAN
avena	Oats	Hafer
banana	Banana	Banane
ben cotta	well done	durchgebraten
bevanda	Drink	trinken
bibita	Drink	trinken
bicchiere di . . .	a glass of . . .	Ein Glas. . .
biscotti	Cookies	kekse
bistecca	beef steak	Rindersteak
bistecca a media cottura	medium steak	Steak-fast durdgebraten
bistecca al sangue	rare steak	Seltene blutig
bistecca ben cotta	well done steak	steak-gut durdgebvatenes
bistecca molto al sangue	very rare steak	Sehr selten sehr blutig
bottiglia	Bottle	Flasche
burro	Butter	Butter
caffè	Coffee	Kaffee
calamari	Squid	tintenfisd
cameriere/cameriera	waiter/waitress	Kellnerin/kellner
caraffa	Carafe	Karaffe
carota	Carrot	Karotte
cavolfiore	Cauliflower	Blumenkohl
cavolo	Cabbage	Kohl
celiaca	Celiac	Celiac
cena	dinner	Abendessen
cervella	brain	Gehirn
cetriolo	cucumber	Gurke
chiara/scura	light/dark	hell /dunkel
ciliegia	cherry	Cherry/kirsche
cinghiale	boar	Wildschwein

ITALIAN	ENGLISH	GERMAN
cioccolata calda	hot chocolate	Heiße Schokolade
cipolla	onion	Zwiebel
colazione	breakfast	Frühstück
con ghiaccio	on the rocks	On the rocks
con latte	with milk	mit Milch
con seltz	with soda	mit Soda
coniglio	rabbit	Kaninchen
coperto	cover charge	kosten für das Giedeck
coppa gelato	cup of ice cream	eisbecher
cornetto/brioche	croissant	Croissant
cozze	mussels	Muscheln
crema di ...	cream of ...	Sahne...
crostata	pie	Pie/pastete
cuoco	chef	Küchenchef
datteri	dates	Termine
di stagione	in season	der Saison
extra	extra fee/charge	Zuschlag/zusatzkosten
fagiano	pheasant	Fasan
fagiolini	green beans	Grüne Bohnen
farina	flour	Mehl
farina di castagne	chestnut flour	Kastanienmehl
farina di frumento	wheat flour	Weizenmehl
farina di mandorle	almond flour	Mandel-Mehl
farina di riso	rice flour	Reismehl
farina di soia	soy flour	Soja-Mehl
farina di tapioca	tapioca flour	Tapioka Mehl
fecola di patate	potato flour/starch	Kartoffel-Mehl/ Stärke
fegato	liver	Leber

ITALIAN	ENGLISH	GERMAN
fichi	figs	Feigen
focaccia	flat bread	Pfannkuchen
fragola	strawberry	Erdbeere
fritto	fried	Fried gebraten
frumento	wheat	Weizen
frutta	fruit	Obst
frutta fresca	fresh fruit	Frisches obst
frutta secca	dried fruit	Trockenfrüchte
frutti di mare	seafood	Meeresfrüchte
funghi	mushroom	Pilz
gelato	ice cream	Eis
granchio	crab	Krabbe
grazie	thank you	danke
hot dog	hot dog	Hot dog
in carpione	cold, with vinegar	Kält, mit Essig
insalata	green salad	Grüner Salat
la birra	beer	Bier
lamponi	raspberries	Himbeeren
latte	milk	Milch
lattuga	lettuce	Kopfsalat
limonata	lemonade	Limonade
limone	lemon	Zitrone
liscio	straight	geradeaus
lista dei vini	wine list	Weinkarte
macedonia di frutta	fruit salad	Obstsalat
mais	sweet corn	Mais (Mais)
mandarino	tangerine	mandarine
mela	apple	Apfel

ITALIAN	ENGLISH	GERMAN
melone	melon	Melone
menu	menu	Menü
merluzzo	cod	Kabeljau
minestrone	vegetable soup	Gemüsesuppe
mirtilli	blueberries	Blaubeeren
more	blackberries	Brombeeren
mousse al cioccolato	chocolate mousse	Mousse au Chocolat
nocepesca	nectarine	Nektarine
omelette / frittata	omelette	Omelett
orzo	barley	Gerste
ostriche	oysters	Austern
pane	bread	Brot
pane grattugiato	breadcrumbs	Paniermehl
paste	pastries	Gebäck
patata	potato	Kartoffel
patate	potato	Kartoffel
patatine fritte	fries	Pommes frites
pâté	pâté	pâté
pepe	pepper	Pfeffer
per favore	please	bitte
per piacere	please	Bitte
pera	pear	Birne
pesca	peach	pfirsich
pesce	fish	Fisch
piselli	peas	Erbsen
pizza	pizza	Pizza
pollo	chicken	Huhn
polpo	octopus	Krake

ITALIAN	ENGLISH	GERMAN
pomodoro	tomato	Tomate
pompelmo	grapefruit	pompelmuse
porro	leek	lauch, porree
pranzo	lunch	Mittagessen
prezzo fisso	fixed menu	bestehendos, uorgeschriebenes menü
prosciutto	ham	Schinken
prugna	plum	Pflaume, zwetschge
prugna secca	prune	Pflaume
rafano	radish	Rettich
ribes	red currant	Rote Johannisbeere
ribes nero	black currant	Schwarze Johannisbeere
ripieno	stuffed	gefüllt
riso	Rice	Reis
sale	salt	Salz
salmone	salmon	Lachs
salsa	sauce	Sauce
scampi /gamberi	prawns / shrimps	Garnelen / Shrimps
segale	rye	Roggen
semolina	semolina	Grieß
senape	mustard	Senf
senza glutine	gluten-free	glutenfrei
sidro	cider	Apfelwein
sogliola	sole	Scholle
sorbetto	sherbet	Limonade
specialità di casa	specialty of the House	Spezialität des Hauses
specialità locale	local specialty	Lokale Spezialität
spuntino	snack	Snack/zwischenmahlzeit
succo d'ananas	pineapple juice	Ananassaft

ITALIAN	ENGLISH	GERMAN
succo d'arancia	orange juice	Orangensaft
succo di mela	apple juice	Apfelsaft
succo di pomodoro	tomato juice	Tomatensaft
tasse	tax	Steuer
Tè	tea	Tee
torta	cake	Kuchen
trota	trout	Forelle
Un pezzo d'agnello	lamb chop	Lamm-Kotelett
Un pezzo di maiale	pork chop	Schweinekotelett
uva	grape	Traube
uva passa	raisins	Rosinen
verdura	vegetables	Gemüse
vino amabile	sweet wine	lieblider Wein
vino bianco/rosso	white wine/red wine	Weißwein/rotwein
vino secco	dry wine	Trockener Wein
vitello	veal	Kalbfleisch
vorrei	I would like	Ich möchte
yoghurt	yogurt	Jogurt
zuppa	soup	Suppe
zuppa di pesce	fish stew	Fisch-Eintopf

ITALIAN	SPANISH	FRENCH
abbacchio	Cordero	agneau
aceto	Vinagre	Vinaigre
acqua	Agua	Eau
acqua minerale	Agua mineral	Eau minérale
affumicato	Ahumado	Fumé
aglio	Ajo	Ail
agnello	Cordero	agmeau
al forno	Al horno	Baked
al sangue	Crudo	Très rare, rouge
albicocca	Albaricoque	Abricot
alla griglia	A la parrilla	Grillé
alla milanese	Batido con huevos y pan rallado y frito	Battues avec des œufs et des miettes de pain et frit avec
alla parmigiana	Con queso parmesano y tomates	Du parmesan et des tomates
alla tartara	Crudo con limón y huevo	Crus avec du citron et l'oeuf
alla valdostana	Con jamón y queso	Avec du jambon et du fromage
amido di frumento	Fecula de trigo	Amidon de blé
amido di mais	De maicena	Fécule de maïs
amido di riso	fecula de arroz	L'amidon de riz
ananas	Piña	Ananas
anatra	Pato	Canard
anguria	Sandía	Pastèque
aragosta	Langosta	Homard
arancia	Naranja	Orange
aringa	Arenque	Hareng
arista	Cerdo asado	Rôti de porc
arrosto	Asado	roti

ITALIAN	SPANISH	FRENCH
avena	Avena	Avoine
banana	Plátano	Banane
ben cotta	Bien cocido	À point ou bien cuit
bevanda	Beber	Un verre
bibita	Bebida	Une boisson
bicchiere di . . .	Un vaso de. . .	Un verre d'. . .
biscotti	Galletas dulces	Cookies
bistecca	El sector de la carne de bistec	Steak de boeuf
bistecca a media cottura	Filete mediano	Moyen steak
bistecca al sangue	bistec crudo	A point steak
bistecca ben cotta	Filete bien cocido	un steak bien cuit
bistecca molto al sangue	Bistec bien crudo	Très rare steak
bottiglia	Botella	Bouteille
burro	Mantequilla	Beurre
caffè	Café	Café
calamari	Calamar	calamars
cameriere/cameriera	Camarero/camarera	serveur/serveuse
caraffa	Jarra	Carafe
carota	Zanahoria	Carotte
cavolfiore	Coliflor	Chou-fleur
cavolo	Repollo	Chou
celiaca	Celiaca	Coeliaque
cena	Cena	Dîner
cervella	Cerebro	Cerveau
cetriolo	Pepino	Concombre
chiara/scura	Claro/oscuro	Clair / foncé
ciliegia	Cereza	cerise
cinghiale	cerdo	Sanglier

ITALIAN	SPANISH	FRENCH
cioccolata calda	Chocolate caliente	Chocolat chaud
cipolla	Cebolla	Oignon
colazione	Desayuno	Petit déjeuner
con ghiaccio	Con hielo	Avec de la glace
con latte	Con leche	Avec du lait
con seltz	Con soda	À la soude
coniglio	Conejo	Lapin
coperto	Cargo de entrada	Couvrir les frais
coppa gelato	Copa de helado	Tune coupe de glace
cornetto/brioche	Croissant	Croissant
cozze	Mejillones	Moules
crema di . . .	De crema. . .	la crème de . . .
crostata	Pastel	Tarte
cuoco	cocinero	Chef
datteri	Fechas	Dates
di stagione	En la temporada	Dans la saison
extra	Suplemento / cargo	Supplément / charge
fagiano	Faisan	Faisan
fagiolini	Judías verdes	Haricots verts
farina	Harina	Farine
farina di castagne	Harina de castaña	Farine de châtaigne
farina di frumento	Harina de trigo	Farine de blé
farina di mandorle	De harina de almendra	Farine d'amande
farina di riso	Harina de arroz	Farine de riz
farina di soia	Harina de soja	Farine de soja
farina di tapioca	Harina de tapioca	Farine de tapioca
fecola di patate	Harina de papa o fecula	Farine de pommes de terre ou amidon
fegato	Hígado	Foie

ITALIAN	SPANISH	FRENCH
fichi	Higos	Figues
focaccia	Panqueque	Crêpe
fragola	Fresa	Fraise
fritto	Frito	Frit
frumento	Trigo	Blé
frutta	Frutas	Fruits
frutta fresca	Frutas frescas	Fruits frais
frutta secca	Frutos secos	Fruits secs
frutti di mare	Mariscos	Fruits de mer
funghi	champinon	champignons
gelato	Helado	glace
granchio	Cangrejo	Crabe
grazie	Gracias	Merci
hot dog	Perro caliente	Hot-dog
in carpione	Fría, con vinagre	Froid, avec du vinaigre
insalata	Ensalada verde	Salade verte
la birra	Cerveza	Bière
lamponi	Frambuesas	Framboises
latte	Leche	Lait
lattuga	Lechuga	Laitue
limonata	Limonada	Limonade
limone	Limón	Citron
lista dei vini	Carta de vinos	Carte des vins
macedonia di frutta	Ensalada de frutas	Salade de fruits
mais	Maíz dulce (maíz)	Maïs doux (maïs)
mandarino	Mandarina	mandarine
mela	Manzana	pomme
melone	Melón	Melon
menu	Menú	Menu

ITALIAN	SPANISH	FRENCH
merluzzo	Bacalao	Morue
minestrone	Sopa de verduras	Soupe aux légumes
mirtilli	Arándanos	myrtilles
more	Moras	Mûres
mousse al cioccolato	Mousse de chocolate	Mousse au chocolat
nocepesca	Nectarina	Nectarine
omelette / frittata	Tortilla	Omelette
orzo	Cebada	Orge
ostriche	Ostras	Les huîtres
pane	Pan	Pain
pane grattugiato	Pan rallado	Chapelure
paste	Pasteles	Pâtisseries
patata	Papa	Pomme de terre
patate	Papa	Pomme de terre
patatine fritte	Papas Fritas	Frites
pâté	Pate	pâté
pepe	Pimienta	Poivre
per favore	por favor	S'il vous plaît
per piacere	Por favor	S'il vous plaît
pera	Pera	Poire
pesca	Melocoton	pêche
pesce	Pescado	Poisson
piselli	Guisantes	Petits pois
pizza	Pizza	Pizza
pollo	Pollo	Poulet
polpo	Pulpo	Pieuvre
pomodoro	Tomate	Tomate
pompelmo	Pomelo	Pamplemousse
porro	Puerro	Poireau

ITALIAN	SPANISH	FRENCH
pranzo	Almuerzo	Déjeuner
prezzo fisso	Menú fijo	Menu fixe
prosciutto	Jamon	jambon
prugna	Ciruela	Prune
prugna secca	Pasa	Pruneau
rafano	Rábano	Radis
ribes	Pasas rojas	groseille
ribes nero	Pasas negras	Cassis
ripieno	Con relleno	Farcis
riso	Arroz	Rice
sale	Sal	Sel
salmone	Salmón	Saumon
salsa	Salsa	Sauce
scampi /gamberi	Camarones / gambas	Crevettes / crevettes
segale	Centeno	froment
semolina	Sémola	Semoule
senape	Mostaza	Moutarde
senza glutine	Sin gluten	Sans gluten
sidro	Sidra	Cidre
sogliola	Lenguado	sole
sorbetto	Sorbete	Sorbet
specialita' di casa	Especialidad de la casa	Spécialité de la maison
specialita' locale	Especialidad local	Spécialité locale
spuntino	Merienda	Snack
succo d'ananas	Jugo de piña	Jus d'ananas
succo d'arancia	Jugo de naranja	Jus d'orange
succo di mela	Jugo de manzana	Jus de pomme
succo di pomodoro	Zumo de tomate	Jus de tomate
tasse	Impuesto	Taxes, impots

ITALIAN	SPANISH	FRENCH
te	Té	Thé
torta	Torta	Gâteau
trota	Trucha	Truite
Un pezzo d'agnello	Chuleta de cordero	Côtes d'agneau
Un pezzo di maiale	chuleta de cerdo	côtes de porc
uva	Uva	Raisin
uva passa	Pasas	Raisins secs
verdura	Vegetales	Légumes
vino amabile	Vino dulce	Vin doux
vino bianco/rosso	Vino blanco/vino tinto	Vin blanc/vin rouge
vino secco	Vino seco	Vin sec
vitello	Ternera	veau
vorrei	Me gustaría	Je voudrais
yoghurt	Yogur	Yogourt
zuppa	Sopa	Soupe
zuppa di pesce	Guiso de pescado	Ragoût de poisson

GLUTEN-FREE
ITALY
BY REGION

ROME AND LAZIO

PLACES IN ROME TO BUY GLUTEN-FREE FOOD PRODUCTS, BY NEIGHBORHOOD

BEYOND CITY CENTER
L'Altro Alimento Gluten Free Shop
Via Antonio Zotti, 122 (In Ostia.)

ESQUILINO
Farmacia Brocchier   Via Orvieto, 33
Farmacia Merulana   Via Merulana, 185

NOMENTANO.
Celidoc   Via Livorno 27

PRATI
Celiachiamo.Com   Via Giulio Venticinque, 32

SAN GIOVANNI.
CeliaMagic   Via Latina 162

SPAGNA
Farmacia Europea   Via Della Croce, 10

STAZIONE TERMINI
Conad   Piazza dei 500-Stazione Termini
Farmacia Indipendenza Dott   Via S.Martino Battaglia, 10

TESTACCIO
Farmacia De Angelis E C   Via Marmorata, 133

TRASTEVERE
NaturaSi'   Via Oderisi da Gubbio, 66
Trastevere Bio   Via di S. Dorotea 11

VATICAN
Farmacia Cola Di Rienzo   Via Cola Di Rienzo, 215
Farmacia Eredi Vincenti   Piazza Della Rovere, 2/C
Farmacia Fabio Massimo   Via Massimo Fabio, 78
Farmacia Mannucci   Via Andrea Doria, 35

PLACES IN ROME TO GET GUARANTEED GLUTEN-FREE GELATO
(SPONSORED BY ITALIAN CELIAC SOCIETY),
BY NEIGHBORHOOD

APPIA ANTICA
Gelateria Labate - Golden Ice   Via M. Menghini, 24

BEYOND CITY CENTER
Il Pinguino   Via Silvestri, 224

BEYOND CITY CENTER (PIAZZA TRIESTE)
Gel'Istria   Piazza Istria, 14

BEYOND CITY CENTER (TUSCOLANO)
Gelateria Greed   Via Vestricio Spurinna, 97
Gelateria Petrini   Piazza Dell'Alberone, 16/A
Grom Tuscolana   Via Tuscolana, 1370

CENTRO STORICO
Grom Giubbonari   Via dei Giubbonari, 53
Grom Maddalena   Via della Maddalena, 30A

CORSO (PIAZZA VENEZIA)
Vacanze Romane   Piazza D'Ara Coeli, 9/10

EUR.
Grom EUR Roma 2   V.le Oceano Pacifico, 83

MAZZINI
Fata Morgana 3   Via Giovanni Bettolo, 7

MONTI
Fata Morgana   Via Lago Di Lesina, 9/11

NAVONA
Grom Navona   P.zza Navona 1

NOMENTANO
Bartocci   Via Alessandria 145
Gel'Istria   P.zza Istria, 14
Cremeria Alpi 2   Via degli Equi, 42

TERMINI
La Romana   Via XX Settembre 60

VATICAN
Al Settimo Gelo   Via Vodice, 21/A

TRASTEVERE
Fata Morgana 4   Via Roma Libera, 11

PRATI.
Gelarmony   Via Marcantonio Colonna 34

ROME B&B'S AND HOTELS LISTED ALPHABETICALLY
(AIC = participates in the Associazione Italiana Celiachia program)

B&B's

Acquedotti Antichi   B&B   AIC
V.le Anicio Gallo, 196/c2   tel. 0645555635 www.acquedottiantichi.com
Notes: Beyond City Center (Along Appian Way). S € 50 D € 70 T € 95

B&B Bio   B&B   AIC
Via Cavalese, 28   tel. 3485500942   www.bedandbreakfastbio.com
Notes: Beyond City Center. S € 55. Located in residential area in Monte Mario Park. Close to Auditorium Music Hall, Maxxi National Museum of Art, Olimpic Stadium (soccer), the Flaminio Stadium, Tennis Centre Foro Italico.

B&B Roma Centro San Pietro   B&B
Via Giorgio Scalia   tel. 0645433333   www.bedandbreakfastromacentro.it
Notes: Vatican. GF breakfast provided upon advance request.

Bed-and-breakfast Roma Centro San Pietro B&B
Via Giorgio Scalia, 39   tel. 0645433333   www.bedandbreakfastromacentro.it
Notes: Vatican. Near the Vatican walls.

Capricci Romani   B&B
Via di Porta Castello, 33   tel. 0668802684   www.bebcapricciromani.com
Notes: Vatican.

Kosher & Gluten-free B&B My Guest Roma B&B
Viale 21 Aprile   tel. 0686324590   www.myguestroma.com
Notes: Bologna. GF breakfast provided upon advance request.

La Papessa   B&B   www.lapapessabb.it
Via del Corso, 241 (corner of Vicolo Sciarra, 61)   tel. 0645439953
Notes: Corso. Walking distance from: Trevi Fountain, Spanish Steps, Colosseum, Pantheon, Vatican Museums. Will provide GF breakfast with advance notice.

My Guest Roma   B&B   www.myguestroma.com
Viale XXIAprile, 12   tel. 686324590
Notes: Provincie. Can do gluten-free and kosher breakfast.

Residenza Piccolo Principe   B&B   €€€€
Via Giovanni Giolitti   tel. 3206993110   www.bbpiccoloprincipe.it
Notes: GF breakfast provided upon advance request.

Town House Fontana di Trevi   B&B
Via de Crociferi, 41   tel. 3336832012   www.bbfontanaditrevi.com
Notes: Spagna. GF breakfast provided upon advance request.

Zaccardi   B&B   , AIC
V.le di Vigna Pia, 40   tel. 0645445503   www.zaccardi.info
Notes: Beyond City Center (In Portuense). Near Trastevere.

HOTELS

Best Western Hotel President   hotel
Via Emanuele Filiberto, 173   tel. 06770121   www.hotelpresidentrome.com
Notes: Colosseo. GF breakfast provided upon advance request.

Dei Consoli Hotel   hotel
Via Varrone, 2/D corner Via Cola di Rienzo   tel. 0668892972
www.hoteldeiconsoli.com
Notes: Vatican. GF breakfast provided upon advance request.

Delle Province hotel
Viale delle Provincie, 103   tel. 0644292670   www.hoteldelleprovince.it
Notes: Tiburtino. GF breakfast provided upon advance request.

Excel Rome St. Peter hotel
Via Catone, 34   tel. 0639735082   www.excelstpeter.it
Notes: Vatican. GF breakfast provided upon advance request.

Franklin Feel the Sound Hotel hotel
Via Rodi, 29   tel. 0639030165   www.franklinhotelrome.it
Notes: Vatican. GF breakfast provided upon advance request.

Gigli d'Oro Suite hotel
Via dei Gigli d'Oro, 12   tel. 0668803579   www.giglidorosuite.com
Notes: Navona. GF breakfast provided upon advance request.

Holiday Inn Parco dei Medici hotel   €€€€, AIC
Via Castello della Magliana, 65   tel. 0665581   www.holidayinn-eur.it
Notes: Beyond City Center (In Eur District).

Hotel Alexandra hotel
Via Vittorio Veneto 18   tel. 064881943   www.hotelalexandraroma.com
Notes: Veneto.

Hotel Claridge hotel
Viale Liegi, 62a   tel. 6845441   www.hotelclaridgerome.com
Notes: Borghese.

Hotel Diana hotel, restaurant   €€€-€€€€, AIC
Via Principe Amedeo, 4   tel. 064786681   www.hoteldianaroma.com
Notes: Esquilino.

Hotel Fori Imperiali Cavalieri hotel   AIC
Via Frangipane, 34   tel. 6.6796246   www.hotelforiimperialicavalieri.com
Notes: Centro Storico.

Hotel Melià - Rist. La Sughereta hotel, restaurant   €€€, AIC
Via degli Aldobrandeschi, 223   tel. 06665441   www.solmelia.com
Notes: Beyond City Center (Near Airport).

Hotel Mozart hotel   AIC
Via dei Greci, 23   tel. 06.360019151   www.hotelmozart.com
Notes: Flaminio, Centro Storico.

Hotel Nord Nuova Roma hotel
Via G. Amendola, 3   tel. 064885441   www.romehotelnord.it
Notes: Termini.

Hotel Rimini hotel
Via Marghera, 17   tel. 064461991   www.hotelriminirome.com
Notes: Termini.

Hotel Spring House (Best Western) hotel   AIC
Via Mocenigo, 7   tel. 0639720948 www.hotelspringhouse.com
Notes: Mazzini.

Hotel Teatro di Pompeo hotel
Largo del Pallaro, 8   tel. 0668300170 www.hotelteatrodipompeo.it
Notes: Pantheon. Will provide GF breakfast with advance notice.

Hotel XX Settembre hotel
Via del Macao, 6   tel. 064467215   www.hotelventisettembre.com
Notes: Veneto.

Holiday Inn Parco dei Medici   hotel (Italian)   €€€€, AIC
Via Castello della Magliana, 65   tel. 0665581   www.holidayinn-eur.it
Notes: Beyond City Center (In Eur District).

Hotel Alexandra   hotel
Via Vittorio Veneto 18   tel. 064881943   www.hotelalexandraroma.com
Notes: Veneto. GF breakfast provided upon advance request.

Hotel Claridge   hotel
Viale Liegi, 62a   tel. 06845441   www.hotelclaridgerome.com
Notes: Borghese. GF breakfast provided upon advance request.

Hotel Diana   hotel, restaurant (Italian)   €€€-€€€€, AIC
Via Principe Amedeo, 4   tel. 064786681   www.hoteldianaroma.com
Notes: Esquilino.

Hotel Melià - Rist. La Sughereta   hotel, restaurant (Italian)   €€€, AIC
Via degli Aldobrandeschi, 223   tel. 06665441   www.solmelia.com
Notes: Beyond City Center (Near Airport).

Hotel Mozart   hotel
Via dei Greci, 23   tel. 0636001915   www.hotelmozart.com
Notes: Spagna. GF breakfast provided upon advance request.

Hotel Napoleon Rome   hotel
Piazza Vittorio Emanuele II   tel. 064467282   www.napoleon.it
Notes: Vittorio Emanuele. GF breakfast provided upon advance request.

Hotel Nord Nuova Roma   hotel
Via G. Amendola, 3   tel. 064885441   www.romehotelnord.it
Notes: Termini. GF breakfast provided upon advance request.

Hotel Rimini   hotel
Via Marghera, 17   tel. 064461991   www.hotelriminirome.com
Notes: Termini. GF breakfast provided upon advance request.

Hotel XX Settembre   hotel
Via del Macao, 6   tel. 064467215   www.hotelventisettembre.com
Notes: Veneto. GF breakfast provided upon advance request.

Hotel Spring House (Best Western)   hotel   AIC
Via Mocenigo, 7   tel. 0639720948   www.hotelspringhouse.com
Notes: Mazzini.

Hotel Teatro di Pompeo   hotel
Largo del Pallaro, 8   tel. 0668300170   www.hotelteatrodipompeo.it
Notes: Pantheon. Will provide GF breakfast with advance notice.

Imperium Suite Navona   hotel
Vicolo della Palomba, 19   tel. 064880628   www.imperiumsuitenavona.com
Notes: Navona. GF breakfast provided upon advance request.

Luana Inn Airport   hotel, restaurant   €€
Via Monte Forcelletta, 23   tel. 3396933742   www.bbluanainn.it
Notes: Airport. Restaurant caters to celiacs. GF breakfast too. Very close to airport.

Radisson Blu Es H.Roma   hotel   AIC
Via Filippo Turati, 171   tel. 06444841   www.radissonblu.com
Notes: Esquillino.

Residence Il Vittoriano   hotel   AIC
Via Giulia, 141   tel. 6.98381849   www.residenceilvittoriano.com
Notes: Campo.

Rome Cavalieri Waldorf Astoria   hotel
Via Alberto Cadlolo, 101   tel. 0635091   www.romecavalieri.it
Notes: Monte Mario.

San Carlo Suite   hotel
Via del Corso, 112   tel. 0668392055
Notes: GF breakfast provided upon advance request.

Sheraton Golf Parco de' Medici   hotel, restaurant (Italian)   €€€-€€€€, AIC
V.le Salvatore Rebecchini, 39   tel. 0665288   www.starwoodhotels.com
Notes: Beyond City Center (Autostrada Airport). Two restaurants. GF breakfast too.

Sunrise Hotel   hotel
Via Cilento, 3   tel. 0682011093   www.sunrisehotel.it
Notes: Sempione. GF breakfast provided upon advance request.

The Duke Hotel Rome   hotel
Via Archemede 69   tel. 06367221   www.thedukehotel.com
Notes: Borghese. GF breakfast provided upon advance request.

SUMMARY INFO: RESTAURANTS IN ROME LISTED BY NEIGHBORHOOD WITH PRICES

Appia Antica
O' Masto   L.go Salinari, 8/16   €€€

Appio
Antica Hostaria Dei Liberti – Ristorante Via Appia Antica, 87   €€-€€€€

Aurelio
Da Arturo   Via Aurelia Antica, 411/413   €€€

Beyond City Center
Circolo Ippico Tor S. Giovanni Via Tor San Giovanni, 245   €
Pomodori Verdi Fritti   Via dei Pescatori, 495   €€
Villa Grant   Via Pratica di Mare, 181   €€€€
Zen Fusion   V.le Eritrea, 69   €€-€€€
V Hugo   Via Cristoforo Colombo, 90   €€-€€€
Millennium   Via Tor Tre Teste, 35   €€€
La Piazzetta   Piazza dei Visconti, 8   €€-€€€

Campo
Da Sergio   Vicolo delle Grotte, 27   €€-€€€
Ditirambo   Piazza della Cancelleria, 74   €€-€€€
Il Sanlorenzo   Via dei Chiavari, 4/5   €€€€
Voglia di Pizza   Via dei Giubbonari, 33   €€

Casolino
La Nduja 2   Via Michele Tenore 21/31   €€-€€€

Centro Storico
Albrecht   Via Rasella 52   €€€
Ciao Checca   P.za di Firenze, 25   €€
Grano Frutta e Farina   Via Della Croce 49A   €€€
Il Vineto   Via Vittorio Veneto 6   €€
Quattro Spicchi   Via della Pisana, 51   €€
Settimio all'Arancio   Via Arancio 50   €€€
Taverna Barberini   Via Delle Quattro Fontane 160   €€
Toto   Via delle Carrozze 10   €€€
Osteria del Pegno   Vicolo di Montevecchio 8   €€€

Colosseo
Ai Tre Scalini   Via SS. Quattro, 30   €€€

Esquilino
Agata e Romeo   Via Carlo Alberto, 45   €€€€
Il Veliero   Via Albalonga, 46   €€
Taberna Recina   Via Elvia Recina, 22   €€€

Ghetto
Al Pompiere   Via Santa Maria dei Calderari, 38 €€-€€€
Sora Lella   Via di Ponte Quattro Capi, 16   €€€

Historic District
Pantharei   Via della Minerva, 18   €€-€€€

Monte Mario
La Pergola   Via Alberto Cadlolo, 101   €€€€

Montesacro/Talenti
Lanificio Cucina   Via di Pietralata, 159   €€

Monti

F.I.S.H.	Via dei Serpenti, 16	€€€€
Ristorante Tema	Via Panisperna, 96/98	€€€€
Sehgal Sanjiv Kumar Ristorante Indiano Maharaja Via Dei Serpenti, 124		€€€€
Zia Rosetta	Via Urbana 54	€€

Navona

Etabli	Vicolo delle Vacche, 9/a	€€€
La Scaletta Degli Artisti Srl	Via di Santa Maria dell'Anima	€€-€€€
Osteria del Gallo	Vicolo di Montevecchio, 27	€€-€€€
Ristorante Bibliothè	Via Celsa, 4	€
Trattoria Pizzeria Fiammetta	Piazza Fiammetta, 10	€€

Nomentano, Pinciano

Ops!	Via Bergamo 56	€€

Ostia

Biorestaunt ZenZero	Viale della Pineta di Ostia 30	€€€

Ostiense

Antico Casale La Carovana	V.le di Vigna Pia, 33	€€-€€€
Hopside	Via Francesco Negri 39	€€
Insomnia	Via Portuense, 469	€€€
Potter Pizza	V.le dei Colli Portuensi, 346	€

Piazza Venezia

Birreria Peroni	Via di San Marcello, 19	€

Pantheon

Armando al Pantheon	Salita de' Crescenzi, 31	€€-€€€
Il Piccolo Mondo	Via delle Coppelle, 16/a	€€€€
La Rosetta	Via della Rosetta, 9	€€€€
La Scaletta	Via della Scala	€€€
Osteria dell'Ingegno	Piazza di Pietra, 45	€€-€€€

Pigneto

Al Country	Via Teano, 243/245	€€
Casa Mangiacotti	Via Gentile da Mogliano 180	€€

Pinciano

Larys Restaurant Rome	Via Basento, 54	€€-€€€

Prati

Da Angelo alla Cupola	Via Aurelia 50	€€€
Dal Toscano	Via Germanico, 58/60	€€€
La Fiorentina	Via Andrea Doria, 24	€€€€
La Soffitta Renovatio	Piazza del Risorgimento 46A	€€
La Pilotta da Mario	Via Porta Cavalleggeri, 35/37	€€-€€€
Taverna Angelica	Piazza A. Capponi, 6	€€€
Baiamonti Lounge Bar	Via Baiamonti, 12	€€
Cesare	Via Crescenzio, 13	€€€

Quirinale

Tullio	Via San Nicola da Tolentino	€€€-€€€€

San Giovanni

Vintage Bistrot	Piazza Tarquinia 4A	€€-€€€

San Lorenzo

Fiorita	Via Bari, 11/B	€€€
Il Bello della Pizza	Via di Portonaccio 33/a	€

Spagna

Caffè Romano dell'Hotel d'Inghilterra	Via Borgongna, 4M	€€€€
Dal Bolognese	Piazza del Popolo, 1	€€€€
El Toulà	Via della Lupa, 29/b	€€€€
Gioia Mia Pisciapiano	Via degli Avignonesi 34	€
Margutta Vegetariano	Via Margutta, 118	€€-€€€

Termini

Mamma Angela's Trattoria	Via Palestro, 53	€€

Trastevere

Alle Fratte di Trastevere	Via delle Fratte di Trastevere	€€
Da Sandri	Via Roma Libera 19	€€-€€€
Il Maggiolino	Via Alessandro Cruto, 9	€-€€
Il Tulipano Nero	Via Roma Libera, 15	€
Jaipur	Via di San Francesco a Ripa, 56	€€
La Gensola	Piazza della Gensola, 15	€€-€€€
Mama.Eat	Via di San Cosimato, 7	€€
Ripa 12 Ristorante	Via San a Franceso Ripa, 12	€€€
Romolo	Via di Porta Settimiana, 8	€€€
Z'Imberto	Piazza San Giovanni della Malva	€€€

Trieste

Mangiafuoco Pizza & Grill	Via Chiana, 37	€€

Tuscolano

Il Portico	P.zza Aruleno C. Sabino, 89	€€-€€€

Vatican

Ad Hoc	Via di Ripetta, 43	
La Veranda dell'Hotel Columbus	Borgo Santo Spirito, 73	€€€-€€€€
Renovatio La Soffitta	P.zza Risorgimento, 46/a	€€€

Veneto

Alex Cafè	Via Vittorio Veneto, 20	€€€€
Hard Rock Cafe	Via Vittorio Veneto, 62	€€-€€€
Il Viaggio	Via Isonzo, 14	€€-€€€
Papá Baccus	Via Toscana, 36	€€€€

Villa Borghese

Al Ceppo	Via Panama, 2	€€€€

Vitinia

Pizza City 2	Via Sant'Arcangelo di Romagna, 55/57	€€

Zona Est

Le Tre Lune a Roma Est	Via di Lunghezzina 75	€€-€€€

Trevi Fountain (D. Frost)

ROME RESTAURANTS AND BAKERIES
LISTED ALPHABETICALLY
(AIC = participates in the Associazione Italiana Celiachia program)

ROMA

Ad Hoc	restaurant	€€
Via di Ripetta, 43	tel. 063233040	www.ristoranteadhoc.com

Notes: Vatican.

Agata e Romeo restaurant €€€€
Via Carlo Alberto, 45 tel. 064466115 www.agataeromeo.it
Notes: Esquilino.

Agrit. Torre Sant'Anastasia agritourism, restaurant, pizzeria €€-€€€, AIC
Via Torre Sant'Anastasia, 83 tel. 0671350361 www.torresantanastasia.it
Notes: Beyond City Center. Also B&B. Closed Monday-Thursday.

Agriturismo Pallotta agritourism
Via delle Selve di Pallotta 2 tel. 06 9486833 www.agriturismopallotta.com

Ai Tre Scalini restaurant €€€
Via SS. Quattro, 30 tel. 067096309 www.aitrescalini.org
Notes: Colosseo. Closed Mondays. Limited selection but will do GF.

Al Ceppo restaurant €€€€
Via Panama, 2 tel. 068419696 www.ristorantealceppo.it
Notes: Villa Borghese. Reservations essential. Closed Mondays.

Al Country restaurant €€, AIC
Via Teano, 243/245 tel. 0621704704 www.ristorantepizzeriaalcountry.it
Notes: Pigneto.

Al Pompiere restaurant €€-€€€
Via Santa Maria dei Calderari, 38 tel. 066868377
Notes: Ghetto. GF pasta. Delicious Jewish dishes. Closed Sundays.

Albrecht restaurant €€€
Via Rasella 52 tel. 06 4880457
Notes: Centro Storico.

Alex Cafè restaurant €€€€, AIC
Via Vittorio Veneto, 20 tel. 064823618
Notes: Veneto.

Alle Fratte di Trastevere restaurant €€
Via delle Fratte di Trastevere tel. 065835775 www.allefratteditrastevere.com
Notes: Trastevere. GF pasta. Many GF options.

Antica Hostaria Dei Liberti - Ristorante restaurant €€-€€€€
Via Appia Antica, 87 tel. 065132888 www.anticaroma.it
Notes: Appio. Outrageously good food and lovely ambience.

Antico Casale La Carovana restaurant, pizzeria €€-€€€, AIC
V.le di Vigna Pia, 33 tel. 065577758 www.lacarovana.info
Notes: Ostiense.

Armando al Pantheon restaurant
Salita de' Crescenzi, 31 tel. 0668803034 www.armandoalpantheon.it
Notes: Pantheon.

Autogrill Aeroporto di Fiumicino autogrill €, AIC
Via dell'Aeroporto di Fiumicino tel. 6.65957477
Notes: airport.

Autogrill Corso autogrill €, AIC
Via del Corso, 181 tel. 6.76789135
Notes: Centro Storico.

Autogrill Stazione Termini autogrill €, AIC
Via Marsala, 25 tel. 6.47823106
Notes: Termini.

Baiamonti Lounge Bar pizzeria, bar €€, AIC
Via Baiamonti, 12 tel. 0637351954 www.baiamontiloungebar.it
Notes: Prati (Mazzini). Closed Sundays.

Bar Napoleoni bar, restaurant €€, AIC
Via Appia Nuova, 592 tel. 6.7804727 www.barnapoleoni.it
Notes: Tuscolano, Appia Antica.

Biorestaunt ZenZero restaurant €€€
Viale della Pineta di Ostia 30 tel. 06 5621293 www.ristozenzero.it
Notes: Ostia.

Birreria Peroni restaurant €
Via di San Marcello, 19 tel. 066795310 www.anticabirreriaperoni.it.
Notes: P.Zza Venezia. Closed Sundays at Saturday at lunch.

Caffe Da Claudia café, restaurant €€€
Piazza Della Rotonda 14A tel. 06 68806127
Notes: Centro Storico.

Caffè Romano dell'Hotel d'Inghilterra restaurant €€€€
Via Borgongna, 4M tel. 0669981500
Notes: Spagna. Already have GF pasta and bread. Still, reservations preferable.

Casa Mangiacotti restaurant, wine bar €€
Via Gentile da Mogliano 180 tel. 392 4319477
Notes: Pigneto.

Celiachiamo.com
Via C.Caneva, 40
Notes: Prati.

bakery
tel. 6.64260188

€, AIC
www.celiachiamo.com

Cesare
Via Crescenzio, 13
Notes: Prati (S.Pietro). Can make many things gluten-free. Preferable to call ahead.

restaurant
tel. 066861227

€€€
www.ristorantecesare.com.

Ciao Checca
P.za di Firenze, 25
Notes: Centro Storico.

tavola calda, gastropub
tel. 6.68300368

€€, AIC
www.ciaochecca.com

Circolo Ippico Tor S. Giovanni
Via Tor San Giovanni, 245
Notes: Beyond City Center. DS pizza point. Closed Mondays.

pizzeria
tel. 0687120537

€, AIC
www.circoloippico.com

Croquembouche
Viale Dell'Arte, 42
Notes: EUR.

bakery, ice cream, chocolates
tel. 6.64651062

€€€, AIC
www.croquembouche.it

Da Angelo alla Cupola
Via Aurelia 50
Notes: Prati.

restaurant, pizzeria
tel. 6.39377133

€€€, AIC
www.angeloallacupola.it

Da Arturo
Via Aurelia Antica, 411/413
Notes: Aurelio. Closed Mondays.

restaurant, pizzeria
tel. 066623408

€€€, AIC
www.ristorantearturo.it

Da Sandri
Via Roma Libera 19
Notes: Trastevere.

restaurant, pizzeria
tel. 6.5816469

€€-€€€, AIC
www.daisandri.it

Da Sergio
Vicolo delle Grotte, 27
Notes: Campo. Closed Sundays. Some choices that can be made GF.

restaurant
tel. 066864293

€€-€€€

Dal Bolognese
Piazza del Popolo, 1
Notes: Spagna. Closed Mondays. Reservations necessary and mention GF.

restaurant
tel. 063222799

€€€€

Dal Toscano
Via Germanico, 58/60
Notes: Prati.

restaurant
tel. 0639723373

€€€
www.ristorantedaltoscano.it

Ditirambo
Piazza della Cancelleria, 74
Notes: Campo.

restaurant
tel. 066871626

€€-€€€
www.ristoranteditirambo.it

El Toulà
Via della Lupa, 29/b
Notes: Spagna. English spoken. Reservations required for dinner. Closed Sundays.

restaurant
tel. 066873750

€€€€
www.toula.it.

Esquilino
Via Carlo Botta 21
Notes: Esquilino.

bakery
tel. 06 70453930

€€€
www.pasticceriacipriani.com

Etabli
Vicolo delle Vacche, 9/a
Notes: Navona. Seeveral dishes are already GF. With notice, will do GF pasta as well.

restaurant
tel. 066871499

€€€
www.etabli.it

F.I.S.H.
Via dei Serpenti, 16
Notes: Monti. Reservations essential.

restaurant
tel. 0647824962

€€€€
www.f-i-s-h.it.

Gioia Mia Pisciapiano   restaurant, pizzeria   €
Via degli Avignonesi 34   tel. 064882784   www.hoteljulia.it/imgioiamia
Notes: Spagna.

Grano Frutta e Farina   sandwich shop, desserts, pizza   €€€
Via Della Croce 49A   www.granofruttaefarina.it
Notes: Centro Storico. They have some GF prepackaged products.

Hard Rock Cafe   restaurant   €€-€€€
Via Vittorio Veneto, 62   tel. 06420304   www.hardrockcafe.com
Notes: Veneto.

Hopside   pub, hamburgers   €€
Via Francesco Negri 39   tel. 06 69313081   www.hopside.it
Notes: Ostiense.

Il Bello della Pizza   pizzeria   €, AIC
Via di Portonaccio 33/a   tel. 6.43253144   www.ilbellodellapizza.com
Notes: San Lorenzo.

Il Maggiolino   restaurant, pizzeria   €-€€, AIC
Via Alessandro Cruto, 9   tel. 065574484   www.ilmaggiolinosrl.com
Notes: Trastevere. DS pizza point. Closed Mondays.

Il Piccolo Mondo   restaurant, bar   €€€€
Via delle Coppelle, 16/a   tel. 0668392065   www.ristorantepiccolomondo.it
Notes: Pantheon. Closed Sundays and month of August.

Il Portico   restaurant, pizzeria   €€-€€€, AIC
P.zza Aruleno C. Sabino, 89   tel. 0671582828
Notes: Tuscolano.

Il Sanlorenzo   restaurant   €€€€
Via dei Chiavari, 4/5   tel. 066865097   www.ilsanlorenzo.it.
Notes: Campo. No lunch Saturday-Monday.

Il Tulipano Nero   restaurant   €
Via Roma Libera, 15   tel. 065818309   www.tulipanonero.biz
Notes: Trastevere. GF pasta.

Il Veliero   restaurant, pizzeria   €€, AIC
Via Albalonga, 46   tel. 6.77209731   ilvelierobar.blogspot.in
Notes: Esquilino.

Il Viaggio   restaurant   €€-€€€, AIC
Via Isonzo, 14   tel. 0697997043   www.ristoranteilviaggio.it
Notes: Veneto.

Il Vineto   restaurant   €€
Via Vittorio Veneto 6   tel. 06 466617
Notes: Centro Storico.

Imperium Suite Navona   hotel
Vicolo della Palomba, 19   tel. 064880628   www.imperiumsuitenavona.com
Notes: Navona.

Insomnia   restaurant, pizzeria   €€€
Via Portuense, 469   tel. 0655389376   www.insomnia.roma.it
Notes: Ostiense. Closed Sundays and at lunch.

Jaipur   restaurant   €€
Via di San Francesco a Ripa, 56   tel. 065803992
Notes: Trastevere. Closed Mondays.

La Cannoleria Sicilia   bakery   €
Via di Monte Brianzo, 66   tel. 0668806874   www.lacannoleriasiciliana.it
Notes: Navona.

La Creperie Di Testaccio   crêperie   €€€
Via Galvani 11   tel. 06 5743814
Notes: Testaccio, Ostiense. They also do take out.

La Fiorentina   restaurant   €€€€
Via Andrea Doria, 24   tel. 063737019   www.lafiorentina.net
Notes: Prati.

La Gensola   restaurant   €€-€€€
Piazza della Gensola, 15   tel. 065816312   www.osterialagensola.it
Notes: Trastevere. GF pasta or pizza, but plenty of dishes can be made GF. Reservations
preferable.

La Mimosa Fiorita   restaurant, pizzeria   €€€, AIC
Via Bari, 11/B   tel. 0644291958
www.facebook.com/pages/La-Mimosa-Fiorita-Roma/167048666667644
Notes: San Lorenzo (Or Tiburtino). Closed Wednesdays. Special GF menu with many options.

La Nduja 2   restaurant, pizzeria   AIC
Via Michele Tenore 21/31   tel. 6.25210654   www.landuja.com
Notes: Casolino.

La Pergola (in Rome Cavalieri/Waldorf Hotel) restaurant   €€€€
Via Alberto Cadlolo, 101   tel. 0635091   www.romecavalieri.it
Notes: Monte Mario.

La Piazzetta   restaurant, pizzeria   €€-€€€, AIC
Piazza dei Visconti, 8   tel. 0666014164   www.giancarlone.com
Notes: Beyond City Center (In Trionfale). DS pizza point. Closed Mondays.

La Rosetta   restaurant   €€€€
Via della Rosetta, 9   tel. 066861002   www.larosetta.com.
Notes: Pantheon. Very small restaurant so better to make reservations. GF pasta and bread.
English spoke.

La Scaletta Degli Artisti Srl restaurant   €€-€€€
Via di Santa Maria dell'Anima   tel. 0668801872   www.lascaletta-roma.it
Notes: Navona.

La Soffitta Renovatio   restaurant, pizzeria   €€
Piazza del Risorgimento 46A   tel. 06 68892977   www.ristoranterenovatio.it
Notes: Prati.

La Veranda dell'Hotel Columbus restaurant   €€€-€€€€
Borgo Santo Spirito, 73   tel. 066872973   www.hotelcolumbus.net
Notes: Vatican. Reservations essential and mention GF. GF pasta.

La Pilotta da Mario   restaurant, pizzeria   €€-€€€
Via Porta Cavalleggeri, 35/37   tel. 06632643   www.lapilotta.com
Notes: Prati.

La Scaletta   restaurant   €€€
Via della Scala   tel. 0'065816317
Notes: Pantheon. Highly recommended. Many celiac clients.

Lanificio Cucina   restaurant   €€, AIC
Via di Pietralata, 159   tel. 6.4501384   www.lanificio.com
Notes: Montesacro/Talenti.

Larys Restaurant Rome   restaurant   €€-€€€, AIC
Via Basento, 54   tel. 6.8530513   www.larys.it
Notes: Pinciano.

Le Ben - Piacere sì, glutine no   bakery   €
Via di Ponziano, 19   tel. 0658332697   www.le-ben.it
Notes: Trastevere. Exclusively GF. Lots of treats.

Le Tre Lune a Roma Est   restaurant, pizzeria   €€-€€€, AIC
Via di Lunghezzina 75- Roma Est   tel. 06.2203031/335.8185144 www.ristoranteletrelune.com
Notes: Zona Est.

Lievito72   hamburger, pizza   €€
Via del Forte Braschi 82A   tel. 06 6142829   www.lievito72.it
Notes: Balduina/Montemario.

Luana Inn Airport   hotel, restaurant   €€
Via Monte Forcelletta, 23   tel. 3396933742   www.bbluanainn.it
Notes: Airport. Restaurant caters to celiacs. GF breakfast too. Very close to airport.

Mama.Eat   restaurant, pizzeria   €€, AIC
Via di San Cosimato, 7   tel. 6.5806222   www.mamaeat.com
Notes: Trastevere.

Mamey_Roma Est   bakery, pizzeria, bar   €, AIC
Via G. Rosaccio, 8/22   tel. 6.41228009   www.mamey.it
Notes: Tiburtino.

Mamma Angela's Trattoria   trattoria   €€
Via Palestro, 53   tel. 0644341317   www.mammaangelas.com
Notes: Termini.

Mangiafuoco Pizza & Grill   restaurant, pizzeria   €€, AIC
Via Chiana, 37   tel. 0685357255   www.mangiafuoco.org
Notes: Trieste.

Margutta Vegetariano   restaurant   €€-€€€
Via Margutta, 118   tel. 0632650577   www.ilmarguttavegetariano.it
Notes: Spagna. Will prepare GF with advance notice.

Millennium   restaurant, pizzeria pub   €€€, AIC
Via Tor Tre Teste, 35   tel. 623269171   www.millenniumcenter.it
Notes: Beyond City Center (In Casilino). Closed at lunch.

Napoleoni   bar, gelato   €€
Via Appia Nuova 592   tel. 06 7804727   www.barnapoleoni.it
Notes: Tuscolano, Appia Antica.

New Food Gluten Free   bakery   €€, AIC
L.go A. Pepere, 25/26   tel. 6.58230394   www.newfoodglutenfree.it

Novotel Roma La Rustica   hotel, restaurant   AIC
Via A. Noale, 291   tel. 6.227661   www.novotel.com
Notes: Beyond City Center.

O' Masto   pizzeria   €€€, AIC
L.go Salinari, 8/16   tel. 065413448   www.omasto.com
Notes: Appia Antica. Closed Mondays. DS pizza point.

Ops!   vegetarian restaurant   €€
Via Bergamo 56   tel. 06 8411769   www.opsveg.com
Notes: Nomentano, Pinciano. GF items indicated on the menu.

Osteria del Gallo restaurant
Vicolo di Montevecchio, 27 tel. 066873781 www.osteriadelgalloroma.it
Notes: Navona.

Osteria del Pegno restaurant €€€
Vicolo di Montevecchio 8 tel. 06 68807025 www.osteriadelpegno.com
Notes: Centro storico (Navona).

Osteria dell'Ingegno restaurant €€-€€€
Piazza di Pietra, 45 tel. 066780662
Notes: Pantheon. GF pasta. Call ahead for reservations and GF requests.

Pantharei restaurant AIC
Via della Minerva, 18 tel. 6.89021922 www.pantharei.it
Notes: Historic District.

Papá Baccus restaurant €€€€
Via Toscana, 36 tel. 0642742808 www.papabaccus.com
Notes: Veneto. With advance notice, will prepare GF.

Pizza City 2 pizzeria €€, AIC
Via Sant'Arcangelo di Romagna, 55/57 - loc.Vitinia tel. 328.3140976
Notes: Vitinia.

Pomodori Verdi Fritti restaurant, pizzeria €€, AIC
Via dei Pescatori, 495 tel. 065212824 www.pomodoriverdifritti.it
Notes: Beyond City Center.

Potter Pizza pizzeria €, AIC
V.le dei Colli Portuensi, 346 tel. 0665740770
Notes: Ostiense.

Primi e Veloci fast food €
Via Sicilia 129 tel. 328 8755900 www.primieveloci.it
Notes: Termini.

Quattro Spicchi pizzeria, bakery €€, AIC
Via della Pisana, 51 tel. 6.64463644 www.quattrospicchi.it
Notes: Centro Storico.

Renovatio La Soffitta restaurant, pizzeria €€€, AIC
P.zza Risorgimento, 46/a (corner of Via Crescenzio) tel. 0668892977
www.ristoranterenovatio.it
Notes: Vatican. Very highly recommended by fellow celiacs. GF pizza, calzone, lasagne, beer.

Resta's Pizza Bar pizzeria, bar €, AIC
L.go La Loggia, 15 tel. 6.60669753

Ripa 12 Ristorante restaurant
Via San a Franceso Ripa, 12 tel. 065809093 www.ripa12.com
Notes: Trastevere.

Ristorante Bibliothè restaurant €
Via Celsa, 4 tel. 066781427 www.bibliothe.net
Notes: Navona.

Ristorante Tema restaurant €€€€
Via Panisperna, 96/98 tel. 06486484 www.ristorantetema.com
Notes: Monti. Very highly recommended by fellow celiacs.

Romolo restaurant €€€
Via di Porta Settimiana, 8 tel. 065818284
Notes: Trastevere. Will do GF with advance notice.

Sale e Argento Via Evandro, 8	restaurant tel. 6.78346526	AIC www.saleeargento.com

San Carlo Suite hotel
Via del Corso, 112 tel. 0668392055 www.sancarlosuite.com
Notes: Centro storico (Spagna).

Sans de Ble' bakery €, AIC
Via G. Chiabrera, 58c tel. 389.9008807 www.sansdeble.it
Notes: Ostiense.

Sehgal Sanjiv Kumar Ristorante Indiano Maharaja restaurant €€€€
Via Dei Serpenti, 124 tel. 064747144
Notes: Monti.

Senza Pensieri Dolci bakery €€
Via dei Campani 53 tel. 340 9724215
Notes: San Giovanni. They specialize in GF.

Settimio all'Arancio restaurant €€€
Via Arancio 50 tel. 06 6876119 www.settimioallarancio.com
Notes: Centro storico.

Sheraton Golf Parco de' Medici hotel, restaurant €€€-€€€€
V.le Salvatore Rebecchini, 39 tel. 0665288 www.starwoodhotels.com
Notes: Beyond City Center (Autostrada Airport). Two restaurants. GF breakfast too.

Sora Lella restaurant €€€
Via di Ponte Quattro Capi, 16 tel. 066861601 www.soralella.com
Notes: Ghetto. Reserve 2 to 3 days ahead for GF.

Taberna Recina restaurant €€€, AIC
Via Elvia Recina, 22 tel. 6.7000413 www.tabernarecina.it
Notes: Esquilino, Aventino.

Taverna Angelica restaurant €€€
Piazza A. Capponi, 6 tel. 066874514 www.tavernaangelica.it
Notes: Prati. Call ahead for GF.

Taverna Barberini restaurant €€
Via Delle Quattro Fontane 160 tel. 06 4883619 www.tavernabarberini.it
Notes: Centro storico.

Toto restaurant €€€
Via delle Carrozze 10 tel. 06 6785558 www.toto1922.it
Notes: Centro Storico.

Trattoria Pizzeria Fiammetta restaurant, pizzeria €€
Piazza Fiammetta, 10 tel. 066875777 www.ristorantefiammetta.it
Notes: Navona. Highly recommended. GF pasta. English spoken. Owner is gluten intolerant.

Tullio restaurant €€€-€€€€
Via San Nicola da Tolentino tel. 064745560 www.tullioristorante.it.
Notes: Quirinale. Near Piazza Barberini. Closed Sundays.

Tutti i gusti gelato, bar €, AIC
Via Casilina, 381 tel. 6.24406269 www.fuoridiglutine.eu

V Hugo restaurant, pizzeria
Via Cristoforo Colombo, 90 tel. 065115709 www.hugorestaurant.it
Notes: Beyond City Center (Eur). Many celiac customers.

Villa Grant — restaurant, reception hall — €€€€, AIC
Via Pratica di Mare, 181 — tel. 0650570832 — www.villagrant.it
Notes: Beyond City Center.

Vintage Bistrot — restaurant — €€
Piazza Tarquinia 4A — tel. 06 64764104 — www.vintagebistrot.com
Notes: San Giovanni.

Voglia di Pizza — restaurant, pizzeria — €€, AIC
Via dei Giubbonari, 33 — tel. 066875293 — www.vogliadipizzaglutenfree.com
Notes: Campo. Very highly recommended by fellow celiacs. Separate gluten-free menu.

Zen Fusion — restaurant — €€-€€€, AIC
V.le Eritrea, 69 — tel. 0686218365 — www.zenfusion.eu
Notes: Beyond City Center (African). Closed Sunday and Monday at lunch. Highly recommended; Japanese and Thai food.

Zia Rosetta — sandwich shop — €€
Via Urbana 54 — www.ziarosetta.com
Notes: Monti.

Z'Imberto — restaurant — €€€
Piazza San Giovanni della Malva — tel. 065816646
Notes: Trastevere. Closed Mondays.

ROMA SUD-EST

Maison del Celiaco — bakery, sandwich shop — €
Via Buscemi 37 — www.maisondelceliaco.it

ROMA-ACILIA

Cremeria Alpi — gelato — €, AIC
Via Sistina 5A — www.cremeriaalpi.it
Notes: Centro Storico.

Il Mulino Celiaco — bakery — €, AIC
Via U. Lilloni, 64/int.23 — tel. 6.60661686 — www.ilmulinoceliaco.it
Notes: Veneto.

ROMA-OSTIA LIDO

Al contadino non far sapere... — restaurant, pizzeria — €€€, AIC
Via della Macchiarella 128 — tel. 0656350219 — www.alcontadinononfarsapere.com
Notes: Ostia

Le Palme — restaurant, bar — AIC
L.re Amerigo Vespucci, 58 — tel. 6.56470131

THE REST OF LAZIO
ACQUAPENDENTE

Agriturismo Belvedere — agritourism, restaurant, pizzeria — €€-€€€, AIC
Loc. Belvedere snc - Torre Alfina — tel. 763.716041
www.belvederetorrealfina.com/index_en.htm
Notes: The chef is a celiac himself.

ALATRI

La Rosetta — pizzeria — €-€€, AIC
Via Duomo, 35 — tel. 0775434642

Papapidò — pizzeria — €, AIC
Via Circonvallazione, sn — tel. 0775442666

Ristorante Sisto — restaurant/pizzeria — € - €€, AIC
Via Circonvallazione Basciano, 55 — tel. 0775409158 — www.ristorantesisto.it

Pantheon (D. Frost)

Villa Scerrato	restaurant	€€-€€€, AIC
Via Madonna della Sanità, 19	tel. 0775440743	

ALBANO LAZIALE

Beccofino	restaurant, pizzeria	€€, AIC
Via Fleming, 5	tel. 0693720309	
Notes: DS pizza point. Closed Mondays.		

ANAGNI

Autogrill La Macchia Ovest	autogrill	€, AIC
A1 Roma - Napoli	tel. 775.768104	
La Rena	restaurant	€€-€€€, AIC
Via La Rena, 10	tel. 07757681	www.ristorantelarena.it
Notes: Closed Tuesdays.		
Villa Sorvillo	B&B	AIC
Via Carlo Alberto dalla Chiesa, 37	tel. 0775727080	www.villasorvillo.it
Zi Luciano	pizzeria	€, AIC
Via Fosso del Lupo, 4	tel. 0775725588	

ANZIO

La Fornace	restaurant, pizzeria	€, AIC
Via della Fornace, 47/a	tel. 069870195	www.lafornacedianzio.it
Maison del Celiaco	bakery, sandwich shop	€, AIC
Viale Antium, 6 C/O Centro Anteo	tel. 6.986385	www.maisondelceliaco.it

APRILIA

Fresche Golosità	sandwich shop, bakery	€, AIC
Via lombardia, 25/ 27	tel. 6.64005936	www.freschegolosita.it

L'Oasi pizzeria €, AIC
Via Del Tronco, 14 tel. 069275334
Notes: Closed Mondays.

ARICCIA

Fori Porta restaurant €€, AIC
Via A. Chigi, 16 tel. 069333661 www.foriporta.it
Notes: Closed Tuesdays.

Taverna Antichi Sapori...e di più restaurant, pizzeria, bar €€, AIC
Via Indipendenza, 30 tel. 06.31055123 www.taverna.antichisapori/ilfroid

ARICCIA-FONTA NA DI PAPA

Zi' Ciana restaurant, pizzeria €€, AIC
Via Nettunense, Km 11 tel. 6.93496158
www.facebook.com/pages/Zi-Ciana/193452074169622

BASSANO IN TEVERINA

Osteria Belvedere restaurant €€€, AIC
Via Belvedere, 1/3 tel. 0761407546 www.osteriabelvedere.it

BELLEGRA

Sancamillo restaurant, hotel, bar AIC
Via San Francesco, 22 tel. 6.95617016 www.hotelsancamillo.it

BOLSENA

Verdeluna restaurant, pizzeria €, AIC
SS Cassia, Km 113,00 tel. 0761799023
Notes: DS pizza point. Closed Wednesdays.

BOMARZO

Il Quadrifoglio restaurant, pizzeria €€, AIC
Via Verga, 19 tel. 0761924281

BRACCIANO

Crazy Bull Cafe' Evolution restaurant, pizzeriaub €€, AIC
P.za Don Cesolini, 4 tel. 6.99802341 www.crazybullcafe.it

Il Grillo restaurant, pizzeria €-€€, AIC
Piazza Don Cesolini, 32 tel. 6.9987685 www.pizzeriailgrillo.com

Pizzando restaurant, pizzeria €€, AIC
Via Cavour, 36 tel. 6.99802932 www.pizzando.com

BROCCOSTELLA

New York Express restaurant €€-€€€, AIC
Via Stella, 96/b tel. 0776.1938150
www.osterianewyork.it/www.osterianewyork.it/Sito_in_allestimento.html

CANALE MONTERANO

Nonsolorose B&B AIC
Via Secchinetto tel. 0699838605 www.digilander.libero.it/bebnonsolorose

CAPODIMONTE

La Piroga pizzeria €, AIC
Via Verentana, km. 13,180 tel. 0761870780
Notes: DS pizza point. Self-service. Closed Tuesdays.

CAPRAROLA

La Bella Venere hotel/restaurant €€€€, AIC
Loc. Scardenato tel. 0761612342 www.labellavenere.it

CARPINETO ROMANO

La Rupe dei 7 Venti   pizzeria   €, AIC
Via Maenza, 26   tel. 069719507   www.pizzeriafeoli.it
Notes: DS pizza point. Closed Mondays.

CASSINO

Rocca Hotel Rist.   hotel, restaurant   €€-€€€, AIC
Via Sferracavalli, 105   tel. 0776311212   www.hotelrocca.it

CASTEL SANT'ELIA

La Vecchia Quercia   restaurant, pizzeria   €€-€€€, AIC
Loc. San Lorenzo   tel. 0761599164
Notes: DS pizza point. Closed Wednesdays.

CASTRO DEI VOLSCI

Il Ruspante   agritourism   €€€, AIC
Località Pozzotello, 18   www.ilruspante.it
Notes: Closed Tuesday-Wednesday.

La Locanda del Ditirambo   inn, restaurant   €€€, AIC
Via dell'Orologio, 11/a   tel. 0775662091
Notes: Closed Monday-Wednesday.

CECCANO

Caffè della Stazione   bar, tavola calda   €, AIC
Via Stazione   tel. 775.604416

Il Giardino dell'Angelo   restaurant, pizzeria   €, AIC
Via Magenta, 51   tel. 0775604463

Il Ristorantino del Rio   restaurant, pizzeria   AIC
Colle Campanaro, 20   tel. 346.7771893

La Cantinella   restaurant   €, AIC
Via Cosa, 20   tel. 0775642019
Notes: Closed Mondays.

Whats App   gelato (€, AIC)   Via per Frosinone, 62

CEPRANO

Hotel Ida   hotel, restaurant   €€-€€€, AIC
Via Caragno, 27   tel. 0775950040   www.hotelida.it

CERVETERI

Il Casale di Montetosto   restaurant, pizzeria   €€-€€€, AIC
Via del Sasso, km.5   tel. 0699079327   www.ilcasaledimontetosto.it
Notes: DS pizza point. Closed Wednesdays.

La Brace da Guerrino   restaurant, pizzeria   €-€€, AIC
Via Fontana Morella, 221   tel. 6.99079202   www.ristorantelabrace.weebly.com

CIVITAVECCHIA

Il Pesce in Bottiglia   restaurant   AIC
Darsena Romana, 10   tel. 0766220699   www.ilpesceinbottiglia.it

L'Angoletto   restaurant   €€€, AIC
Via P. Guglielmotti, 2   tel. 076632825   www.langoletto.com
Notes: Closed Mondays and Sunday nights.

Le Delizie   bar   €, AIC
Via G. Baccelli, 128   tel. 766.672477

| Lo Stuzzichino | restaurant | €€-€€€, AIC |
| Via P. Manzi, 30 | tel. 766.32945 | www.lostuzzichino.com |

| Ostaria La Babbiona | restaurant | €€€, AIC |
| Via Padri Domenicani, 11 | tel. 0766560649 | www.lababbiona.it |

| Pizzaland | restaurant, pizzeria bar | €, AIC |
| Via Enrico Berlinguer | tel. 3289596358 | |

| Taverna dell'Olmo | restaurant | €-€€, AIC |
| Via Tevere,4 | tel. 766.501331 | www.ristorantetavernadellolmo.it |

COLONNA

| Pause | restaurant, pizzeria | €-€€, AIC |
| Via Frascati, 23 | tel. 6.9438097 | www.pausebirroteca.it |

FERENTINO

| Il Giardino | restaurant | €, AIC |
| Via Stazione 37 | tel. 0775244128 | www.pizzeriailgiardino.it |

| Primavera | restaurant | €€€-€€€€, AIC |
| Via Casilina Nord Km 70, 254 | tel. 0775246521 | www.ristorante-primavera.com |
Notes: Closed Mondays and Sunday nights.

FIUGGI

| Forum et Ludus | restaurant, pizzeria | €-€€, AIC |
| Via delle Felci | tel. 0775506058 | www.fiuggi.org/rforum.htm |
Notes: Closed Tuesdays.

| Hotel Olimpic | hotel, restaurant | €€€, AIC |
| Via Prenestina sud, 63 | tel. 0775515584 | |

FIUMICINO

| Autogrill Fiumicino Satellite Ovest | autogrill | €, AIC |
| Via Dell'Aeroporto, 1 | tel. 6.65011112 | |

| Luana | restaurant, pizzeria, B&B | AIC |
| Via Monte Nozzolo, 3 | tel. 066520231 | www.bbluanainn.it |

| Mychef Aeroporto Fiumicino Satellite C | mychef | €, AIC |
| Fiumicino | tel. 6.65019911 | www.mychef.it |

| Mychef Aeroporto Fiumicino Terminal A | mychef | €, AIC |
| Fiumicino | tel. 6.65019911 | www.mychef.it |

| Pizzeria Rosticceria del Porto | pizzeria, tavola calda | €, AIC |
| V.le Traiano, 101 | tel. 6.6521539 | |
www.facebook.com/PizzeriaRosticceriaDelPortoDarsena

FONDI

| Cantina di Galba | restaurant | €€€, AIC |
| Via Fabio Filzi, 29 | tel. 0771523648 | |
Notes: Closed Mondays.

| Il Mulino | restaurant, pizzeria | €, AIC |
| Via Rene, 5 | tel. 0771502891 | |

| Martino Club Hotel | hotel, restaurant | €€€, AIC |
| Via Flacca, km 4.150 | tel. 77.157464 | www.hotelmartino.it |

FORMIA

| Chinappi | restaurant, pizzeria | €€€€, AIC |
| Via Anfiteatro, 8/10 | tel. 0771790002 | |

| **I Dolci Pensieri** | gelato (€, AIC) | Via dei Frassini |

La Villetta restaurant €€€€, AIC
Via del Porticciolo Romano tel. 0771723113
Notes: Closed Tuesdays.

Ristopub Cook restaurant, pizzeria €€, AIC
Via S. Maria Cerquito tel. 0771720436

FRASCATI

Gamela Arte Pasticcera cupcake shop €, AIC
Via San Francesco D'Assisi, 10 tel. 6.9424148
www.facebook.com/GamelaArtePasticcera
Notes: 100% gluten-free.

Il Campo restaurant, pizzeria €€, AIC
Via Lunati, 3 tel. 6.942453 www.ilcampofrascati.it
Notes: 100% gluten-free.

FRASSO SABINO

La Taverna del Tiranno restaurant, pizzeria €€, AIC
Via Mirtense, Km 1 tel. 765.841708 www.latavernadeltiranno.com

FRAZ. GIULIANELLO

Al Ponte restaurant, pizzeria €, AIC
Via Velletri, 52 tel. 069665430 www.massimoalponte.it
Notes: DS pizza point. Closed Mondays, Tuesdays.

FROSINONE

La Ginestra restaurant €€-€€€, AIC
Via Adige, 1 tel. 0775824261

GAETA

B&B Elena B&B AIC
L.re Caboto,488 tel. 0771460466 www.elenabebgaeta.it

Il Follaro restaurant €€, AIC
L.mare Caboto, 624 A/D tel. 771.18942 www.ristoranteilfollaro.it

Il Gazebo restaurant, pizzeria €€€, AIC
Via Flacca Km.20,600 tel. 3405838052

Tuttigusti gelato (€, AIC) P.zza Libertà, 22

GENZANO DI ROMA

Da Elio restaurant, pizzeria €, AIC
Via Emilia Romagna, 04 tel. 6.9391466

Papillon Club restaurant, pizzeria €€, AIC
Via Lucrezio, 9 - Colli di Cicerone tel. 069370555
www.sites.google.com/site/papillonclubsrl

Piazza Margherita restaurant, pizzeria €, AIC
Via Ettore Ronconi, 1 tel. 0693953062 www.piazza-margherita.it

Pizzeria MA.MI pizzeria €, AIC
Via S.Silvestri, 208 tel. 0694426685

Trattoria dei Cacciatori restaurant €€€, AIC
Via Italo Belardi, 76 tel. 069396060 www.trattoria-cacciatori.com

GROTTAFERRATA

Maison del Celiaco bakery, sandwich shop €
Via Delle Sorgenti 98 - Squarciarelli www.maisondelceliaco.it

GUIDONIA

La Taverna   restaurant, pizzeria   €€€, AIC
Via G. Motta, 36   tel. 0774304179   www.latrattoriaguidonia.it

GUIDONIA MONTECELIO

Pizza Pazza   restaurant/pizzeria   € - €€, AIC
Via Arsoli, 21   tel. 3453327162

ITRI

Buenavistasurfmed   B&B   AIC
Contrada Campanaro, 21   tel. 3473792183   www.buenavistasurfmed.it

La Maison Galu'   B&B   AIC
Strada Prov. Itri/Sperlonga - Loc. Corano 9   tel. 771.728325   www.lamaisongalu.it

La Torre Rossa   agritourism, B&B   €€€, AIC
Contrada S. Stefano   tel. 0771729102   www.latorrerossa.com

LABICO

Magic Garden   B&B   AIC
Via Colle Pirro, 1   tel. 6.9510926   www.bbmagicgarden.com

LADISPOLI

La Piana di Alsium   agritourism   €€€, AIC
Via Longarina dei Caselli, 7   tel. 6.9946734   www.pianadialsium.com

Ristorante Roma   restaurant, pizzeria   AIC
L.mare Regina Elena, 35   tel. 6.83083267

LANUVIO

Al Tempio   restaurant, pizzeria   €€€€, AIC
Via G. Matteotti, 16   tel. 069375614

LATINA

Fattoria Prato di Coppola   restaurant   €€-€€€, AIC
Via del Lido Km.4,200   tel. 0773273411
I Milli   gelato (€, AIC)   Largo Cesti
Notes: Also GF crêpes. Closed Mondays.

I Milli 2   gelato (€, AIC)   Strade Acque Alte, snc

Il Funghetto   restaurant   €€€€, AIC
Strada Litoranea, 11412   tel. 0773208009
Notes: Closed Wednesdays and Sunday nights.

La Ginestra   restaurant   €€, AIC
Via dei Piceni, 63   tel. 0773266021   www.laginestravegetariano.it

La Pasticelia   bakery   €, AIC
Via Oslavia, 11   tel. 340.3232905   www.facebook.com/LaPasticelia

L'Euro   restaurant, pizzeria   €€, AIC
Via Isonzo, 269   tel. 773.242415

Punto Snack   pizzeria   €, AIC
Viale P.L.Nervi, 166   tel. 0773601512

LAVINIO DI ANZIO

Breezy   gelato (€, AIC)   Via Leonardo da Vinci, 21

Follia   restaurant, pizzeria   €€, AIC
Via Ardeatina, 632   tel. 3318065876

MAGLIANO SABINA

Il Giglio restaurant, pizzeria, B&B €€, AIC
Vocabolo Colle Croce tel. 0744910078 www.agriturismoilgiglio.it

MARINA DI S. NICOLA / LADISPOLI

Polipetto Goloso gelato (€, AIC) Via Orione, 1

MARINO

Forgione restaurant, pizzeria €€€, AIC
Via Pal. Colonna, 32

MENTANA

Il Sole e la Luna sandwich shop, bakery €, AIC
P.zza Moscatelli, 36 tel. 6.9001566 www.labilsoleelaluna.it

Sporting Life restaurant, pizzeria €€€, AIC
Via Cannetacci, 50 tel. 0690015826

MONTALTO DI CASTRO

Stella Polare restaurant €€€, AIC
Viale Harmine, 58/a tel. 0766801276 www.ristorantestellapolare.com
Notes: Closed Wednesdays.

MONTE COMPATRI

Il Rifugio dei Cacciatori restaurant, pizzeria €€€, AIC
Via Tuscolana, km 26,700 tel. 069406293

MONTE SAN BIAGIO

Piccola Caffetteria del Corso bar €, AIC
V.le Littoria, 1 tel. 348.8556153

MONTEROTONDO

Maculato restaurant, pizzeria €€-€€€€, AIC
Via Castelchiodato, 9 tel. 069066065 www.maculato.it

MOROLO

La Mola restaurant €€-€€€, AIC
Via Recinto della Mola, 67 tel. 0775229059

NETTUNO

Al Centro restaurant, pizzeria €€-€€€, AIC
Piazza Colonna, 13 tel. 6.9880946 www.ristoranteosteriaalcentro.com

ORTE

Garibaldi 148 bar €, AIC
Corso Garibaldi, 148 tel. 338.4280271

OSTIA LIDO

Don Pepe restaurant €€-€€€, AIC
L.re P. Toscanelli, 125 tel. 065672408

Il Corsaro restaurant €€€-€€€€, AIC
L.re Amerigo Vespucci, 164 tel. 055600317 www.ilcorsaro beach.it
Notes: Closed Mondays at lunch.

Il Mare del Gelato gelato (€, AIC) Via Pietro Rosa, 27

Mamey_Ro ma Ostia Lido bar €, AIC
Via dei Pescherecci, 5 tel. 6.64670436

Peccati di Gola gelato (€, AIC) Via Danilo Stiepovich, 245

Peppino a Mare restaurant €€€€, AIC
L.re Amerigo Vespucci, 102 tel. 6.56320247 www.peppinoamare.it

Pinzirò
Via Mar dei Sargassi, 68

restaurant
tel. 0656362203

€€-€€€, AIC
www.pinziro.it

PATRICA

Bar L'Incontro
Via Morolense, Km.5,500

tavola calda, bar
tel. 775.200734

€, AIC

POGGIO MIRTETO

Peter Pan 2
P.za della Vetreria 12

restaurant, pizzeria
tel. 765.24183

€-€€, AIC
www.ristorantepeterpan2.it

POMEZIA

Agriturismo Tonelli
Via Cesena, 15

agritourism
tel. 333.3300612

AIC
www.agriturismotonelli.it

Pizzeria Caroli
Via Catullo, 22

pizzeria
tel. 6.91620051

€€, AIC
www.pizzeriacaroli.com

PONTINIA

L'Arca
Via Migliara, 53 corner of Via Della Torre   tel. 0773853338

restaurant

€€€, AIC

POSTA FIBRENO

Ben Posta
Via Vicenne, 3

B&B
tel. 3391240889

AIC
www.benposta.it

RIETI

Al Bersagliere da Gualtiero
Via Castagneto, loc. S. Elia
Notes: Closed Tuesdays.

restaurant, pizzeria
tel. 0746210253

€€, AIC

Al Pincetto
Piazza Oberdan, 2

restaurant, pizzeria
tel. 746.272092

€-€€, AIC
www.ristorantealpincetto.com

Borgo Margherita
Via Sandro Pertini, 667

restaurant, pizzeria
tel. 0746218239

AIC

Cintia
Via Sandro Pertini, 667

restaurant, pizzeria
tel. 0746251527

€€, AIC

Da Valerio
Via Salaria per Roma

restaurant, pizzeria, hotel
tel. 746.606047

AIC
www.ristorantehoteldavalerio.it

Gelateria Crosby

gelato (€, AIC)

P.zza Marconi, 22

Il Picchio Allegro
Via Criano, 18

pizzeria
tel. 0746271826

AIC
www.picchioallegro.com

La Corte
Via Bevilacqua, 12

restaurant
tel. 746.218597

€€, AIC
www.lacortecatering.it

La Foresta
Via Foresta, 51

restaurant
tel. 0746220455

€€€-€€€€, AIC
www.ristorantelaforesta.it

La Lisca
Via Salaria per L'Aquila, 52

restaurant, hotel
tel. 746.271409

€€-€€€, AIC
www.laliscarieti.it

La Locanda del Carro
P.za S. Rufo, 7/8

restaurant
tel. 746.218507

€-€€, AIC

Lungovelino Cafè
Via Salaria, 26

wine bar, restaurant
tel. 0746.1970108

€€-€€€, AIC
www.lungovelino.it

Mondo Antico
Via Comunali, 23

restaurant, pizzeria
tel. 0746201665

€€, AIC

Notes: Closed Mondays.

Park Hotel Villa Potenziani hotel, restaurant AIC
Via San Mauro, 6 tel. 0746202765 www.villapotenziani.it
Notes: Closed Mondays and at lunch.

Quelli de Il Carro al Coccio restaurant, pizzeria €-€€, AIC
Via P. Borsellino, 11 tel. 746.760078
Notes: Great reviews.

Fontana (S. Wolozin)

RIETI - TERMINILLO ROSCE
Rosce Caffe' restaurant, B&B €€-€€€, AIC
Via degli Appennini,18 tel. 335.71026

RIGNANO FLAMINIO
Mediterranea cupcake shop, deli €, AIC
Via dei Montaroni, 26 tel. 320.3346866
www.facebook.com/pages/Laboratorio-Mediterranea-Senza-Glutine/156179137739726

RIVODUTRI
Agriturismo Tenuta Due Laghi agritourism, restaurant AIC
Via Campigliana, 29 tel. 746.685206 www.tenutaduelaghi.com

ROCCA PRIORA
Al Ritrovo da Uccia restaurant, pizzeria AIC
Via Mediana, 12 tel. 069406081 www.alritrovodauccia.it

S. MARTINO AL CIMINO-VITERBO
Balletti Park Hotel hotel AIC
Via Umbria, 2 tel. 07613771 www.balletti.com

Gelateria Balletti gelato (€, AIC) Via Umbria, 2

Tavernetta Il Cavaliere restaurant, pizzeria €€€, AIC
Via Umbria, 2/a tel. 07613771 www.balletti.com

SABAUDIA

La Capricciosa   restaurant, pizzeria
€€, AIC   Via Tortini 33
tel. 0773515677
www.lacapricciosa.it

SAN MARTINO AL CIMINO

Ristorante Pizzeria da Saverio
restaurant, pizzeria   €€, AIC
Piazza Del Duomo, 2
tel. 761.379643
www.dasaverio.com

Cinquecento classico (J. Lubin)

SAN POLO DEI CAVALIERI

L'Agrifoglio   restaurant   €, AIC
Via Santa Liberata, 14   tel. 0774416384

SANTA MARINELLA

Girogustando   gelato (€, AIC)   Via Aurelia, 248

SERMONETA SCALO

La Valle dell'Usignolo   agritourism   €€, AIC
Via Vigna Riccelli, 2   tel. 0773318629   www.lavalledellusignolo.it

SERRONE

Belsito   restaurant   €€€€, AIC
Via delle Rimembranze, 17/29   tel. 0775523106   www.belsitoserrone.com
Notes: Closed Wednesdays.

SPIGNO SATURNIA

Der Keller   pub   €, AIC
Via Grata, 8   tel. 077164187

TARQUINIA

L'Ambaradan   restaurant   €€€€, AIC
P.zza G. Matteotti, 14   tel. 0766857073
Notes: Closed Wednesdays.

Quadrifoglio   agritourism   €€€, AIC
Loc. Selciatella   tel. 3358080415   www.agriturismoquadrifoglio.it
Notes: Closed Tuesdays. Rooms for rent.

Valle del Marta   agritourism   AIC
Via St. Aurelia Vecchia Km.93   tel. 0766855475   www.valledelmarta.it

TERRACINA

La Perla   pizzeria   €, AIC
Via Grata, 8   tel. 0773730691

TOBIA

Poggio della Guardia   pizzeria, trattoria   €€€€, AIC
Str. Ciavaletta 15   tel. 0761263570   www.poggiodellaguardia.it

TOLFA

Tolfa Hotel
Via Lizzera, 44
Notes: Restaurant is closed Mondays.

hotel restaurant
tel. 076693286

€€€, AIC
www.tolfahotel.it

TORRICE

Drago Rosso
Via Piana, 50

restaurant, pizzeria
tel. 0775301675

€, AIC
www.trattoriadragorosso.com

VALENTANO

La Voltarella
Via Solferino, 25
Notes: 100% gluten-free. Closed Tuesdays.

restaurant
tel. 0761422197 www.facebook.com/locanda.lavoltarella

€€, AIC

VALMONTONE

Fashion Hotel
Via della Pace 1/2

hotel
tel. 6.9599631

AIC
www.fashion-hotel.it

Mone'
Via della Pace 1/2

restaurant, pizzeria, bar
tel. 6.95994751

€€€, AIC
www.fashionristorazione.com

VELLETRI

La Forbice
C.so della Repubblica, 466

restaurant, pizzeria
tel. 069638812

€, AIC
www.laforbice.it

VILLA S. GIOVANNI IN TUSCIA

Da Peppone
V.le Europa, 8

restaurant, pizzeria
tel. 761.476287

€€€, AIC
www.dapeppone.com

VITERBO

Da Oliviera
Str. Cassia Sud Km. 76 113/c

restaurant
tel. 761.263001

AIC
www.ristorantedaoliviera.it

Gustosi senza glutine
Piazza Santa Maria Nuova, 7

bakery
tel. 0761.1706154

€, AIC
www.gustosisenzaglutine.it

FLORENCE AND TOSCANA

PLACES IN FLORENCE TO BUY GLUTEN-FREE FOOD PRODUCTS

Esselunga	Via Galliano, 136
Esselunga	Via Pisana, 130
Esselunga	Via Milanesi, 32/34
Esselunga	Via del Gignoro
Esselunga	Viale Gianotti, 75/77
Esselunga	Via Masaccio, 274
Esselunga	Via Di Novoli, 61
Esselunga	Via Canova, 164
Esselunga	Via del Argingrosso, 47
Farmacia all'insegna	Piazza S.Giovanni, 20 R
Farmacia Camilli	P.zza Degli OttaViani, 8/r
Farmacia Del Cinghiale	Piazza Mercato Nuovo, 4/R
Farmacia Paglici	Via Della Scala, 61R
Farmacia Zanobini	Via Pagnini, 17/R

GUARANTEED GLUTEN-FREE GELATO PLACES
(Sponsored by the Italian celiac society)

Antica Gelateria Fiorentina   Via Faenza, 2/a
Notes: Santa Maria Novella.

Ciolli   Via Ramazzini, 35/r
Notes: Campo di Marte.

Damiani   Via Burchiello, 20/r
Notes: Monticelli.

Gelateria Conti   Viale dei Mille 1A
Notes: Campo di Marte.

Gelateria Malotti   Via di Novoli, 42/6

Gelateria Mascia   Via Torcicoda, 60

Gelateria Senza Glutine   Via 20 Settembre 126
Notes: Fortezza Basso.

Grom   Via dell'Oche, 24/R
Notes: Duomo.

Il Gelato Gourmet   Via M. Palmieri, 34/R
Notes: Santa Croce.

La Bottega del Gelato   Via Por Santa Maria 33
Notes: Duomo.

La Sorbettiera   P.zza Tasso, 11/r
Notes: Palazzo Pitti. Closed Wednesdays.

Mandorla e Limone 2   Via Passavanti, 18/r

Roberto   Via Mariti, 3/a
          Notes: Novoli.

FLORENCE B&B'S AND HOTELS LISTED ALPHABETICALLY
(AIC = participates in the Associazione Italiana Celiachia program)

HOTELS

Albergo Londra
Via Jacopo di Diacceto, 16/20   hotel, restaurant
tel. 05527390   www.hotellondra.com
Notes: Santa Maria Novella.

B&B Cimatori
Via Dante Alighieri, 14   B&B
tel. 0552655000   www.cimatori.it
Notes: Duomo.

B&B Il Marzocco
V.le Fratelli Rosselli 78   tel. 055 274 1444   www.bbilmarzoccoflorence.net
Notes: Stazione Ferroviaria Santa Maria Novella.

B&B L'Argentiere
via G. Borelli 8   tel. 335 528 3741   www.largentiere.it
Notes: San Gaggio.

B&B La Mongolfiera
Via Guido Guinizzelli 1   tel. 055 553 5141   www.residenzelamongolfiera.it
Notes: Centro Storico Minore.

B&B Leopoldo Florence
Via Fabbroni 78   tel. 055 384 1202   www.leopoldohouse.it
Notes: Piazza Leopoldo.

B&B Monte Oliveto
Via Domenico Burchiello 67   tel. 055 231 3484   www.bebmonteoliveto.it
Notes: Monticelli.

B&B Villa La Sosta
Via Bolognese 83   tel. 055 495 073   www.villalasosta.com
Notes: Fortezza Basso.

Best Western Grand Hotel Adriatico
Via Maso Finiguerra 9   tel. 055 279 31   www.hoteladriatico.it
Notes: Santa Maria Novella.

Best Western Hotel Villa Gabriele D'Annunzio
Via G. D'Annunzio 141/a-b   tel. 055 602 960   www.dannunziohotel.it
Notes: Campo di Marte.

Casa di Barbano
Via Di Barbano 1   tel. 055 475 016   www.casadibarbano.it
Notes: Indipendenza.

Casa Toselli
Via Toselli 67   tel. 055 332 202   www.casatoselli.it
Notes: San Lorenzo.

Classic Hotel
Viale Machiavelli 25   tel. 055 22 93 51   www.classichotel.it
Notes: Michelangelo.

Dante e Beatrice relais
via Cavour 90   tel. 55 579232   www.danteandbeatrice.com
Notes: Indipendenza.

Eden Rock Resort
Via Clemente Biondetti 7   tel. 055 400 331   www.edenrockresort.it
Notes: Just outside city.

The Galileo Hotel
Via Nazionale 22/a   tel. 055 496 645   www.galileohotel.it
Notes: Santa Maria Novella.

Grand Hotel Baglioni
Piazza Unità Italiana 6   tel. 055 23 580   www.hotelbaglioni.it
Notes: Santa Maria Novella.

Grand Hotel Villa Medici
Via Il Prato 42   tel. 55 277 171   www.villamedicihotel.com
Notes: Stazione Ferroviaria Santa Maria Novella.

Hilton Florence Metropole
Via del Cavallaccio 36   tel. 055 787 11   www3.hilton.com
Notes: Just outside city.

Hotel Adler Cavalieri
Via Della Scala 40   tel. 055 277 810   www.hoteladlercavalieri.com
Notes: Stazione Ferroviaria Santa Maria Novella.

Hotel Alba
Via della Scala 22/38r   tel. 055 282 610   www.hotelalbafirenze.it/en
Notes: Stazione Ferroviaria Santa Maria Novella.

Hotel Albani Firenze
Via Fiume 12   tel. 055 26 030   www.albanihotels.com/firenze
Notes: Santa Maria Novella.

Hotel Alessandra
Borgo SS. Apostoli 17   tel. 055 283 438   www.hotelalessandra.com
Notes: Duomo.

Hotel Angelica
via Fiume 11   tel. 055210229   www.hotelangelicafirenze.com
Notes: Santa Maria Novella.

Hotel Annalena
Via Romana 34   tel. 055 222 402   www.annalenahotel.com
Notes: Palazzo Pitti.

Hotel Arizona
Via Luigi Carlo Farini 2   tel. 055 245 321   www.arizonahotel.it/en
Notes: Santa Croce.

Hotel Atlantic Palace
Via Nazionale 10   tel. 055 213 031   www.atlanticpalace.it
Notes: Santa Maria Novella.

Hotel Axial
Via dei Calzaiuoli 11   tel. 055 218 984   www.hotelaxial.it
Notes: Duomo.

Hotel Fiorino   inn   AIC
Via Osteria del Guanto, 6   tel. 055210579   www.hotelfiorino.it
Notes: Duomo. Only GF breakfast.

Il Guelfo Bianco   hotel   €€, AIC
Via Cavour, 29   tel. 0552883300   www.ilguelfobianco.it
Notes: Santa Maria Novella.

SUMMARY INFO: RESTAURANTS IN FLORENCE
LISTED ALPHABETICALLY WITH PRICES

Airport

Da Tito i Sette Peccati	Via Alderotti, 87/a	€-€€
Mychef Aeroporto Firenze A. Vespucci	Via del Termine	€

Campo di Marte

Aviazione Campo di Marte	Viale Malta, 8	€€
Ciolli	Via Ramazzini, 35/r	€€
Gelateria Conti	Viale dei Mille 1A	€€
Il Girasole	Via Aretina, 138/C r	€€
Il Povero Pesce	Via P.F. Calvi, 8	€€-€€€
Piazza del Vino	Via della Torretta, 18/r	€€-€€€
Pizza Man	Via Carlo del Prete, 10 R	€€
Pizza Man	Viale de Amicis 47R	€€
Trilli	Viale Marconi 19R	€

Duomo

La Bottega del Gelato	Via Por Santa Maria 33	€
B&B Cimatori	Via Dante Alighieri, 14	
Buca Lapi	Via del Trebbio, 1	€€€€
Cantinetta Antinori	Piazza Antinori 3	€€€
Cantinetta del Verrazzano	Via dei Tavolini, 18-20	€€€
Chiaroscuro	Via del Corso, 36r	€€
Da Pennello	Via Dante Alighieri, 4	€€
Giannino in S. Lorenzo	Borgo S. Lorenzo, 35/37 R	€€
Grom	Via dell'Oche, 24/R	€
Gustavino	Via della Condotta 37R	€€€
Hostaria Il Desco	Via delle Terme, 23/R	€€-€€€
Hotel Fiorino	Via Osteria del Guanto, 6	
La Giostra	Borgo Pinti, 12	€€€
Le Botteghe di Donatello	Piazza Duomo, 28/r	€€€
Oliviero	Via delle Terme, 51	€€€
Panino Vegano	Via M. Bufalini, 19/R	€€
Vecchia Firenze	Borgo degli Albizi, 18	€€

Fortezza Basso

Gelateria Senza Glutine	Via 20 Settembre 126	€-€€

Fucecchio

Osteria Numero Uno	Via del Moro, 18-20	€€€€

Indipendenza

Cafaggi	Via Guelfa 35	€€€-€€€€
Il Fresco Senza Glutine	Viale Spartaco Lavagnini 2	€-€€
La Cucina del Garga	Via S. Zanobi, 33 a/r	€€€€

Michelangelo

I Tarocchi	Via dei Renai, 14 R	€€

Monticelli

Damiani	Via Burchiello, 20/r	€
Pizza Man	Via Sansovino, 191	€€

Novoli

Baraka Cafè	Via di Novoli, 75/r	€
Pistocchi	Via del Ponte di Mezzo 20	€€
Roberto	Via Mariti, 3/a	€
Starbene Senza Glutine	Viale Alessandro Guidoni 83B	€

Oberdan

Grand Hotel Mediterraneo	Lungarno del Tempio, 44	
La Luna Nuova	Via Gioberti, 93/r	€€

Palazzo Pitti

Cammillo	B.go S. Jacopo, 57	€€€€
Fuor d'Acqua	Via Pisana, 37r	€€€€
La Sorbettiera	P.zza Tasso, 11/r	€€
Mamma Gina	Borgo San Jacopo, 37	€€€
Munaciello	Via Maffia 31	€€
Oronero	Piazza Pitti 1R	€€
Pasticceria Gualtieri	Via Senese, 18/R	€
Trattoria Cammillo	Borgo Sant Jacopo, 57R	€€€€
Vivanda	Via Santa Monaca 7R	€€

Piazza della Liberta/Savonarola

I Cinque Sensi	Via Pier Capponi, 3 a/r	€€€

Piazza San Martino

Ristorante Paoli	Via dei Tavolini, 12R	€€€€

Santa Croce

Bacca Rossa	Via Ghibellina, 46/r	€€€-€€€€
Cibreino	Via de' Macci, 118	€-€€
Don Chisciotte	Via Cosimo Ridolfi, 4	€€€€
Il Gelato Gourmet	Via M. Palmieri, 34/R	€
La Brasserie	Via dei Macci 77	€€€€
Nencioni	Via Pietrapiana 24R	€€
Trattoria Cibreo	Via de' Macci, 118	€€€

Santa Maria Novella

Albergo Londra	Via Jacopo di Diacceto, 16/20	
Antica Gelateria Fiorentina	Via Faenza, 2/a	€
Buca Mario	Piazza degli Ottaviani, 16/r	€€€€
Ciro & Son's	Via del Giglio, 26/28 R	€€€€
Coccole Cioccolato	Via dei Ginori 55	€
Etichetta Pinchiorri	Piazza Ognissanti 1	€€€
Harry's Bar	22R Lungarno Amerigo Vespucci	€€€€
I' Toscano	Via Guelfa, 70/r	€€€
Il Desco Bistrot	Via Cavour, 55/r	€€
Il Guelfo Bianco	Via Cavour, 29	€€
La Gratella	Via Guelfa, 81 R	€€
Quinoa	Vicolo Santa Maria Maggiore, 1	€€€
Ristorante Sabatini	Via Panzani, 9	€€€€
The Club House	Via De Ginori 10r	€€
Trattoria Antellesi	Via Faenza, 9R	€€€

Sascaro

L' Antica Badia	Via Faentina, 342	€€

Stazione Ferroviaria Santa Maria Novella

Bar Deanna	Piazza Stazione, 52/55 r	€€
Deanna - Terravision	Piazza della Stazione 52R	€€
Enotria Ristorante	Via delle Porte Nuove, 50	€€€
Il Portale	Via C. Alamanni, 29/r	€€€
La Carabaccia	Via Palazzuolo, 190/r	€€€

View of Florence (D. Frost)

FLORENCE RESTAURANTS AND BAKERIES
LISTED ALPHABETICALLY

Aviazione Campo di Marte pizzeria, sandwich shop, pub €€, AIC
Viale Malta, 8 tel. 55.5381058 www.aviazionecampodimarte.it
Notes: Campo di Marte.

Bacca Rossa restaurant €€€-€€€€, AIC
Via Ghibellina, 46/r tel. 055240620 www.baccarossa.it
Notes: Santa Croce.

Bar Abbecedario bar, tavola calda/fredda €€, AIC
Viale Pieraccini, 22A tel. 338.4483006

Bar Deanna bar, tavola calda/fredda €€, AIC
Piazza Stazione, 52/55 r tel. 55.284092
Notes: Stazione Ferroviaria Santa Maria Novella.

Baraka Cafè bar, tavola calda/fredda €, AIC
Via di Novoli, 75/r tel. 55.431495 www.barakacafe.it
Notes: Novoli.

Buca Lapi restaurant €€€€
Via del Trebbio, 1 tel. 055213768 www.bucalapi.com
Notes: Duomo. Reservations required for dinner.

Buca Mario restaurant €€€€
Piazza degli Ottaviani, 16/r tel. 055214179 www.bucamario.it
Notes: Santa Maria Novella. GF pasta. English spoken. Closed in August.

Cafaggi restaurant €€€-€€€€
Via Guelfa 35 tel. 055294989 www.ristorantecafaggi.com
Notes: Indipendenza.

Caffetteria Raffaella - Tapinassi Bar bar, tavola calda   €, AIC
Via S. Caterina d'Alessandria, 26   tel. 055486268

Cammillo   trattoria   €€€€, AIC
B.go S. Jacopo, 57   tel. 055212427
Notes: Palazzo Pitti. Closed Tuesday-Wednesday.

Cantinetta Antinori   restaurant   €€€
Piazza Antinori 3   tel. 055292234   www.antinori.it
Notes: Duomo. Reservations recommended.

Cantinetta del Verrazzano   restaurant   €€€
Via dei Tavolini, 18-20   tel. 055268590   www.verrazzano.com
Notes: Duomo. Reservations recommended. Closed Tuesdays. English spoken.

Chiaroscuro   bar, tavola calda   €€, AIC
Via del Corso, 36r   tel. 055214247   www.chiaroscurofirenze.it
Notes: Duomo.

Cibreino   restaurant   €-€€
Via de' Macci, 118   tel. 0552341100 www.edizioniteatrodelsalecibreofirenze.it
Notes: Santa Croce. Small sister restaurant of Cibreo; same food, less pricey. No reservations nor credit cards accepted.

Ciro & Son's   restaurant, pizzeria   €€€€, AIC
Via del Giglio, 26/28 R   tel. 055289694   www.ciroandsons.com
Notes: Santa Maria Novella.

Coccole Cioccolato   tea salon, desserts   €
Via dei Ginori 55   tel. 05 5294750   www.coccolecioccolato.it
Notes: Santa Maria Novella.

Da Pennello   restaurant   €€
Via Dante Alighieri, 4   tel. 055294848   www.ristoranteilpennello.it
Notes: Duomo.

Da Tito i Peccati di Gola   restaurant, pizzeria   €€, AIC
Via Baracca, 149 rosso   tel. 055416726   www.datitoipeccatidigola.it

Da Tito i Sette Peccati   restaurant, pizzeria   €-€€, AIC
Via Alderotti, 87/a   tel. 0554360470

Da Tito il Sesto Girone   restaurant, pizzeria   €€-€€€, AIC
Via Villamagna, 77/a   tel. 0556530695

Deanna - Terravision   café, desserts   €€
Piazza della Stazione 52R   tel. 05 5284092
Notes: Stazione Ferroviaria Santa Maria Novella.

Don Chisciotte   restaurant   €€€€
Via Cosimo Ridolfi, 4   tel. 055475430   www.ristorantedonchisciotte.it
Notes: Santa Croce. Reservations recommended.

Enotria Ristorante   restaurant   €€€, AIC
Via delle Porte Nuove, 50   tel. 055354350   www.enotriawine.it
Notes: Stazione Ferroviaria Santa Maria Novella.

Etichetta Pinchiorri   restaurant   €€€
Piazza Ognissanti 1   tel. 05 527163770   www.stregisflorence.com
Notes: Santa Maria Novella.

Fuor d'Acqua   restaurant   €€€€
Via Pisana, 37r   tel. 055222299   www.fuordacqua.it
Notes: Palazzo Pitti. Highly recommended seafood restaurant.

Giannino in S. Lorenzo   restaurant   €€, AIC
Borgo S. Lorenzo, 35/37 R   tel. 0552333799   www.gianninoinflorence.com
Notes: Duomo.

Grand Hotel Mediterraneo   hotel, restaurant, reception hall   AIC
Lungarno del Tempio, 44   tel. 055660241   www.hotelmediterraneo.com
Notes: Oberdan.

Gustavino   wine bar, restaurant   €€€
Via della Condotta 37R   tel. 05 52399806   www.gustavino.it
Notes: Duomo.

Harry's Bar   restaurant   €€€€
22R Lungarno Amerigo Vespucci (Grand Hotel)   tel. 0552396700   www.harrysbarfirenze.it
Notes: Santa Maria Novella. Reservations required. English spoken.

Hostaria Il Desco   restaurant   €€-€€€, AIC
Via delle Terme, 23/R   tel. 055294882   www.hostariaildesco.com
Notes: Duomo.

I Cinque Sensi   restaurant   €€€, AIC
Via Pier Capponi, 3 a/r   tel. 55.5000315   www.ristoranteicinquesensi.com
Notes: Piazza della Liberta/Savonarola.

I Tarocchi   restaurant, pizzeria   €€, AIC
Via dei Renai, 14 R   tel. 55.2343912
Notes: Michelangelo.

I' Toscano   restaurant   €€€, AIC
Via Guelfa, 70/r   tel. 055215475   www.itoscano.it
Notes: Santa Maria Novella. Closed Tuesdays.

Il Desco Bistrot   sandwich shop   €€, AIC
Via Cavour, 55/r   tel. 055288330   www.ildescofirenze.it
Notes: Santa Maria Novella. Closed at dinner.

Il Fresco Senza Glutine   desserts, sandwich shop   €-€€
Viale Spartaco Lavagnini 2   tel. 05 5491884
Notes: Indipendenza.

Il Girasole   crepes, gelato   €€, AIC
Via Aretina, 138/C r   tel. 05 52477587   www.gelateriailgirasole.com
Notes: Campo di Marte.

Il Portale   restaurant   €€€, AIC
Via C. Alamanni, 29/r   tel. 055212992
Notes: Stazione Ferroviaria Santa Maria Novella. Closed Sundays.

Il Povero Pesce   restaurant   €€-€€€, AIC
Via P.F. Calvi, 8   tel. 055671218   www.poveropesce.it
Notes: Campo di Marte.

L' Antica Badia   pizzeria   €€, AIC
Via Faentina, 342   tel. 0555002153   www.pizzerialalauna.it

La Brasserie   French restaurant   €€€€
Via dei Macci 77   tel. 05 52478326   www.labrasseriefirenze.it
Notes: Santa Croce.

Closeup of Duomo (S. Amatangelo)

La Carabaccia   restaurant   €€€
Via Palazzuolo, 190/r   tel. 055214782   www.trattorialacarabaccia.com
Notes: Stazione Ferroviaria Santa Maria Novella. English spoken. Reservations recommended.

La Cucina del Garga   cooking school, restaurant   €€€€, AIC
Via S. Zanobi, 33 a/r   tel. 055475286   www.garga.it
Notes: Indipendenza.

La Giostra   restaurant   €€€
Borgo Pinti, 12   tel. 055241341   www.ristorantelagiostra.com
Notes: Duomo. English spoken. Reservations required.

La Gratella   trattoria   €€, AIC
Via Guelfa, 81 R   tel. 055211292
Notes: Santa Maria Novella.

La Luna Nuova   pizzeria, restaurant   €€, AIC
Via Gioberti, 93/r   tel. 055663810   www.pizzerialaluna.net
Notes: Oberdan.

Le Botteghe di Donatello   restaurant, pizzeria   €€€, AIC
Piazza Duomo, 28/r   tel. 055216678   www.botteghedidonatello.com
Notes: Duomo.

Lo Strettoio   restaurant   €€€€, AIC
Via di Serpiolle, 7   tel. 0554250044   www.lostrettoio.com
Notes: Closed Mondays and Sundays at dinner.

Mamey Firenze Ovest   bar   €, AIC
Via Pratese,211   tel. 055319223   www.mamey.it/firenze-ovest.html

Mamma Gina   restaurant   €€€
Borgo San Jacopo, 37   tel. 0552396009   www.mammagina.it
Notes: Palazzo Pitti. Reservations required for dinner.

Munaciello   restaurant, pizzeria   €€
Via Maffia 31   tel. 05 5287198   www.munaciello.it
Notes: Palazzo Pitti.

Mychef Aeroporto Firenze A. Vespucci mychef   €, AIC
Via del Termine   tel. 55.3427495   www.mychef.it

Nencioni   café   €€
Via Pietrapiana 24R   tel. 05 5241012
Notes: Santa Croce.

Oliviero   restaurant   €€€
Via delle Terme, 51   tel. 055287643   www.ristorante-oliviero.it
Notes: Duomo. GF pasta. Reservations required.

Oronero   café   €€
Piazza Pitti 1R   tel. 05 52302473   www.oronero-firenze.blogspot.com
Notes: Palazzo Pitti.

Osteria de' benci   osteria   €€€
Via de' Benci, 13   tel. 0552344923   www.debencisuite.com
Notes: English spoken. Reservations essential. Closed Sunday.

Osteria Numero Uno   osteria   €€€€
Via del Moro, 18-20   tel. 055284897   www.osteriadigiovanni.com
Notes: Fucecchio. English spoken. Reservations essential. Closed Sunday.

Panino Vegano   sandwich shop   €€, AIC
Via M. Bufalini, 19/R   tel. 333.8359787   www.paninovegano.it
Notes: Duomo.

Pasticceria Gualtieri   bakery   €, AIC
Via Senese, 18/R   tel. 55.221771   www.pasticceriagualtieri.com
Notes: Palazzo Pitti. Also vegan.

Piazza del Vino   restaurant, wine bar   €€-€€€, AIC
Via della Torretta, 18/r   tel. 055671404   www.piazzadelvino.eu
Notes: Campo di Marte.

Pistocchi   desserts   €€
Via del Ponte di Mezzo 20   tel. 05 50516939
Notes: Novoli.

Pizza Man   restaurant, pizzeria   €, AIC
Via Baracca, 148 A/B   tel. 0554379931   www.pizzaman.it

Pizza Man   restaurant, pizzeria   €€, AIC
Via Carlo del Prete, 10 R   tel. 55.433849   www.pizzaman.it
Notes: Campo di Marte.

Pizza Man   restaurant, pizzeria   €€, AIC
Via Sansovino, 191   tel. 055712738   www.pizzaman.it
Notes: Monticelli. DS pizza point.

Pizza Man   restaurant, pizzeria   €€, AIC
Viale de Amicis 47R   tel. 0550510049   www.pizzaman.it
Notes: Campo di Marte. DS pizza point.

Quinoa   restaurant, bar   €€€, AIC
Vicolo Santa Maria Maggiore, 1   tel. 55.290876   www.ristorantequinoa.it
Notes: Santa Maria Novella.

Ristorante Paoli   restaurant   €€€€
Via dei Tavolini, 12R   tel. 055216215   www.casatrattoria.com
Notes: Piazza San Martino. Reservations required.

Ristorante Sabatini
Via Panzani, 9
Notes: Santa Maria Novella.

restaurant
tel. 055282802

€€€€
www.ristorantesabatini.it

San Marcellino
Via Chiantigiana,28
www.facebook.com/sanmarcellinoristorantebarpizzeria

restaurant, pizzeria
tel. 0553921039

€, AIC

Star Bene Senza Glutine
Viale S. Lavagnini
Via Di Ripoli 4/6r

bar, desserts
tel. 055/491884
tel. 055/6587549

€
www.starbenesenzaglutine.it
www.starbenesenzaglutine.it

Starbene Senza Glutine
Viale Alessandro Guidoni 83B
www.starbenesenzaglutine.it/firenze-novoli.html
Notes: Novoli.

bakery, sandwich shop
tel. 05 59338350

€

The Club House
Via De Ginori 10r
Notes: Santa Maria Novella. American food.

restaurant
tel. 055211427

€€
www.theclubhouse.it

Trattoria Antellesi
Via Faenza, 9R
Notes: Santa Maria Novella.

trattoria
tel. 055216990

€€€

Trattoria Cammillo
Borgo Sant Jacopo, 57R
Notes: Palazzo Pitti. Reservations required.

trattoria
tel. 055212427

€€€€

Trattoria Cibreo
Via de' Macci, 118
Notes: Santa Croce.

restaurant
tel. 0552341100 www.edizioniteatrodelsalecibreofirenze.it

€€€

Trattoria da Garibaldi
Piazza del Mercato Centrale, 38

trattoria
tel. 055212267

€€, AIC
www.garibaldi.it

Trilli
Viale Marconi 19R
Notes: Campo di Marte.

café

€

Vecchia Firenze
Borgo degli Albizi, 18
Notes: Duomo.

restaurant
tel. 0552340361

€€
www.vecchiafirenze.eu

Vivanda
Via Santa Monaca 7R
Notes: Palazzo Pitti.

restaurant
tel. 05 52381208

€€
www.vivandafirenze.it

THE REST OF TOSCANA

ALBERESE

Agriturismo Le Due Ruote
Strada Antica Dogana, 44
Notes: Must make reservations.

agritourism
tel. 0564405361

€€€€, AIC
www.agriturismoledueruote.it

ALTOPASCIO

Hotel Cavalieri del Tau
Via Gavinana, 56

hotel, restaurant
tel. 583.25131

AIC
www.cavalierideltau.it

ANTIGNANO

In Caciaia
Via Dei Bagni, 38

restaurant
tel. 0586580403

AIC

ARBIA-ASCIANO

Piccola Oasi — restaurant, pizzeria — €-€€, AIC
Piazza della Repubblica, 70 — tel. 0577365367

AREZZO

A Casa Tua — B&B — AIC
Via Montale, 85 — tel. 3291774790
Notes: S € 35 D € 50

Gelateria Cremì — gelato (€, AIC) — C.so Italia, 100

Gelateria Cremì — gelato (€, AIC) — Via Fiorentina,1 83 C

Gustolandia — pizzeria — €, AIC
Via Case Nuove di Ceciliano, 73/15 — tel. 0575320056

Il Sogno di Tutti — bar, tavola calda — €, AIC
Piazza Giotto, 17 — tel. 0575403590

La Bottega di Nonna Tina — sandwiches, bakery — €, AIC
Via Antonio Pizzuto, 46/a — tel. 575.27678 — www.labottegadinonnatina.it
Via Pietro Aretino, 11 — tel. 575.27678 — www.labottegadinonnatina.it

La Gola Non Ha Ora — restaurant — €-€€, AIC
Via Piave, 23 — tel. 0575905249 — www.lagolanonhaora.it

Minerva — hotel, restaurant — €€, AIC
Via Fiorentina, 4 — tel. 0575370390

Mivà — restaurant, pizzeria — €€, AIC
Via San Lorentino, 20 — tel. 0575. 300300 — www.mivaarezzo.com

Mivà di più — restaurant, pizzeria — €, AIC
Via Garibaldi, 36/38 — tel. 0575352182 — www.mivadipiu.com

Non Solo Caffè — bar, tavola calda — €, AIC
Via Giotto, 27 — tel. 3487956703

San Marco — gelato (€, AIC) — Via Romana, 66/a

Star Bene Senza Glutine — bar, desserts — €
Via Turati 57 — tel. 389.0357468 — www.starbenesenzaglutine.it

Vinosteria 4 Chiacchiere — restaurant — €€€ - €€€€, AIC
Via Guelfa, 14/16 — tel. 0575902524

AULLA

da Giovanna — restaurant — AIC
Località Bettola-Aulla — tel. 0187414117 — www.ristorantedagiovanna.com

AVENZA CARRARA

Il Giardino Antico — B&B — AIC
Via Toniolo, 8/bis — tel. 0585859667 — www.giardinoantico.it

Lavenza — pizzeria — €, AIC
Via Gino Menconi, 53 — tel. 058552451

BAGNI DI LUCCA

Antico Albergo Terme — hotel — €€-€€€, AIC
Via Paretaio, 1 — tel. 058386034

La Lira — restaurant, pizzeria — €-€€, AIC
P.zza Vitt. Veneto — tel. 0583867708 — www.lalirapub.it
Notes: Closed Wednesdays and lunch.

Autogrill Chianti
A1 Firenze - Roma

BAGNO A RIPOLI
autogrill
tel. 55.6560063

€, AIC

BAGNO VIGNONI

Hotel Posta Marcucci
Via Ara Urcea, 43

B&B
tel. 0577887112

AIC
www.hotelpostamarcucci.it

Il Barrino
Via del Gorello, 44

bar, tavola calda
tel. 0577887112

€, AIC

BARBERINO DEL MUGELLO

Vanilla & Cioccolato

gelato (€, AIC)

Largo Nilde Iotti

BARBERINO DI MUGELLO

C.lo M.C.L. S. M.le Montecuccoli restaurant
Via Rocca Cerbaia, 3

tel. 055841035

€€ - €€€€, AIC

Lo Scricciolo
Via delle Voltate, 2

restaurant, pizzeria
tel. 558423116

€-€€, AIC
www.ristoranteloscricciolo.it

Mychef Aglio Est
A1 Firenze - Milano

mychef
tel. 55.841085

€, AIC
www.mychef.it

BARBERINO VAL D'ELSA

Il Paese dei Campanelli
Loc. Petrognano

restaurant
tel. 0558075318

€€€€, AIC
www.ilpaesedeicampanelli.it

BARGA

Bar Pizzeria F.lli Rossi
Via P. Funai, 86/88

bar, restaurant, pizzeria
tel. '0583710193

€, AIC

Renaissance Tuscany Il Ciocco Hotels & Resort hotel, restaurant
Loc. Castelvecchio Pascoli

tel. 0583719478

€€€-€€€€, AIC
www.ciocco.it

BETTOLLE

Walter Redaelli
Via XXI Aprile, 10

restaurant
tel. 0577623447

€€€-€€€€, AIC
www.ristoranteredaelli.it

BIBBIENA

Bar Gelateria Edi
Notes: Closed Tuesdays.

gelato (€, AIC)   Via Marcucci Poltri -p.zza Stazione

Glutenfreedesi
Via Carlo Marx, 5

bakery, pizzeria
tel. 348.0905883

€, AIC
www.glutenfreedesi.it

BIENTINA

Succo d'Uva
Via XX Settembre, 2

restaurant, pizzeria, bar
tel. 0587757548

€€-€€€€, AIC

Villa delle Mimose
Via Corte Betti, 26/a

restaurant, pizzeria
tel. 0587714038

€€€-€€€€, AIC
www.villadellemimose.it

BORGO A BUGGIANO

La Fiamma
Via Cavour, 77/79

restaurant, pizzeria
tel. 0572318116

AIC

BORGO SAN LORENZO

I' Corbezzolo
Via P. Caiani

restaurant/pizzeria
tel. 0558402197

€ - €€, AIC

Gluten-Free Italy by Region

Il Feriolo	restaurant	€€-€€€, AIC
Via Faentina, 32	tel. 0558409928	www.ristoranteilferiolo.it
La Griglia	restaurant	€-€€€, AIC
V.le IV Novembre, 91	tel. 0558458527	
Star Bene Senza Glutine	bar, desserts	€
Via Trieste n. 4/1	tel. 055/0503822	www.starbenesenzaglutine.it

BUCINE

Le Mura	agritourism	€€, AIC
Loc. Le Mura, 31	tel. 055992297	www.agrilemura.it
Locanda Casariccio	agritourism	AIC
Loc. Casariccio, San Leolino	tel. 338.5679126	www.agricolasanleolino.it

CALENZANO

Happy Ice	gelato (€, AIC)	Via Giusti, 59
Il Borgo	restaurant, pizzeria	AIC
Via del Molino, 87	tel. 0558811377	

CAMPAGNATICO

La Vecchia Oliviera	restaurant, pizzeria	€€, AIC
Via Piave	tel. 0564996462	

CAMPI BISENZIO

Da Que' Grulli	restaurant	AIC
Via Confini, 162	tel. 3937461913	www.daquegrulli.it
Don Chisciotte	restaurant, pizzeria	€€, AIC
Via Barberinese, 157	tel. 55.8954319	
La Gelateca	gelato (€, AIC)	Via S. Quirico, 165 (int I Gigli)
Sottozero	gelato	€, AIC
Via Barberinese 157	tel. 055 8970971	www.gelateriasottozero.com

CAMPIGLIA D'ORCIA

I Tre Rioni	restaurant	€€€, AIC
Via Campotondo, 3	tel. 0577872015	www.itrerioni.com

CAMPO NELL'ELBA

Select	inn	AIC
Via per Portoferraio, 30	tel. 0565976734	

CAMPO NELL'ELBA-ISOLD D'ELBA

Gelateria Ghibli	gelato	€, AIC
P.zza Torino, 5	tel. 565.976156	
Piccolo Hotel Versilia	inn, restaurant	AIC
Via dell'Acqued otto, 1580	tel. 0565976123	www.piccolohotelversilia.it

CAPALBIO

Villaggio Capalbio	resort	AIC
Str. Pedemontana, 58	tel. 0564899017	www.villaggiocapalbio.it

CAPOLIVERI- ISOLA D'ELBA

Angiò	bar restaurant, pizzeria	€-€€€, AIC
Via del Pinone, 144 loc. Lacona	tel. 0565964412	
Capo di Stella	inn	AIC
Loc. Capo di Stella-Lacona	tel. 0565964052	www.capodistella.com

Pienza Val d'Orcia – "Falling into a painting" (J.Coyne)

Zero Gradi
gelato (€, AIC)
Via Roma, 38

CAPRAIAE LIMITE

Lowengrube
pub
€, AIC
Via pr.le Limitese
tel. 0571979253

CAPRESE

Il Rifugio
restaurant, pizzeria
€€-€€€, AIC
Lama di Caprese
tel. 0575793968

CARMIGNANO

Agrit. Casa Belvedere
agritourism restaurant
€€€, AIC
Via S. Biagio, 10
tel. 0558717301   www.agriturismobelvedere.it

CARRARA

Golosità Senza Glutine
pizzeria
€€, AIC
Via Carriona, 265
tel. 0585842409

CASCIANA TERME

Il Merlo
restaurant, pizzeria
€-€€€€, AIC
P.zza C. Minati, 5
tel. 0587644040

CASTAGNETO-CARDUCCI

Il Vecchio Frantoio
restaurant
€€, AIC
Via Gramsci, 8 /A
tel. 0565763731

CASTELFIORENTINO

Il Cigliere del Rustico
restaurant
€-€€€, AIC
Via O. Di Paolo, 24/e loc. Bellosguardo   tel. 0571582154
Notes: Closed Monday-Wednesday.

Peter Pan
gelato (€, AIC)
C.so Matteotti, 36

Special Pizza
restaurant, pizzeria
AIC
Via Masini, 11
tel. 571.633367

CASTELFRANCO DI SOPRA

Enjoy Toscano
restaurant, bar
€€€, AIC
P.zza V. Emanuele, 1-2
tel. 0559149763

CASTELLINA IN CHIANTI

Albergaccio di Castellina
Via Fiorentina, 63
Notes: Closed Sundays.
restaurant
tel. 0577741042
€€€€, AIC

L'Antica Delizia
Notes: Closed Tuesdays.
gelato (€, AIC)
Via Fiorentina, 4

CASTELMARTINI

Caffè Mirò
Via Martiri del Padule, 75
Notes: Closed Mondays.
restaurant, pizzeria, bar
tel. 3392837117
AIC
www.caffemiro.com

CASTELNUOVO BERARDENGA

Il Convito di Curina/Villa Curina restaurant
Loc. Curina
Notes: Also B&B. Closed Wednesdays.
tel. 0577355647
AIC
www.ilconvitodicurina.it

CASTELNUOVO DI GARFAGNANA

Il Baretto
Via Farini, 5
restaurant, pizzeria
tel. 0583639136
€€, AIC
www.ilbaretto.org

Il Ciulè
Via Giovanni Pascoli, 1
restaurant/pizzeria
tel. 058362643
€€, AIC

Osteria Vecchio Mulino
Via Vittorio Emanuele, 12
osteria
tel. 583.62192
AIC

Osteria Vecchio Mulino
Via Vittorio Emanuele, 12
osteria
tel. 058362192
€-€€, AIC
www.ilvecchiomulino.com

CASTIGLION FIORENTINO

Babette - Casale di Brolio
Via di Brolio, 74
restaurant, B&B
tel. 0575652054
€€€, AIC
www.babetteristorante.it

Il Passaggio
Via Adua, 68
restaurant
tel. 575.659639
AIC

La Fenice
Via Santa Cristina - loc. Taragnano, 25   tel. 0575650176
B&B
AIC

CASTIGLIONCELLO

Bagno Bar Salvadori
L.re Colombo, 16
restaurant, pizzeria
tel. 0586754194
€-€€, AIC
www.bagnisalvadori.it

Il Coccodrillo
Lungomare Colombo, 18
restaurant
tel. 0586752627
€€-€€€, AIC

CASTIGLIONE DELLA PESCAIA

Bagno Bruna
Via Isola Clodia
bar, tavola calda
tel. 0564933613
€, AIC
www.bagnobruna.it

L'Approdo
Via Ponte Giorgini, 29
hotel, restaurant
tel. 0564933466
€€€, AIC
www.approdo.it

Roma Hotel
Via C. Colombo, 14
Notes: Closed at lunch.
hotel
tel. 0564933542
AIC
www.hoteromacastiglione.it

CAVRIGLIA

Locanda Cuccuini
V.le Caduti, 32
B&B
tel. 0559166419
AIC
www.locanda-cuccuini.com

Il Cedrino
Via Aurelia Sud, 30

CECINA
restaurant, pizzeria
tel. 0586682233

€€€, AIC

L'Acquapazza
Via Ginori, 89

restaurant
tel. 0586621219

€€€, AIC
www.ristorantelacquapazza.com

Mangia e Bevi
Via 2 Giugno, 7

pizzeria
tel. 586.62285

AIC

Marina (2 locations)
V.le Galliano, 23
Via della Vittoria, 61

gelato (€, AIC)

Slap

CECINA MARE
gelato (€, AIC)

Viale Galliano, 10

PS
Pianello Val Tidone, 41

CERRETO GUIDI
restaurant
tel. 0571559242

AIC
www.ps-ristorante.it

Il Parco
Via Agnoletti, 316

CERTALDO
pizzeria, tavola calda
tel. 571.65241

€, AIC

Il Rabarbaro
Loc. La Maglianella, 30

CHIANCIANO TERME
restaurant, pizzeria
tel. 057864592

€, AIC

Villa Maria
Via Macerina, 19
Notes: Closed October-April.

inn, restaurant
tel. 057863003

€€, AIC
www.villamariachianciano.it

Az. Bioagritur.Poggio ai Lupi
Loc. I Renicci

CHIANNI
agritourism
tel. 0587648163

€€-€€€€, AIC

Rist.Nonna Rosa/H. Rosati
Via dei Tulipani, 1 loc. Querce al Pino   tel. 0578274408
Notes: DS pizza point. Closed Mondays.

CHIUSI
hotel, restaurant

€€€-€€€€, AIC
www.hotelrosati.it

Terme della Versilia
Via Gramsci, 2

CINQUALE DI MONTIGNOSO
restaurant reception hall inn
tel. 0585807792

€€€, AIC

Il Caggio di Sotto
Loc. Il Gaggio, 26/Lano

COLLE VAL D'ELSA
agritourism
tel. 0577971255

AIC
www.caggiodisotto.com

C.lo Arci Corniola
Via di Corniola, 34/36

CORNIOLA EMPOLI
pizzeria
tel. 0571922202

€ - €€, AIC

Hotel Farneta
Località Farneta, 3

CORTONA
inn, restaurant
tel. 0575610241

€€-€€€€, AIC

La Tufa
Loc. Ossaia 67/a

restaurant, pizzeria
tel. 0575677717

€-€€€, AIC
www.hostarialatufa.it

DICOMANO

Il Geko
V.le Vittorio Veneto, 10/12
Notes: Closed Tuesdays.

restaurant, pizzeria
tel. 0558387672

€-€€€, AIC

Vigna la Corte
Loc. Rimaggio

B&B
tel. 0558397027

AIC
www.vignalacorte.com

DONORATICO

Ristorante Pizza In da Franco
Via Aurelia, 1/ C

restaurant, pizzeria
tel. 565.775343

AIC

ELLERA - FIESOLE

B&B Eridu
Via Murri, 16/a

B&B
tel. 55.6592036

AIC

EMPOLI

Cucina S. Andrea
Via Salvagnoli,43/47
Notes: Closed Mondays.

restaurant
tel. 057173657

€€-€€€€, AIC

La Fortuna
P.zza G. Guerra, 40

restaurant
tel. 571.700377

AIC

Millevoglie senza glutine
Via Carrucci, 78

sandwich shop
tel. 571.74232

€, AIC

Star Bene Senza Glutine
P.zza Guido Guerra, 29

bar
tel. 0571527259

€, AIC
www.starbenesenzaglutine.it

Un Monte di Bontà

gelato (€, AIC)

Via Ridolfi, 7/9

Zero
Via Volontari della Libertà, 21/23

restaurant
tel. 0571930099

€, AIC

EMPOLI - PONTE A ELSA

Pizza e Godi
Via Due Giugno, 63

pizzeria
tel. 571.932124

€-€€, AIC

FARNETA

Osteria da Mangiafoco
Via per Chiatri, 820/B
Notes: Closed Tuesdays.

restaurant, pizzeria
tel. 0583327288

€-€€, AIC

FIESOLE

Le Lance
Via Mantellini, 2/b

restaurant, pizzeria
tel. 055599595

AIC
www.lelance.it

Trattoria Le Cave di Maiano
Via Cave di Maiano 16

restaurant
tel. 05 559133

€€€

FIGLINE VAL D'ARNO

Pasticceria Napoletana Delizie
Via Fiorentina, 19/A

bar
tel. 55.9157053

€-€€, AIC

FOIANO DELLA CHIANA

C'era una volta

gelato (€, AIC)

Piazza Garibaldi, 4

La Lodola
Via Piana, 19

B&B
tel. 0575649660

AIC
wwwlalodola.com

FOLLONICA

Caribia

gelato (€, AIC)

Viale Italia, 212

La Lanternina 2 di Palmieri	restaurant, pizzeria	AIC
V.le Italia, 160	tel. 056642679	www.ristorantepalmieri.com

FORNACI DI BARGA

La Bionda di Nonna Mary	restaurant, pizzeria	€-€€€, AIC
Via della Repubblica, 254	tel. 058375624	
Notes: Closed Wednesdays.		

Mara Meo	pizzeria	€, AIC
Via Provinciale, 18	tel. 0583758982	

FORTE DEI MARMI

Imperiale	gelato (€, AIC)	Via Colombo, 97/a

Posidonia	restaurant, bar	€€-€€€, AIC
Via Mazzini, 202/d	tel. 0584752843	

GABBRO ROSIGNANO M.MO

Villa Edera	restaurant	€€-€€€€, AIC
Via Ornellini, 90	tel. 0586742535	

GALLICANO

Il Baretto	restaurant, pizzeria	€, AIC
Via Serchio, 17	tel. 058374066	

GALLUZZO

Star Bene Senza Glutine	bar, desserts	€
Via Gherardo Silvani, 51	tel. 329.2616608	www.starbenesenzaglutine.it

GREVE IN CHIANTI

La Cantina	restaurant, pizzeria	AIC
Piazza Trento, 3	tel. 55.854097	

GROSSETO

Bar Perugina	bar	€, AIC
Via Manin, 26	tel. 564.22263	

Caffè del Teatro	restaurant, pizzeria	AIC
Via Goldoni, 12	tel. 3285633674	

Caffè Nazionale	bar, tavola calda	€, AIC
P.zza Gioberti, 4	tel. 0564450601	

Gelateria Papavera	gelato, crêperie	€, AIC
Piazza Gioberti, 6	tel. 348.2465214	

Gli Attortellati	restaurant	€€, AIC
S.P. 40 La Trappola, 39	tel. 564.400059	www.gliattortellati.com

Hungry Years	pub, restaurant	€€, AIC
Via Vinzaglio, 20	tel. 564.413351	www.hungryyears.it

Il Carrettino	restaurant, pizzeria	AIC
Via Bengasi, 7	tel. 056428421	www.ilcarrettinogr.it

In Florida	gelato (€, AIC)	Viale Giusti, 55

L'Uva e il Malto	restaurant	€€-€€€, AIC
Via Mazzini, 165	tel. 0564411211	www.luvaeilmalto.it
Notes: Closed Sundays.		

Mangiar Bene	tavola calda	€, AIC
Via Tazzoli, 5	tel. 3282913764	

IMPRUNETA

Nyx — pizzeria — €, AIC
Via Imprunetana per Tavarnuzze, 8/c   tel. 0552312262

Terzotempo — restaurant, pizzeria — €-€€€, AIC
Via Achille Grandi, 2 loc. Tavarnuzze   tel. 0552373364   www.ristoranteterzotempo.it
Notes: Closed Saturday at lunch.

INCISA VAL D'ARNO

La Casa di Rita — B&B — AIC
Via S. Maria Maddalena, 27   tel. 0558330099   www.lacasadirita.it

IOLO

Bar Giotto — gelato (€, AIC) — Via Guazzalotri, 15

I Cavalieri — restaurant, pizzeria — AIC
Via Didaco Bessi, 3   tel. 574.622573

ISTIA D'OMBRON E

Ristorante Poggio Cavallo — restaurant — AIC
Loc. Poggio Cavallo - SP30 Sante Mariae   tel. 564.409021

LAJATICO

Bellavista Toscana — agritourism — €€€, AIC
Via Aldo Moro, 11   tel. 0587643308   www.ristorantebellavistatoscana.it

LAMMARI CAPANNORI

Mara Meo — pizzeria — €, AIC
V.le Europa, 46   tel. 0583436400

LAMPORECCHIO

Il Poderino — agritourism — €€, AIC
Via Giugnano, 158   tel. 057388109

LASTRA A SIGNA

La...Strapizza — grocery store — €, AIC
Via Diaz, 132   tel. 0558723138   www.lastrapizza.com

LATERINA

Lo Strettoio — restaurant, pizzeria — €€, AIC
Via Agna -Loc. Pian di Chena   tel. 057589161   www.ristorantelostrettoio.it
Notes: DS pizza point. Closed Wednesdays.

London Bar — gelato (€, AIC) — Via Vecchia Aretina, 60

LE CROCI - CALENZANO

Antica Sosta a Combiate — restaurant — €€€€, AIC
Via di barberino, 71   tel. 0558876980   www.anticasostacombiate.it

LE FONTANELLE

Le Fontanelle — hotel, restaurant — AIC
Via Trav. del Crocifisso, 7   tel. 0574730373   www.hotelfontanelle.com

LIDO DI CAMAIORE

Petit Hotel / Ristorante Piattofondo hotel, restaurant — AIC
Via Don Minzoni, 22   tel. 584.619374   www.ptithotel.com

LIVORNO

All'Improvviso Pizzeria — pizzeria — AIC
Via Toscana, 69/69a   tel. 586.903023

Aragosta
Piazza dell'Arsenal e, 6

restaurant
tel. 586.895395

€€€, AIC
www.aragostasrl.com

Bella Napoli
Via Sardi, 41
Notes: Closed Wednesdays.

restaurant, pizzeria
tel. 0586898731

€€, AIC
www.pizzeriabellanapoli.it

Bistrot Manalù
Piazza della Vittoria, 9

restaurant
tel. 586.958326

€€, AIC
www.facebook.com/bistrotmanalu

Caciaia in Banditella
Via Puini, 97

restaurant
tel. 0586 580403

€€€€, AIC

Chez Ugo
Scali del Monte Pio, 35
Notes: Closed Mondays.

pizzeria
tel. 0586219230

€, AIC

In Vernice
Via Sproni, 32/34
Notes: Closed Sundays.

restaurant
tel. 0586219546

€€, AIC

La Grotta delle Fate
Via Grotta delle Fate, 157
Notes: Closed at lunch.

restaurant
tel. 0586503162

€€, AIC
www.grottadellefate.net

L'Origine
Via dell'Origine, 14
Notes: Closed Mondays.

pizzeria
tel. 0586210157

€, AIC

Orlandi Montallegro
P.zza di Montenero, 3
Notes: Closed Tuesdays.

restaurant inn
tel. 0586579030

€€, AIC

Star Bene Senza Glutine
Mercato Centrale Livorno Box n° 47/48-49/50

bar, desserts

€
www.starbenesenzaglutine.it

Trattoria L'Angelo d'Oro
Piazza Mazzini, 15

trattoria
tel. 0'0586881295

€€, AIC

LOC. FRATTA DI CORTONA

Gina
P.zza S. Margherita

pub, tavola calda
tel. 3662747657

€, AIC

LOC. OLMO FIESOLE

Il Trebbiolo Relais
Via del Trebbiolo, 8

hotel, restaurant
tel. 0558300583

€€€, AIC
www.iltrebbiolo.it

LOC. STABBIA - CERRETO GUIDI

Pizza Pazza a Pezzi
Via Provinciale Francesca, 139

pizzeria
tel. 0571956029

€, AIC

LONDA

Da Fischio
Loc. Il Lago
Notes: Closed Mondays.

restaurant, pizzeria
tel. 0558351608

AIC

LORENZANA

Osteria Pian di Laura
Via Papa Karol Wojtyla ,3

osteria
tel. 050662610

€-€€, AIC
www.osteriapiandilaura.com

LUCCA

A Palazzo Busdraghi Residenza d'Epoca hotel
Via Fillungo, 170

tel. 0583950856

€€€€, AIC
www.apalazzobusdraghi.it

Albergo Celide   hotel   AIC
Viale G.Giusti, 25   tel. 0583954106
Notes: GF breakfast only.

Ammodonostro   restaurant   €€€-€€€€, AIC
Via della Fratta, 22   tel. 0583953828   www.ristoranteammodonostro.com

Antica Tratt. Stefani da Benedetto restaurant   €€-€€€, AIC
Via Borgo, 55- S.Lorenzo a Vaccoli tel. 0583379031
Notes: Closed Tuesday-Wednesday.

Bar Caffetteria Moriani   bar   €, AIC
Via Nuova per Pisa 5634/b   tel. 583.378324

Bontà Yogurt   gelato (€, AIC)   V.le Puccini, 183/187

Buca di S. Antonio   restaurant   €€€-€€€€, AIC
Via della Cervia, 3   tel. 058355881   www.bucadisantantonio.com
Notes: Closed Mondays and Sunday evenings.

Cremeria Opera   gelato (€, AIC)   Viale Luporini, 951

El Paso   restaurant, pizzeria   €, AIC
Via per Camaiore, 679   tel. 0583341273
Notes: DS pizza point. Closed Mondays.

Gelateria de' Coltelli   gelato (€, AIC)   Via San Paolino, 10

Gli Orti di Via Elisa   restaurant   €€€, AIC
Via Elisa, 17   tel. 0583491241   www.ristorantegliorti.it

Grand Hotel Guinigi   hotel, restaurant   AIC
Via Romana, 1247   tel. 05834991   www.grandhotelguinigi.it

Grom   gelato   €, AIC
Via Fillungo, 56   tel. 583.436455   www.grom.it

Mara Meo   pizzeria   €, AIC
P.zza S. Francesco, 17   tel. 0583467084

Pizzeria Felice   restaurant, pizzeria   AIC
Via Buonamici, 352   tel. 0583587412   www.pizzeriafelice.it
Notes: DS pizza point. Closed Mondays.

Ristorante Giglio   restaurant   €€€-€€€€, AIC
Piazza del Giglio, 2   tel. 0583494058   www.ristorantegiglio.com

Star Bene Senza Glutine   bar, desserts   €
Via Catalani 200   tel. 338.8496184   www.starbenesenzaglutine.it

LUCCA-S. LORENZO A VACCOLI

Botton d'Oro   restaurant   €€€, AIC
Via del Ponte Guasperini, 873   tel. 0583370101   www.albergovillamarta.it
Notes: Closed Sundays.

LUCIGNANO

La Maggiolata   restaurant   €€, AIC
Via G. Matteotti, 60   tel. 0575819008   www.ristorantelamaggiolata.it
Notes: Closed Wednesdays.

La Rocca   restaurant   AIC
Piazza Ser Vanni, 1   tel. 0575836775   www.larocca-ristorante.it

Snoopy   gelato (€, AIC)   Via Rosini, 20

LUCO DI MUGELLO

L'Orto sull'Uscio   B&B   AIC
Via Campagna, 48/1   tel. 0558401197   www.lortosulluscio.com

MARCIANA MARINA

Il Gastronomo   restaurant, tavola calda   €€, AIC
Via del Sette, 10   tel. 0565997021
Notes: Closed Wednesdays.

Isola Verde   hotel, restaurant   €€, AIC
Via San Giovanni   tel. 0565904291   www.hotelisolaverde.it

Publius   restaurant   AIC
P.za del Castagneto-Loc. Poggio   tel. 056599208
Notes: Closed November-March and Mondays.

Scaraboci   restaurant   €€€€, AIC
Via XX Settembre, 29   tel. 0565996868
Notes: Closed January-April and at lunch.

Zero Gradi   gelato (€, AIC)   P.zza For di Porta, 8

MARCIANO DELLA CHIANA

Albatros   restaurant, pizzeria   €€-€€€, AIC
Via Culle, 37   tel. 0575845464   www.albatrosristorante.it
Notes: Closed Monday-Thursday and at lunch.

MARINA DI ALBERESE

La Viola Ristoro   bar, tavola calda/fredda   €, AIC
c/o Parco della Maremma   tel. 335.7066047

MARINA DI BIBBONA

Gasperini & Zoppi   gelato (€, AIC)   Via dei Melograni lotto H 1

Il Ghiottone   gelato (€, AIC)   Piazza dei Gerani, 1
Notes: Closed Tuesdays.

Paradiso Verde   hotel, restaurant   AIC
P.zza del Forte, 1   tel. 0586600022   www.hotelparadisoverde.it

MARINA DI CAMPO-ISOLA D'ELBA

Bologna   restaurant, pizzeria   €€, AIC
Via delle Case Nuove, 71   tel. 0565976105   www.ristorantebologna.it

Zero Gradi   gelato (€, AIC)   Via per Portoferraio, 9

MARINA DI CARRARA

Bar Gelateria Bristol   gelato (€, AIC)   Via Rinchiosa, 40

Gelateria Paradiso   gelato (€, AIC)   Viale Colombo, 119/bis
Gelateria Samba - Giorgia   gelato (€, AIC)   Via Genova, 14 bis

MARINA DI GROSSETO

Bagno Le Poste Marina   bar, tavola calda   €-€€, AIC
Via Leopoldo di Lorena   tel. 0564337811

Bagno Moderno   restaurant   €€€, AIC
L.re Leopoldo II di Lorena, 47   tel. 056434255   www.bagnomoderno.it

Ristorante Pantagruel   restaurant   AIC
Via Bellini, 5a   tel. 340.0781754

MARINA DI MASSA

Bagno Arlecchino Via L.re di Levante, 14	restaurant tel. 3939387076	€, AIC
Bagno Hermitage L.re di Levante, 128	bar, tavola calda tel. 585.245341	€, AIC
Casa Faci Via Ernesto Lombardo, 16	inn tel. 0585869556	AIC www.casafaci.it
Excelsior/Rist. Il Sestante V. Cesari Battisti, 1	hotel, restaurant tel. 05858601	AIC www.hotelexcelsior.it
Gelateria Aruè	gelato (€, AIC)	P.zza Pellerano, 12
Hermitage L.re di Levante, 128	bar, tavola calda tel. 0585245341	€, AIC www.hotelhermitage.net
Hotel Italia V.le Amerigo Vespucci, 3 Notes: Closed October-March.	hotel tel. 0585240606	€€, AIC www.hotelitaliamarinadimassa.com
Roby Via Casamicciola, 3	hotel tel. 0585240686	AIC www.hotelroby.net
Tiffany Via Fosdinovo, 14	hotel, restaurant tel. 0585241196	AIC www.tiffany-hotel.it
Villa Tiziana Via delle Pinete, 266	hotel tel. 0585869724	AIC www.tizianahotel.com

MARINA DI PIETRASANTA

Da Totò e un Po' di Napoli Via L. da Vinci, 65 Notes: Closed Mondays and lunch.	pizzeria tel. 058423947	€, AIC
Hotel Esplanade Viale Roma, 235	hotel tel. 0584754883	€€€€, AIC www.hotelesplanadeversilia.it
Hotel Milton Via Puccini, 15	hotel tel. 058420258	€€€, AIC www.albergomilton.com
Hotel Villa Marzia Via Corridoni, 5	hotel, restaurant tel. 0584745818	€€€€, AIC www.hotelvillamarzia.it
Ivana e Daniela Via Dalmazia,38	restaurant tel. 584.20113	AIC
Nuova Sabrina Via Ugo Foscolo, 11	hotel tel. 058420253	AIC www.nuovasabrina.com
Villa Amelia Via Ugo Foscolo, 18	B&B tel. 3498526517	AIC www.villa-amelia.com

MARLIA

Granozero Tutto il Fresco Senza Glutine Viale Europa, 271/A	pizza, desserts tel. 583.929896	€-€€, AIC

MASSA

Caffè Gambrinus Via Democrazia, 15	bar, tavola calda tel. 585.41371	€, AIC
Haziel	gelato (€, AIC)	P.zza Aranci, 30

MASSA E COZZILE

Bar Si.Ba
Via Biscolla, 48
bar, tavola calda
tel. 572.70633
€, AIC

MERCATALE VAL DI PESA

Circolo M.C.L. - Il circolino
Via Gramsci, 6
restaurant
tel. 55.821586
AIC

MONSUMMANO TERME

Da Libe
Via Francesca Uggia 542
pizzeria, bar
tel. 572.62583
€-€€, AIC

MONTALCINO

Boccon Divino
Trav. Dei Monti, 201 loc. Colombaio
restaurant
tel. 0577848233
€€€€, AIC

MONTALE

Azzurra
gelato (€, AIC)
Via Martiri della Libertà, 119

MONTAVARCHI

Star Bene Senza Glutine
Via Mincio 46
bar, desserts
tel. 055/980216
€
www.starbenesenzaglutine.it

MONTE S. SAVINO

Bar Gelateria La Castiglia
Notes: Closed Mondays.
gelato (€, AIC)
Via della Riconoscenza, 7

Il Cioccolato di Carlo
Corso Sangallo, 22
gelato, bar
tel. 575.810586
€, AIC

La Torre di Gargonza
Loc. Gargonza
Notes: Closed Tuesdays.
inn, restaurant
tel. 0575847065
€€€-€€€€, AIC
www.gargonza.it

Podere Pendolino by Albatros
Loc. Castellare, 44
restaurant, pizzeria, B&B
tel. 0575849697
€-€€€, AIC

MONTECARLO

Antica Dimora Patrizia
Piazza Carmignani, 12
B&B
tel. 583.1797017
AIC

Circolo Acsi-La Torre
Via Provinciale, 7
restaurant, wine bar
tel. 05832298298
€€€€, AIC

MONTECATINI TERME

Hotel Adua Regina di Saba
V.le Manzoni, 46
hotel
tel. 057278134
€€€€, AIC
www.hoteladua.it

MONTELUPO

Lo Spigo
Via di Pulica, 139
Notes: Closed Mondays.
restaurant
tel. 0571929111
€-€€, AIC

MONTELUPO FIORENTINO

Antica Trattoria del Turbone
Via Turbone, 35-37-39
trattoria, pizzeria
tel. 0571542035
€-€€, AIC
www.anticatrattoriadelturbone.it

Il Coriandolo
Piazza S. Rocco, 1
restaurant, pizzeria
tel. 0571541021
AIC

Le Scuderie dell'Antinoro
Via Tosco Romagnola Nord, 6
restaurant, pizzeria
tel. 0571913079
€-€€€€, AIC
www.scuderieantinoro.it

MONTEMURLO

Sglutinando
Via Udine, 19/23
sandwich shop, bakery
tel. 328.8827111
€, AIC

MONTEPULCI ANO OVEST

Il Grifo
Via Milazzo, 19
B&B
tel. 578.738702
AIC

MONTERIGGIONI

Maison del Celiaco
Via Sandro Pertini 15/16
bakery, sandwich shop
www.maisondelceliaco.it
€

MONTERONI D'ARBIA

Gelateria Byblos
Notes: Closed Mondays.
gelato (€, AIC)
Via Roma, 199-203

MONTESCUDAIO

Bibere
Via della Libertà. 59 A
restaurant, wine bar
tel. 586.685888
AIC

MONTEVARCHI

Bar Pinco Pallino
Via Mincio, 46
bar
tel. 55.980215
€, AIC

Coffee Gallo
Via Leopardi, 27
restaurant, pizzeria
tel. 0559850530
€€, AIC
www.coffeegallo.com

MONTIANO

da Ghigo
P.zza Cappellini, 4
restaurant
tel. 0564589643
€€€, AIC
www.ristorantedaghigo.it

MONTICIANO

Castello di Tocchi
Loc. Tocchi Podere La Ripa
B&B
tel. 0577757102
AIC
www.castelloditocchi.it

Villa Ferraia
Loc. Tocchi
B&B
tel. 0577757102
AIC
www.villaferraio.com

MONTIERI

Al Pozzolone
Str. Delle Galleraie, 55
B&B
tel. 0566914314
AIC
www.pozzolone.it

MONTIGNOSO

Bar del Re
Via Romana Ovest, 19
sandwiches, crêpes
tel. 39329210009
€-€€, AIC

MULAZZO

Abramo
Via Provinciale, 23
restaurant
tel. 0187439388
€-€€, AIC
Notes: Closed Mondays and at lunch.

ORBETELLO

Gallery
Via Gioberti, 91
restaurant, B&B
tel. 0564860474
€€€-€€€€, AIC
www.orbetelloturismo.it/ristorante-gallery

Mixer
gelato (€, AIC)
C.so Italia, 78
Notes: They also have crêpes. Closed Wednesdays.

PELAGO

Boccon Divino
Via Cafaggiolo, 10 Loc. Palaie
restaurant
tel. 0558311279
€€-€€€€, AIC
www.boccondivinofirenze.it
Notes: Closed Tuesdays at lunch.

La Fonte
Loc. Trebbio, 34
Notes: Closed Tuesdays and at lunch.

PESCAGLIA
restaurant, pizzeria
tel. 0583359815

AIC
www.ristorantelafonte.com

Pizzeria La Diga
Viale Beatrice, 122

PIAN DEGLI ONTANI
restaurant, pizzeria
tel. 573.67307

AIC
pizzerialadiga@live.it

Silvio la Storia a Tavola
Via Brennero, 181/183

PIANOSINATICO
restaurant
tel. 0573629204

€€, AIC
www.ristorantesilvioabetone.com

Il Tavolello
Via Comunale del Colli, 9
Notes: Closed Wednesdays.

PIAZZA AL SERCHIO
pizzeria
tel. 058360477

€, AIC

La Terrazza del Chiostro
Corso del Rossellino, 26
Notes: Closed Mondays and from November to March.

PIENZA
restaurant
tel. 0578748183

€€€€, AIC
www.laterrazzadelchiostro.it

La Rocchetta
Via Montiscendi, 172

PIETRASANTA
restaurant
tel. 584.799728

AIC
ristoranterocchetta@yahoo.it

La Volpe e l'Uva
P.zza Matteotti, 42

osteria
tel. 058472570

€€€-€€€€, AIC
www.trovavetrine.it/la-volpe-e-luva

Star Bene Senza Glutine
Via Barsanti 40

bar, desserts
tel. 584.283279

€
www.starbenesenzaglutine.it

Clarabella Caffè
Via Marconi, 41/b

PIEVE A NEVOLE
bar
tel. 572.954307

€, AIC

Gelateria 7 Nani

gelato (€, AIC)

Via Empolese, 90

Paso
Via di Tiglio, 88
Notes: DS pizza point. Closed Tuesdays.

PIEVE S. PAOLO-CAPANNORI
pizzeria
tel. 0583981750

€, AIC

Il Garibaldi Innamorato
Via G.Garibaldi, 5

PIOMBINO
restaurant
tel. 056549410

€€€, AIC
www.ilgaribaldiinnamorato.it

Il Tiramestoli
Loc. Carbonifera

restaurant
tel. 565.20945

€€€, AIC
www.iltiramestoli.it

Biba Bar
Via Turati, 57

PISA
bar
tel. 389.0357468

€, AIC
www.bibabar-pisa.it

Caffè Letterario Voltapagina
Via San Martino, 71

bar
tel. 50.5202716

€, AIC
www.caffeletterariovoltapagina.it

Da Peppone
Via Fiorentina, 449

osteria, pizzeria
tel. 50.6203882

AIC
www.pizzeriadapeppone.com

Gelateria de' Coltelli

gelato (€, AIC)

Lungarno Pacinotti

La Pizza Magica
Via Vittorio Veneto, 3
pizzeria
tel. 3931824268
€, AIC

Pizza Magica City
Via Palestro, 29/33
restaurant, pizzeria
tel. 50.580794
AIC

Rist. Squisitia/H. San Ranieri
Via Mazzei ang via S. Biagio
hotel, restaurant
tel. 0509719555
€€-€€€€, AIC
www.sanranierihotel.com

PISTOIA

Gelateria Cipriani
gelato (€, AIC)
Via Curtatone e Montanara, 65

La Diligenza
Viale Adua, 306
restaurant, pizzeria
tel. 573.90417
AIC

La Diligenza In...
V.le Adua, 308
Notes: Closed Sundays and Monday mornings.
bar, sandwich shop
tel. 0573904170
€€, AIC

La Fenice
Via Dalmazia, 73
Notes: Closed Tuesdays.
restaurant, pizzeria
tel. 057321167
€-€€€, AIC
www.lafenicecistorante.it

Parè
gelato (€-€€, AIC)
Via Pacinotti, 83

Pizza Mania
Via Udine, 4
Notes: Closed Sundays.
pizzeria
tel. 0573976063
€-€€, AIC

Verde Paradiso
P.zza della Resistenza, 15
B&B
tel. 05731780352
AIC
www.verdeparadiso.com

PODENZANA

La Gavarina d'Oro
Via Provinciale, 23
restaurant
tel. 0187410021
€€, AIC
www.lagavarinadoro.com

Mirador
Via del Gaggio, 22
inn, restaurant
tel. 0187410064
€-€€, AIC

POGGIBONSI

Da Poldo Food&Love
Largo Usilia, 24
sandwich shop
tel. 329.0806318
€, AIC

POGGIO A CAIANO

La Bottega del Gelato (ex Nonna Luisa) gelato (€, AIC)
Via Soffici, 47

PONTASSIEVE

Al Trebbio
Via Montetrini, 10 Molino del Piano
restaurant, pizzeria
tel. 0558317292
€€, AIC
www.castellodeltrebbio.com

Le Fate Golose
Notes: Closed Mondays.
gelato(€, AIC)
P.zza Libero Grassi, 22

Locanda Toscani da Sempre
Via F.lli Monzecchi, 13
Notes: Also B&B.
restaurant
tel. 0558392952
€€€, AIC
www.toscanidasempre.it

Tenuta dei Cavalieri
Via Santa Brigida, 3
agritourism, restaurant
tel. 0558364332
€€, AIC
www.tenutadeicavalieri.com

PONTE A POPPI

Gelateria Edi
gelato (€, AIC)
Via Roma, 45

PONTEDERA

Il Marathoneta   restaurant, pizzeria   €€, AIC
Via R. Piaggio, 54/56   tel. 587.293152
www.facebook.com/pages/Il-Marathoneta-pizzeria-focacceria-e/514544348556462

La Losanga   restaurant, pizzeria   €-€€€€, AIC
Via Pisana, 157   tel. 0587562323
Notes: Closed Wednesdays.

La Polveriera   restaurant   €€€€, AIC
Via Marconcini, 54   tel. 058754765
Notes: Closed Sundays.

Pane per Noi   sandwich shop, bakery   €, AIC
Via della Repubblica 3   tel. 587.980426   www.facebook.com/pane.pernoi.1

Pizzeria Pasquale   pizzeria, osteria   €€, AIC
Via Roma, 110 ang R. Piaggio   tel. 0587290633
Notes: Closed Sundays.

PONTREMOLI

Ca' del Moro   restaurant   €€€-€€€€, AIC
Loc. Casa Corvi, 9   tel. 0187830588   www.cadelmororesort.it

POPPI

Tutto Pizza   pizzeria   €€, AIC
Via Roma, 124   tel. 575.520482

PORCARI

Bar Caffetteria Moriani   bar   €, AIC
Viale Puccini, 1995   tel. 583.29587

Happy Time   pizzeria, restaurant   €€, AIC
Via Fratina, 23   tel. 0583297289   www.happytimeparcogiochi.it

Mara Meo   pizzeria   €, AIC
Via Roma, 120   tel. 058329113

Stefy 3   pizzeria   €, AIC
Via Capannori, 59   tel. 0583210662
Notes: Closed Mondays and at lunch.

PORTO ERCOLE

Gelateria Creola   gelato (€, AIC)   Via Lungomare Strozzi, 8

PORTO S. STEFANO

Gelateria La Bontà   gelato   €, AIC
Via Corso Umberto   tel. 328.7318428

PORTOFERRAIO-ISOLA D'ELBA

Viticcio   hotel, restaurant   AIC
Loc. Biodola, 1   tel. 0565939058   www.hotelviticcio.it

Zero Gradi   gelato (€, AIC)   Via Vittorio Emanuele, 18

PRATO

Antichi Sapori   restaurant, pizzeria   AIC
Via V. Da Filicaia   tel. 0574461189
Notes: Closed Mondays.

Aroma di Vino   osteria   €€, AIC
Via Santo Stefano, 24   tel. 0574433800   www.pratoaromadivino.it

Circolo la Libertà Via Pistoiese, 659	restaurant, pizzeria tel. 0574810618	€€, AIC

Gelateria Sanmarco Viale Vittorio Veneto, 16	gelato tel. 340.9939636	€, AIC www.gelateriasanmarcoprato.it

Il Pirana Via G. Valentini, 110	restaurant tel. 057425746	€€€€, AIC www.ristorantepirana.it

Pepe Nero Via Zarini, 289	restaurant tel. 0574550353	€€-€€€, AIC

Ristorante Sabatini Via Ferrucci, 162-164	restaurant tel. 574.070038	€€€, AIC

www.facebook.com/RistorantePizzeriaSabatini

Rosso Pomodoro Prato Via delle Pleiadi, 16 c/o Omnia Center	pizzeria tel. 574.056138	€€, AIC www.rossopomodoro.it

Sans Gluten Viale Montegrapp a, 298	sandwich shop, bakery tel. 574.830242	€, AIC www.sansgluten.it

Sottozero (5 locations) Via Montalese, 12 Via Roma, 312/b	gelato (€, AIC) Via Garibaldi, 112 Viale Piave, 20	www.gelateriasottozero.com Piazza Mercatale, 4/5

Star Bene Senza Glutine Via Frà Bartolomeo n. 203	bar, desserts tel. 0574/726422	€ www.starbenesenzaglutine.it

Starbene Senza Glutine Via Frà Bartolomeo, 23	bakery tel. 574.726422	€, AIC www.gelateriasottozero.com

PRINCIPINA TERRA

Hotel Fattoria La Principina Via San Rocco, 465	hotel, restaurant tel. 056444141	€€, AIC www.fattorialaprincipina.it

PROCCHIO-MARCIANA

Monna Lisa Via Fonte Leccio, 10	hotel, restaurant tel. 0565907904	AIC www.hotelmonnalisa.it

QUARRATA

Il Calesse Via Carraia, 215	agritourism, B&B tel. 0573750344	AIC www.agriturismoilcalesse.it

Il Mondo senza glutine Via Montalbano, 154	sandwich shop tel. 573.774123	€-€€, AIC

www.facebook.com/il.mondo.senza.glutine33

Pizza & Co Via Ceccarelli, 159/a	pizzeria tel. 0573717686	€-€€, AIC

QUATTRO STRADE LARI

Prima Gelateria Notes: Closed Tuesdays.	gelato (€, AIC)	Via Livornese ovest, 91

RAPOLANO TERME

La Taverna Toscana Loc. Laticastelli	restaurant tel. 0577725513	€€€, AIC www.latavernatoscana.it

REGGELLO

Il Muretto	gelato (€, AIC)	Via Gramsci, 50

Villa Pitiana	hotel, restaurant	€€€€, AIC
Via Pr.le per Tosi	tel. 055860012	www.villapitiana.com

ROCCATEDERIGHI

La Conchiglia	restaurant, pizzeria	€€€, AIC
Via Roma, 24/c	tel. 0564567430	

RONCHI

Bagno Europa	bar, tavola calda	€, AIC
Viale Lungomare di Levante, 106	tel. 585.241474	www.bagnoeuropa.com
Cavalieri del Mare	hotel	€€€, AIC
Via Veterani dello Sport	tel. 0585868010	www.cavalieridelmare.net
Notes: Closed September-May.		
Villa Elsa	hotel	AIC
Via Pistoia, 2	tel. 0585241097	

ROSIGNANO MARITTIMO

Le simpatiche canaglie	pizzeria	€-€€, AIC
Via Gramsci, 55	tel. 586.790139	

ROSIGNANO SOLVAY

Lo Scoglietto	restaurant	€€€-€€€€, AIC
L.re Monte alla Rena, 13	tel. 0586767962	
Notes: Closed October-April.		

RUFINA

Il Ritrovo	restaurant, pizzeria	€-€€€, AIC
P.zza Umberto I,32	tel. 0558396219	

S. ALBINO MONTEPULCIANO

La Locanda del Vino Nobile	restaurant	€€€ - €€€€, AIC
Via dei Lillà, 1/3	tel. 0578798064	www.lalocandadelvinonobile.it

S. BRIGIDA-PONTASSIEVE

Nappino	restaurant/pizzeria	€€€ - €€€€, AIC
Via S. Chiari, 1	tel. 0558300439	www.nappino.it

S. CARLO TERME-MASSA

Alb. S. Carlo/Rist. Panoramique	inn, restaurant	€€-€€€, AIC
Via Nicola Zonder, 3	tel. 058543193	
Buongustaio	hotel, restaurant	€€-€€€, AIC
Via Belvedere, 90	tel. 058545741	

S. CASCIANO VAL DI PESA

B&B Art	B&B	AIC
Via della Volta, 6	tel. 0558290372	www.bbart.eu
Da I' Moro	gelato (€, AIC)	Via Empolese, 228
I Pini	gelato (€, AIC)	P.zza G. Matteotti, 7
Mamma Rosa	restaurant, trattoria	€€€€, AIC
Via Cassia per Siena	tel. 0558249454	www.trattoriamammarosa.it

S. FREDIANO A SETTIMO

Gelateria Sighieri	gelato (€, AIC)	Via T. Romagnola,1078
Notes: Closed Wednesdays.		

S. GIMIGNANO

Taverna del Granducato	restaurant	€€, AIC
Piazza Martiri di Montemaggio	tel. 0577940824	

S. GIOVANNI VALDARNO

Il Gelatone   gelato (€, AIC)   Corso Italia, 9

S. GIULIANO TERME

Io e Gelato   gelato (€, AIC)   Via Calcesana, 499 - loc. Mezzana

S. MARIA A MONTE

Black - White   restaurant, pizzeria   €€, AIC
Via San Donato, 106   tel. 0587473322
Notes: Closed Mondays and at lunch.

Il Germoglio-Bar Miro e Giusy-H.Da Neide restaurant, pizzeria, bar   €-€€, AIC
Via Francesca, 144   tel. 0587706286

Il Poeta/Il Verde Melograno   hotel, restaurant   €€, AIC
Via Francesca Nord, 248   tel. 0587709090   www.hotelilpoeta.it

Oasi al Lago   restaurant, pizzeria   €-€€€, AIC
Via Arnovecchio S. Donato, 1   tel. 0587709201
Notes: Closed Mondays.

S. MARIA DEL GIUDICE

Marta Guest House   B&B   AIC
Via del Querceto, 47   tel. 0583378555   www.martaguesthouse.it

S. QUIRICO D'ORCIA

La Taverna del Barbarossa/Casanova restaurant, pizzeria, inn   €€€€, AIC
SS.146 Loc. Casanova, 6 c   tel. 0577898299   www.tavernadelbarbarossa.com

S.FREDIANO A SETTIMO

Gelateria Sighieri   gelato (€, AIC)   Via T. Romagnola, 1078

SAN GIMIGNANO

Bar Combattenti Gelateria   gelato (€, AIC)   Via S. Giovanni, 124

Le Vecchie Mura   restaurant   €€€€, AIC
Via Piandornella, 15   tel. 577.94027   www.vecchiemura.it

SAN CASCIANO

I Pini   gelato (€, AIC)   Via Volterrana, 142

Osteria Cinque Divino   osteria   €€€-€€€€, AIC
V.le S. Francesco   tel. 0558228116   www.cinquedivino.it
Notes: Closed Mondays.

SAN MINIATO

Az. Agricola Marrucola   agritourism   €€-€€€, AIC
Via Calenzano, 40   tel. 0571418306   www.marrucola.it

SAN PIERO A SIEVE

I' Regolo   pizzeria   €€, AIC
Via Calimara, 4/a   tel. 55.849824   www.i-regolo.it

La Nuova Bisboccina   restaurant, pizzeria   €-€€€, AIC
Via Provinciale, 38   tel. 0558486950

SAN ROMANO

Dumbo   restaurant, pizzeria   €-€€, AIC
Via Cavour, 30/32   tel. 0571450999

Ristorante Lupo Càntero
Via Vittorio Emanuele, 10

SAN VINCENZO
restaurant €€€, AIC
tel. 565.704651 www.facebook.com/ristorantelupocantero

Al Coccio
Via N. Aggiunti, 83

SANSEPOLCRO
restaurant €€, AIC
tel. 0575741468 www.alcoccio.com

Don Chisciotte
Via G. Marcelli, 3

restaurant, pizzeria, pub €€, AIC
tel. 575.741134

Ghignoni
Via Tiberina Sud, 850

gelato €, AIC
tel. 575.7419 www.ghignoni.it

Hotel La Balestra
Via dei Montefeltro, 1

hotel, restaurant €€, AIC
tel. 0575735151 www.labalestra.it

SANTA LUCIA - UZZANO

Pizza ... e altri rimedi
Via Provinciale Lucchese, 248

restaurant, pizzeria €€, AIC
tel. 572.444085 www.pizzaealtririmedi.it

SANTA MARIA DEGLI ANGELI

Villa Cherubino
Via P. d'Italia, 39

restaurant €€, AIC
tel. 0758040226

SCANDICCI

Gelatando

gelato (€, AIC) Piazza Togliatti, 61

Gelateria Malotti

gelato (€, AIC) P.zza Cavour, 14/15/16

La Taverna di Castruccio
Via Pisana, 129/A

restaurant €€-€€€, AIC
tel. 55.751198 www.tavernadicastruccio.it

Maranatha
Via del Pantano, 1

B&B AIC
tel. 55.751123 www.bedandbreakfast.it

Pizzeria Il Moro
Via G. Donizzetti, 29

pizzeria €€, AIC
tel. 328.6621909 www.pizzeriailmoro.com

Star Bene Senza Glutine
ViaTurri, 29 A

bar, creperie €, AIC
tel. 55.730927 www.starbenesenzaglutine.it

SEANO

I' Prugnolo
P.zza IV Novembre, 4
Notes: Closed Mondays-Tuesdays.

restaurant, pizzeria €-€€, AIC
tel. 0558706933 www.ristoranteiprugnolo.it

SERRAVALLE PISTOIESE

Agriturismo Terra Mia
Via Lipe, 7

agritourism €€, AIC
tel. 05731940064 www.terramiatoscana.it

SERRE DI RAPOLANO

Grand Hotel Serre
Racc. Autostr. Siena-Bettolle

hotel AIC
tel. 0577704777 www.hotelserre.it

La Sosta
Via Serraia
Notes: Closed Mondays.

restaurant €€€€, AIC
tel. 0577704177 www.lasostaristorante.it

SESTO DI MORIANO

Antica Locanda di Sesto
Via Lodovica, 1660
Notes: Closed Saturdays.

restaurant €€€-€€€€, AIC
tel. 0583578181

Gluten-Free Italy by Region

SESTO FIORENTINO

Bar Baraonda Viale Ariosto,44	bar, tavola calda/fredda tel. 55.446352	€, AIC
Gelato Coop.Fi	gelato (€, AIC)	Via Petrosa, 19-23 (int. Centro Sesto)
Mandorla e Limone	gelato (€, AIC)	Via Verdi, 95
Matam Via Lucchese, 160	restaurant, pizzeria tel. 55.3454158	AIC
Novotel Firenze/Novotelcafé Via Tevere, 23	hotel, restaurant tel. 055308338	€€€-€€€€, AIC www.novotel.com
Star Bene Senza Glutine Via Di Calenzano 101	bar, desserts tel. 557950783	€ www.starbenesenzaglutine.it

SIENA

B&B Quattrocantoni Via San Pietro, 30	B&B tel. 338.1414094	AIC
Borgo Grondaie Via delle Grondaie, 15	B&B tel. 0577332539	AIC www.borgogrondaie.com
Garden Via Custoza, 2	hotel tel. 0577567111	€€€€, AIC
Grom	gelato (€, AIC)	Via Banchi di Sopra, 13
Grotta Gallo Nero Via del Porrione, 65	restaurant tel. 0577284356	AIC www.gallonero.it
Hotel Italia V.le Cavour, 67	B&B tel. 057744248	AIC www.hotelitalia.it
Il Camerlengo	gelato (€, AIC)	P.zza del Campo, 6
Il Campino Via Vittorio Veneto, 29 Notes: Closed Wednesdays.	osteria tel. 0577236545	€€-€€€, AIC www.ilcampino.com
Il Ghibellino Via dei Pellegrini, 26	restaurant tel. 0577288079	€€, AIC
Villa Liberty V.le Vittorio Veneto, 11	B&B www.villaliberty.it	AIC

SPAZZAVENTO - CARMIGNANO

Agriturismo Podere Midolla Via della Torre di Sant'Alluccio,10	agritourism, restaurant, B&B tel. 0558717086	€€€, AIC www.poderemidolla.com

SPICCHIO-VINCI

Osteria de'Nichi Via Limitese, 109	osteria tel. 3668093274 www.osteriadenichi.oneminutesite.it	€€€, AIC

TAVARNELLE VAL DI PESA

Osteria La Gramola Via delle Fonti, 1 Notes: Closed Tuesdays.	restaurant, catering tel. 0558050321	€-€€€€, AIC www.gramola.it

TERRANUOVA BRACCIOLINI

Acquolina Fraz. Cicogna, 96/E Notes: Request GF when you make a reservation.	osteria tel. 055977497	€€€, AIC

Il Canto del Maggio
Via Penna,30/d
osteria
tel. 0559705147
€€€, AIC
www.cantodelmaggio.com

Il Casolare
Fraz. Persignano, 111
osteria
tel. 55.96939
AIC

Piansa
Via Poggi Lupi, 580
tavola calda, bar
tel. 0559737166
€, AIC

Podere San Lorenzo
IV Str. Lungarno
agritourism
tel. 0559199176
€€, AIC

TERRICCIOLA

Da Pasquino
Via Volterrana, 308 - Loc. La Sterza
Notes: Closed Fridays.
inn, restaurant
tel. 0587674000
€€, AIC

TIRLI-CASTIGLIONE DELLA PESCAIA

Il Poggetto
Loc. Fonte Poderana
restaurant
tel. 3476761061
€€€, AIC
www.ristoranteilpoggettotirli.com

TORRE DEL LAGO

L'Ocanda
Viale Europa, 31
Notes: Not great reviews.
restaurant
tel. 584.47446
€€€€, AIC
www.locandamilu.it

VADA

Il Casale Mancini
Strada Provinciale La Torre,41
B&B, restaurant, pizzeria
tel. 586.789028
AIC
www.casalemancini.it

La Ventola
Via Dei Cavalleggeri, 171/b
inn, restaurant, pizzeria
tel. 0586770170
€€€-€€€€, AIC
www.laventola.it

VIAREGGIO

Barca Bertilla / Vela Mare Sportiva Dilettantistic a bar
Darsena Italia Porto di Viareggio
tel. 584.40727
€, AIC

Gran Varignano
Via Paladini, 27
Notes: Closed Mondays.
pizzeria
tel. 0584395734
€, AIC

Grom
V.le Marconi, 77
gelato
tel. 584.962263
AIC
www.grom.it

La Posteria
Via Fratti, 386
restaurant, pizzeria
tel. 3477351890
€€€, AIC

Marechiaro
V.le Europa, 14
restaurant
tel. 0584391244
€-€€€, AIC
www.bagnomarechiaro.it

Stabilimento Balneare De Pinedo
Viale Europa, 3
bar, tavola calda
tel. 584.39213
€-€€, AIC

Star Bene Senza Glutine
Via Mazzini 151
bar, desserts
tel. 584.631736
€
www.starbenesenzaglutine.it

VICCHIO

Agrit. Fattoria I Ricci
Via Rostolena, 14
agritourism
tel. 055844784
€€€€, AIC
www.fattoriairicci.com

La Casa Matta
Viale Beato Angelico, 79/81
restaurant, pizzeria
tel. 55.8497104
AIC
www.lacasamatta.eu

Locanda Antica Porta di Levante
P.zza Vitt. Veneto, 5
hotel, restaurant
tel. 055844050
AIC
www.anticaportadilevante.it

VICOPISANO

D'Antonio restaurant, pizzeria €-€€, AIC
Via Prov.le Vicarese, 161 tel. 50702001

VOLTERRA

Don Beta restaurant €€€-€€€€, AIC
Via Matteotti, 39 tel. 058886730 www.donbeta.it

Il Pozzo degli Etruschi restaurant €€, AIC
Via delle Prigioni, 28/30 tel. 058880608 www.ilpozzodeglietruschi.com

Il Ritrovo restaurant, pizzeria €-€€, AIC
B.go S. Lazzero, 7 tel. 058880122 www.ilritrovo-volterra.it
Notes: Pizza only at dinner.

La Vecchia Lira restaurant €-€€€€, AIC
Via Matteotti, 19 tel. 058886180 www.vecchialira.com

Ombra della Sera pizzeria, tavola calda €€€, AIC
Via Gramsci, 70 tel. 058886663 www.ristoranteombradellasera.it
Via Guarnacci, 16 tel. 058886663 www.ristoranteombradellasera.it

Modern Couple (A. Smith)

VENICE AND VENETO

PLACES IN VENICE TO BUY GLUTEN-FREE FOOD PRODUCTS

Calle Dei Sapori
Sestiere Cannaregio, 2892, Venetian Ghetto

Erborista Cibele
Campielo dell Anconetta (near Calle del Pistor)

Farmacia Alla Vecchia
Sestiere San Marco, 4598

Farmacia Alle due Colonne
Via Cannareggio, 6045

Farmacia Dezuanni   Via San Salvador, 21

Farmacia Italo Inglese   Via San Marco, 3717

Farmacia S.S. Cosma e Damiano   Isola Giudeca, 446

Mea Libera Tutti Sas   Sestiere Cannaregio, 3803

Minimarket   Via Tiro, 14 Lido

Salumeria Bellenzier   San Polo1472

PLACES IN VENICE TO GET GUARANTEED GLUTEN-FREE GELATO (SPONSORED BY ITALIAN CELIAC SOCIETY)

Grom
Strada Nuova Cannaregio, 3844

Grom
Campo S.Barnaba - Dorsoduro 2852

Grom
Campo dei Frari

Gelateria Nico
Dorsoduro, 922 Zattere

B&B'S AND HOTELS IN VENICE LISTED ALPHABETICALLY

AD Place Venice
Fondamenta della Fenice, 2557/A, San Marco   tel. 041 241 32 34   www.adplacevenice.com

Aqua Palace
Calle de la Malvasia 5492 Castello   tel. 041 296 0442   www.aquapalace.it

Bella Venezia Hotel Venice
San Marco, 4710   tel. 0415288779   www.hotelbellavenezia.com

Best Western Hotel Ala
San Marco 2494   tel. 041 520 8333   www.hotelala.it

Best Western Hotel Biasutti
Via Enrico Dandolo,27/29   tel. 041 526 0120   www.hotelbiasutti.it

Best Western Premier Hotel Sant'Elena
Calle Buccari, 10   tel. 041 271 7811
www.book.bestwestern.it/EN/hotel_in_Venice_98238.aspx

Bonotto Hotel Belvedere
Via Generale Giardino, 14, 36065   tel. 0424529845   www.bonotto.it

Cà Pisani
Dorsoduro 979   tel. 041 240 1411   www.capisanihotel.it

Ca' Vendramin di Santa Fosca
Cannaregio 2400   tel. 041 275 0125   www.hotelcavendramin.it

Ca' del Campo
Campo della Guerra, San Marco 51   tel. 041 241 1660   www.cadelcampo.it

Ca' della Loggia
San Marco, Calle San Gallo 921/a   tel. 041 241 1267   www.cadellaloggia.it

Casa del Melograno
Cannaregio 2022   tel. 041 520 8807   www.locandadelmelograno.it

Ca' Nigra Lagoon Resort
Santa Croce 927   tel. 412750047   www.hotelcanigra.com

Domina Home Cà Zusto
Campo Rielo, Santa Croce 1358   tel. 041 524 2991   www.dominahomecazusto.com/en

Domina Home GiudeccaSt
Corte Ferrando 409C   tel. 041 296 0168   www.dominahome.it

Hotel A la Commedia
San Marco 4596/A, Corte del Teatro Goldoni   tel. 041 277 0235
www.commediahotel.com

Hotel Ai Due Principi
Castello 4971   tel. 041 241 3979   www.hotelaidueprincipi.com

Hotel Ai Mori d' Oriente
Fondamenta Della Sensa, Cannaregio 331   tel. 041 711 001   www.morihotel.com

Hotel Al Gazzettino
San Marco, 4971   tel. 041 528 6523   www.algazzettino.com

Hotel Al Piave
Ruga Giuffa Castello, 4838/40   tel. 41.5238512   www.hotelalpiave.com

Hotel Bonvecchiati
San Marco, Calle Goldoni 4488   tel. 041 528 5017   www.hotelbonvecchiati.it

Hotel Bucintoro
Castello 2135/a   tel. 041 528 9909   www.hotelbucintoro.com

Hotel Canal Grande
Santa Croce, 932, Campo San Simeon Grande   tel. 041 24 40 148
www.hotelcanalgrande.it

Hotel Da Bruno
Castello 5726/A   tel. 041 523 0452   www.hoteldabruno.com

Hotel Danieli
Riva degli Schiavoni 4196   tel. 041 522 6480
www.danielihotelvenice.com/?EM=GFHG_LC_72_ICM_EAME
Notes: GFM.

Hotel De L'Alboro Venice
Sestiere San Marco, 3894   tel. 0415206977   www.alborohotel.it
Notes: GF breakfast. Great location.

Hotel Dell'Opera
San Marco 2009   tel. 041 520 5243   www.hoteldelloperavenice.com

Hotel Donà Palace
San Marco 391   tel. 041 274 3511   www.donapalace.it

Hotel Excelsior Hotel
Via Zara, 3, Lido   tel. 0421370934   www.excelsior-jesolo.it

Hotel Rialto
Riva del Ferro, San Marco   tel. 0415209166   www.rialtohotel.com
Notes: GF breakfast on request.

Hotel Villa Beatrice
4 Via dei Villini, 30126 Lido di Venezia   tel. 041 731 072   www.hotelbeatrice.com

Il Glicine Fiorito Bed and Breakfast B&B
Via Orsmida Rosada, 32, Venice-Lido Venezia   tel. 041770537   www.ilglicinefiorito.com
Notes: GF breakfast.

Park Hotel Brasilia Hotel
Via Levantina, 2° acc. al mare, 3   tel. 0421380851   www.parkhotelbrasilia.com
Notes: GF breakfast on request.

Russott Hotel Venice
Via Orlanda, 4 I   tel. 0415310500   www.russotthotels.com

Reflections in the Grand Canal (A. Smith)

VENICE RESTAURANTS AND BAKERIES
LISTED ALPHABETICALLY
(AIC = participates in the Associazione Italiana Celiachia program)
(V=vaporetto stop)

RESTAURANTS

A la Vecia Cavana   restaurant
Cannaregio 4624   tel. 0415238644   www.veciacavana.it
Notes: Special celiac menu. Restaurant highly recommended.

Ai Gondolieri   restaurant   €€€€
Fondamenta dell'Ospedaletto, Dorsoduro 366   tel. 0415286396   www.aigondolieri.it
Notes: English spoken. Closed Tuesdays.

Al Giardinetto "da Severino "   restaurant   €€€€, AIC
Castello, 4928   tel. 0415285332   www.algiardinetto.it

Algiubagio'   restaurant   €€€€
Cannaregio 5039, Fondamenta Nuove   tel. 0415236084   www.algiubagio.net
Notes: English spoken. V: Fondamente Nuove.

Alla Vedova   restaurant   €-€€€€
Calle del Pistor 3912   tel. 0415285324
Notes: Highly recommended. No credit cards.V: Ca'D'Oro.

Antico Gatoleto   restaurant, pizzeria   €€€
Sestiere Cannaregio 6055   tel. 04 15221883   www.anticogatoleto.com

Aromi Restaurant and Aromi Bar restaurant   €€€
Giudecca 810   tel. 0412723311

Bancogiro   restaurant   €€-€€€

Avogaria   hotel, restaurant   €€€€
Calle Avogaria, Dorsoduro 1629   tel. 041296049   www.avogaria.com
Notes: GF with advance notice.

Campo San Giacometto, Santa Croce 122 (under porch)   tel. 0415232061
Notes: V:Rialto.

Cips Club   restaurant   €€€
at hotel Cipriani - Giudecca 10, 30133   tel. 0415207744
Notes: Reservations recommended. V: Zitelle.

Corte Sconta   restaurant   €€-€€€
Calle del Pestrin, Castello 3886   tel. 0415227024
Notes: GF pasta. English spoken. Reservations essential. Closed Sun., Mon. months of Jan.,
Feb., July and Aug. V: Arsenale.

Da Leoni   restaurant   €€€€
Riva degli Schiavoni, Castello 4171   tel. 0412700680   www.hotellondra.it
Notes: No GF pasta. English spoken. In Hotel Londra Palace. Reservations essential. V:San
Zaccaria.

da Poggi   restaurant   €€, AIC
Rio terrà de La Madalena, 2103 Cannaregio   tel. 3926818463 www.ristorantedapoggi.it

Fortuny Restaurant   restaurant   €€€€
at the hotel Cipriani Giudecca 10, 30133   tel. 0415207744   www.hotelcipriani.it.
Notes: V: Zitelle. Reservations essential, jacket required, no children under 8 in evening.

Frary's   restaurant   €€, AIC
San Polo, 2558   tel. 41.72005
www.facebook.com/pages/Frarys/605774209449317

Gastronomia Le Quattro Stagioni restaurant, fast food   €€
Corso Mazzini 34   tel. 345 2695635

Il Molino   restaurant   €€€-€€€€
At the Hilton - Giudecca 810   tel. 0412723311

La Bitta   restaurant   €€
Calle lunga San Barbara, Dorsoduro 2753   tel. 0415230531
Notes: English spoken. Closed Sun. No lunch. V:Ca' Rezzonico.

La Favorita   restaurant, pizzeria   €€-€€€
Via Giovanni Rizzetti 18   tel. 04 23723474   www.lafavoritapizzeria.com

La Fontanella   restaurant   €€€-€€€€
Via Orlanda, 4 I   tel. 0415310500   www.russotthotels.com

La Zucca   restaurant   €
1762 Santa Croce, close to San Giacomo square   tel. 0415241570   www.lazucca.it
Notes: Reservations essential.

Oke Zattere   restaurant, pizzeria   €€-€€€, AIC
Dorsoduro, 1414   tel. 041.5206601/340.4529035

Ostaria al Garanghelo   restaurant   €
Via Garibaldi, 1621   tel. 0415204697   www.garanghelo.com

Ostaria Antico Dolo   restaurant   €€€€
Ruga Rialto, 778   tel. 0415226546   www.anticodolo.it
Notes: Many celiac customers. GF pasta. Highly recommended.

Osteria All Ombra   restaurant   €€-€€€
Canneregio 5603   tel. 041611905
Notes: In a small square bet. Campo die SS. Apostoli and Salizzada S. Giovanni Crisostomo.

Pane Vino e San Daniele   restaurant   €€-€€€
Calle dei Botteri, San Polo   tel. 0415237456   www.panevinoesandaniele.net

Restaurant da fiore   restaurant   €€€€
S. Polo, 2002 (Calle del Scaleter)   tel. 041721308   www.dafiore.net

Parking (A. Smith)

Ristorante Gianni	restaurant	€€-€€€
Dorsoduro 918, Zattere	tel. 0415237210	

Ristorante Le Maschere	restaurant	€€€-€€€€

in San Clemente Palace hotel - Isola di San Clemente 1   tel. 0412445001
www.sanclemente.thi.it
Notes: GF with advance notice.

Trattoria AL Gazzettino	restaurant	€€€-€€€€
Sestiere San Marco 4972	tel. 04 15210497	

Trattoria da Fiore	restaurant	€€€€

San Marco, Calle de le Botteghe, 3461   tel. 0415235310   www.dafiore.it
Notes: Very highly recommended but also very expensive. Near San Polo square.

Trattoria Da Nino	restaurant	€€€
Sestiere Castello 4668	tel. 04 15235886	www.trattoriadanino.com

Trattoria dai Peochi	restaurant	€€
Canneregio 2232	tel. 041721555	

Vini da Gigio	restaurant	€€€
Sestiere Cannaregio, 3628	tel. 0415285140	www.vinidagigio.com

Notes: Great reviews.

VENEZIA - LIDO

Hotel Villa Beatrice	hotel	AIC
Via dei Villini, 4	tel. 41.731072	www.hotelbeatrice.com

THE REST OF VENETO
(AIC = participates in the Associazione Italiana Celiachia program)

ADRIA

Gastronomia Le Quattro Stagioni	tavola calda	€€€, AIC
Corso Mazzini, 34	tel. 345.2695635	www.gastronomialequattrostagioni.it

ARBIZZANO

La Sfera	pizzeria	€, AIC
Via Valpolicella, 21	tel. 0456020018	

Enrico VIII
Via Spianzana, 20

ARCUGNANO
restaurant
tel. 0444550440

€€-€€€, AIC
www.enricoottavo.it

ARIANO NEL POLESINE

Antico Delta
Via San Basilio 139

pizzeria
tel. 426.378403

€€, AIC
www.anticodelta.it

ARQUÀ POLESINE

Locanda Valmolin
Via Marzara, 694

restaurant, pizzeria
tel. 347.1334411

€€€€, AIC
www.locandavalmolin.com

Trattoria degli Amici
Via Quirina, 4

restaurant
tel. 042591045

€€, AIC
www.trattoriadegliamici.it

ARZIGNANO

Pizzeria Pasticceria Majn
Via Main, 7/B

pizzeria, bakery, gelato
tel. 444.674438

€, AIC
www.pizzeriamajn.it

ASIAGO

Albergo Rendola
Via Rendola, 41

inn, restaurant, pizzeria
tel. 0424464148

AIC
www.albergorendola.it

La Tana c/o Sporting Residence H. Asiago restaurant
Via 4 Novembre, 77   tel. 0424462521
Notes: Closed Mondays.

€€€, AIC

Magia
Viale Trento Trieste, 31

pizzeria
tel. 424.463338

€€, AIC

Pizzeria Ristorante Rendola
Via Rendola, 41

restaurant, pizzeria
tel. 0424600500

€€-€€€, AIC

Sporting Residence Hotel
Via 4 Novembre, 77

hotel
tel. 0424462177

AIC
www.sportingasiago.com

ASOLO

Villa Razzolin Loredana
Via Schiavonesca Marosticana, 15   tel. 0423951088
Notes: Closed Mondays.

restaurant

€€, AIC

BELLUNO

Al Borgo
Via Anconetta, 8

restaurant
tel. 0437926755

€€€, AIC

Notes: Closed Mondays at dinner, Tuesdays.

Alla Bella Napoli
Via Feltre, 240

restaurant, pizzeria
tel. 437.944054

€€-€€€, AIC

Excalibur
Via Tiziano Vecellio, 5/A

pizzeria
tel. 437.932078

€€, AIC
www.excaliburweb.it

La Delizia

gelato (€, AIC)

P.zza V.Emanuele, 9

Zodiaco
Via Travazzoi, 8
Notes: Closed Mondays.

restaurant, pizzeria
tel. 0437941478

€, AIC

BIBIONE

Al Villaggio c/o V.T.I.
Via Delle Colonie 2

restaurant/pizzeria
tel. 0431442630

€€, AIC
www.vti.it

BOLZANO VICENTINO

Nuvole di Latte   gelato (€, AIC)   Via Roma, 56

BOSCO CHIESANUOVA

Lenci Tre   pizzeria   €, AIC
Via M. Piccoli, 61   tel. 0457050057

BREDA DI PIAVE

Da Teddy   trattoria, pizzeria   €, AIC
Via Giuseppe Garibaldi, 44 loc. Pero   tel. 0422904418

BREDA DI PIAVE - LOC PERO

Antica Bassa Da Teddy   restaurant, pizzeria   €€-€€€, AIC
Via Giuseppe Garibaldi, 44 loc. Pero   tel. 422.904418   www.anticabassadateddy.it

BRENZONE

Hotel Eden   hotel, restaurant   AIC
Via Zanardelli, 6   tel. 45.7420102   www.consolinihotels.com

CADONEGHE

Da Silvio   pizzeria   €€, AIC
Via L. Bordin, 39   tel. 049702150
Notes: Closed Mondays.

CALDOGNO

Al Marinante   restaurant   €€€-€€€€, AIC
Via Cà Alta, 111   tel. 0444986039   www.almarinante.it
Notes: Closed Mondays, Tuesdays, and at lunch.

Molin Vecio   trattoria   €€€-€€€€, AIC
Via Giaroni, 116   tel. 0444585168   www.molinvecio.it
Notes: Closed Tuesdays.

CAMPODARSEGO

Ariston   hotel   AIC
Via Antoniana, 230   tel. 0499314401

Il Dolce Incontro   gelato (€, AIC)   Via Caltana, 48

CAORLE

Cleofe   hotel, restaurant   €€€-€€€€
Via Altinate, 2   tel. 042181082   www.hotelcleofe.it

Hotel Angelo   hotel   AIC
Via dei Calamari, 6   tel. 0421211728

Hotel Doriana   hotel   AIC
L.re Trieste, 48   tel. 042181104   www.hoteldoriana.it

CAPRINO VERONESE

Athena   pizzeria   €, AIC
Via Pertini, 10/h   tel. 0456230813

CASELLE DI SOMMACAMPAGNA

da Brinchi   trattoria   €€-€€€, AIC
Via Tezze, 82   tel. 0458581106   www.trattoriadabrinchi.com

CASSOLA LOC. SAN GIUSEPPE

Alla Torre   restaurant, pizzeria   €€, AIC
Via Leonardo da Vinci, 23   tel. 424.33081   www.pizzeriallatorre.it

CASTEL D'AZZANO

Al Ventaglio restaurant, pizzeria €€-€€€, AIC
Via Pietro Mascagni, 92 tel. 045512591 www.pizzerialventaglio.it

CASTELCUCCO

Montegrappa hotel, restaurant, pizzeria €€, AIC
Viale Montegrappa, 8 tel. 0423563123 www.hotelmontegrappa.it

CASTELFRANCO VENETO

Da Gennaro restaurant, pizzeria AIC
Via Castellana 17 tel. 423.482188

CASTELGOMBERTO

Al Ponte pizzeria €€, AIC
Via S. Cecilia, 73 tel. 445.491045 www.pizzeriaalponte.it

CASTELNUOVO DEL GARDA

Agrit. Casa San Marco B&B AIC
Via Verona, 1 tel. 0456458906 www.agriturismocasasanmarco.com

CAVALLINO TREPORTI

Alla Fattoria c/o Union Lido restaurant €€-€€€€, AIC
Via Fausta, 245 tel. 041968376 www.lafattoria.it

Art & Park Union Lido Hotel hotel AIC
Via Fausta, 270 tel. 041968043 www.parkhotelunionlido.com

Carpaccio restaurant €€-€€€€, AIC
Via Fausta, 266 tel. 41.3098632
www.unionlido.com/en/things-to-do-en/gourmet-club/carpaccio-3

Cavallo Marino c/o Union Lido restaurant €€, AIC
Via Fausta, 258 tel. 0415370840

Riviera c/o Union Lido restaurant €, AIC
Via Fausta, 258 tel. 0415371344

CAZZANO DI TRAMIGNA

Corte del Sole pizzeria €€, AIC
Via Costeggiola, 38 tel. 45.7675369 cortedelsole@yahoo.it

CENCENIGHE

Da Makram restaurant, pizzeria €, AIC
Via Roma, 62 tel. 0437580328
Notes: DS pizza point. Closed Mondays.

CESSALTO

Airest Ristop Calstorta fast food €, AIC
Via Calstorta, 3 tel. 421.327179

CHIES D'ALPAGO

Locanda San Martino restaurant bar €€€-€€€€, AIC
Via Don Ermolao Barattin, 23 tel. 043740111
Notes: Closed Mondays, Tuesdays at dinner, Wednesdays.

CHIOGGIA

Grom gelato (€, AIC) P.zza del Quartiere Latino, 16

CHIRIGNAGO

Icebear gelato (€, AIC) Via Miranese, 286/M

CISMON DEL GRAPPA

Val Goccia
Via Giarre di Sicilia, 5
Notes: Closed Tuesdays.

restaurant, pizzeria
tel. 0424432126

€€, AIC
www.valgoccia.com

CITTADELLA

Antica Porta

gelato (€, AIC)

Via Garibaldi, 55

Torre di Malta
Via Ca' Nave, 2/d

restaurant/pizzeria
tel. 0499401761

€€, AIC
www.ristorantepizzeriatorredimalta.it

CODOGNÈ

Giancarlo
Via Farmacia, 57

restaurant
tel. 3480177072

€€€-€€€€, AIC
www.resortmarcopolo.it

COGOLLO DEL CENGIO

Barricatella
Via Strada del Costo, 1

trattoria, bar, gelato
tel. 445.320158

€€, AIC
www.facebook.com/home.php

COLOGNA VENETA

Acquario
Via S.Andrea 27

pizzeria
tel. 044285667

€, AIC

Rio (A. Smith)

COLOGNOLA AI COLLI

Chocolat

gelato (€, AIC)

Via Strà, 35

COSTA DI ROVIGO

La Rosa
P.zza San Rocco, 41

pizzeria
tel. 0425497197

€, AIC

COSTABISSARA

Ca' Nostra
Via Mazzini, 8/10

pizzeria
tel. 0444971181

AIC
www.canostra .it

Dal Gelatiere

ERACLEA MARE
gelato (€, AIC)

Via Marinella, 12

Stella Alpina
Piazza Municipio, 7

FALCADE
hotel, restaurant, bar
tel. 437.599046

€€€€, AIC
www.hotelstellalpina.com

Bar Gelat. Centrale

FORNO DI ZOLDO
gelato (€, AIC)

P.zza A. Santin, 4

Villa Gardenia
Via S. Giorgio, 188
Notes: Closed Tuesdays.

FRATTA POLESINE
restaurant
tel. 0425668497

€€, AIC
www.villa-gardenia.it

Pizzeria La Capannina
Via Poiano 23

GARDA
pizzeria
tel. 45.6279159

€€-€€€, AIC
www.lacapanninagarda.com

Pila Vecia
Via Saccovener, 9
Notes: 100% gluten-free.

ISOLA DELLA SCALA
restaurant
tel. 45.6630642

€€€, AIC
www.risoferron.com

da Guido
Via Roma Sinistra, 25

JESOLO
restaurant
tel. 0421350380

€€€€
www.ristorantedaguido.com

Gelateria Lovat

gelato (€, AIC)

Piazza I Maggio, 15

Stefania
Via Pordenone, 12
Notes: S € 23 D € 46

B&B
tel. 3201776184

AIC

Hotel Domingo
Via Gorizia, 31

JESOLO LIDO
hotel
tel. 0421971922

€, AIC

Hotel Europa
Via Bafile, 361

hotel
tel. 0421371631

AIC
www.hoteleuropajesolo.it

Hotel Galassia
Via Treviso, 7

hotel
tel. 0421370677

AIC
www.hotelgalassia.it

Hotel Imperia
Via Gorizia, 31

hotel
tel. 0421370718

AIC
www.hotelimperia.com

Hotel Nettuno
Via Bafile XXIII A.M. 2

hotel
tel. 0421370301

AIC
www.hotel-nettuno.com

Hotel Stockholm
Via dei Mille, 15

hotel
tel. 0421371235

AIC
www.hotelstockholm.it

Hotel Universo
Via Treviso, 9/11

hotel
tel. 0421972298

AIC

Ristorante Frontemare
Via Bafile, 23° accesso al mare

restaurant
tel. 0421370301

€€-€€€, AIC
www.hotelnettuno.com

Teverone
Piazza Roma, 9

LAMOSANO DI CHIES
pizzeria
tel. 437.40189

€€, AIC

LIMANA

Az. Agric. I Boschi del Castagno B&B   AIC
Via I Boschi, 1   tel. 0437970114

L'Oasi   trattoria   €€€, AIC
Via Triches, 25   tel. 0437967298
Notes: Closed Sundays at dinner, Mondays.

LONIGO

Mondo nuovo   sandwich shop, bakery   €, AIC
Via Cesare Battisti, 168/F   tel. 3485422421
www.facebook.com/mondonuovoglutenfree

The Bridge   pizzeria   €, AIC
Via Madonna, 44   tel. 0444835460

MALO

Il Fornino   pizzeria, pub   €, AIC
Via Pace, 3   tel. 0445581427

MARGHERA

Grom   gelato   €, AIC
Via Pietro Arduino c/o Centro Comm.le Navedevero   tel. 041/920648   www.grom.it

MAROSTICA

Lunaelaltro   pizzeria   €-€€€, AIC
Corso della Ceramica, 33   tel. 424.478098   www.osterialunaelaltro.com

MARTELLAGO

Zeus Pizza   pizzeria   €€, AIC
Via Berna, 2   tel. 41.0994487

MASON VICENTINO

Icio & Paola   pizzeria   €, AIC
Via S. Pietro, 6   tel. 0424708232

MEL

Col di Neve   B&B   €€€, AIC
Via Tiago, 90   tel. 0437540342

MERLENGO PONZANO VENETO

Le Querce   restaurant   AIC
Via Talponera 130/A   tel. 422.99043

MESTRE

Al Corso   pizzeria   €, AIC
C.so del Popolo, 37   tel. 041981642

Gelateria Artigianale Al Parco   gelato (€, AIC)   Via Casona 23

Grom   gelato (€, AIC)   Via Palazzo, 37

Novotel Venezia/Novotelcafé   hotel, restaurant   €€€€, AIC
Via A. Ceccherini, 21   tel. 0415066511   www.novotel.com

RossoPomodoro   restaurant, pizzeria   €€, AIC
Via Don Federico Tosatto 26   tel. 41.2001288   www.rossopomodoro.it

MESTRE-ZELARINO

Antico Moro   hotel   AIC
Via Castellana, 149   tel. 41.5461834   www.anticomoro.com

MIRA

Isola di Caprera   hotel   €€€€, AIC
Riviera S. Trentin, 13   tel. 0414265255   www.isoladicaprera.com

MIRANO

Ostaria Nova   restaurant   €€€€, AIC
Via Cavin di Sala, 12   tel. 41.5700761   www.ostarianova.it

MOGLIANO VENETO

ICapriccio   restaurant, bar   €€€, AIC
Via Toti dal Monte, 29/31   tel. 415905304   www.icapriccio.com

MONTEBELLUNA

Al Grappolo d'Oro   pizzeria   €, AIC
Via Feltrina Sud, 181   tel. 0423303516   www.grappolodoro.com

MONTECCHIA DI CROSARA

Tregnago   restaurant   €€-€€€, AIC
Via Campitelli, 1   tel. 0457460036   www.ristorantetregnago.com

MONTEFORTE D'ALPONE

Abbazia   pizzeria   €€, AIC
Via Giuseppe Garibaldi, 24   tel. 45.7613796   www.monteolivetomaggiore.it

MONTEGROTTO TERME

Caffè del Corso   tavola calda   €, AIC
Corso delle Terme, 108/a   tel. 3402952513

Hotel Garden Terme   hotel, restaurant   AIC
Corso Terme, 7   tel. 49.8911699   www.gardenterme.it

MONTEMEZZO DI SOVIZZO

La Grippia   pizzeria   €, AIC
Via Fontanalunga, 13   tel. 0444551011
Notes: Closed Mondays and at lunch.

MONTICELLO CONTEOTTO

Ristorante Hotel Rizzi   hotel, restaurant, pizzeria €€€-€€€€, AIC
Via Revoloni, 2   tel. 0444946099
Notes: Closed Tuesdays.

MUSILE DI PIAVE

Antica Trattoria alla Fossetta restaurant bar   €€, AIC
Via Fossetta, 31   tel. 0421330296   www.fossetta.it

NERVESA DELLA BATTAGLIA

La Strana Coppia   restaurant, pizzeria   €€, AIC
Via Lungo Piave G. Da Bologna, 1 tel. 422.77931
www.facebook.com/pages/Pizzeria-La-Strana-Coppia/323934487343

NOALE

Zeus Pizza   pizzeria   €€, AIC
Via Tempesta, 75   tel. 41.822257

ORSAGO

La Dolce Flavia   gelato (€, AIC)   Via G. Mazzini, 22

PADOVA

Al Carmine   restaurant, pizzeria   €€, AIC
P.zza Petrarca, 8   tel. 0498764952
Notes: Closed Mondays, Saturday and Sunday lunch.

Autogrill Limena
A4 Brescia - Padova

autogrill
tel. 49.8648057

€, AIC

Bastioni del Moro
Via P. Bronzetti, 18
Notes: Closed Sundays.

restaurant
tel. 0498710006

€€€, AIC
www.bastionidelmoro.it

Da Nadia
Via A. da Bassano, 45-47

hotel, restaurant, pizzeria
tel. 0498641661

€€, AIC

Forcellini 172
Via Forcellini, 172

pizzeria, restaurant
tel. 0498033722

€€, AIC
www.forcellini172.it

Grom
Grom
www.grom.it

gelato (€, AIC)
gelato (€, AIC)

P.zza dei Signori, 33
Via Roma, 101

Per Bacco
Piazzale Pontecorvo, 10
Notes: Closed Sundays.

restaurant
tel. 0498752883

€€€€, AIC
www.per-bacco.it

Perdinci
Via C. Callegari, 43

pizzeria
tel. 49.604578

€, AIC
www.perdinci.it

PAESE

Zeus Pizza
Via Marconi, 36

pizzeria
tel. 422.1564431

€€, AIC
www.misterimprese.it

PALAZZOLO DI SONA

Cà Fileno
Via Prele, 48

restaurant
tel. 0456080891

€€-€€€, AIC
www.ristorantecafileno.com

PEDAVENA

La Birreria Pedavena
Viale Vittorio Veneto, 76

restaurant
tel. 439.304402

€-€€, AIC
www.labirreriapedavena.com

PERAGA DI VIGONZA

Le Midì Ristoservice
Via Germania, 9
Notes: Closed Saturdays, Sundays, and at dinner.

restaurant, tavola calda
tel. 049629675

€, AIC
www.lemidi.it

PERAROLO DI VIGONZA

Mai Sazio
Via A. Diaz, 160

pizzeria
tel. 0496226588

€, AIC
www.maisazio.it

PESCHIERA DEL GARDA

Bellavista
Lungolago Mazzini, 1

pizzeria
tel. 0457553252

€€, AIC

Tortuga Cafè

gelato (€, AIC)

Via Lungolago Mazzini, 2/b

PESEGGIA

La Torre
Via Vecchia Mogliese, 186

pizzeria
tel. 0415830590

€, AIC
www.pizzerialatorre.it

PIAZZOLA SUL BRENTA

Alle Logge
Via delle Logge Palladiane, 6

restaurant
tel. 0499601432

€€€€, AIC
www.ristoranteallelogge.it

PIEVE DI CADORE

Cavallino
Via Nazionale, 4

inn, restaurant
tel. 0435500467

€€-€€€, AIC
www.hotelcavallinodolomiti.it

PIEVE DI SOLIGO

Agli Angeli   pizzeria   €, AIC
Via Tacchini, 45   tel. 04381794966   www.angeli.it
Notes: Closed Wednesdays at dinner.

PONTE DI NANTO

El Rosedal   pizzeria   €, AIC
Via Mercato, 48   tel. 444639044

PONTE NELLE ALPI

Mychef Ponte nelle Alpi Ovest   mychef   €, AIC
A27 Venezia - Belluno   tel. 437.990613   www.mychef.it

PONTE SAN NICOLÒ

Al Ponte   pizzeria   €, AIC
Via Roma, 37   tel. 49717437   www.pizzeriaristorantealponte.it

PORTO TOLLE

La Fraterna   B&B   AIC
Via Mentone, 13   tel. 0426384128   www.agriturismolafraterna.it

Nottedì   B&B   AIC
Via Alicata, 10 - loc. Cà Mello   tel. 3497237930

PREGANZIOL

Glutine Zero   sandwich shop, bakery   €, AIC
Via Veneto 1   tel. 422.1571101   www.glutinezero.it

L'Albera di Zeus   pizzeria   €, AIC
Via Terraglio, 249   tel. 04221721856

QUINTO DI TREVISO

Best Western Premier Bhr Treviso Hotel hotel, restaurant   €€€€, AIC
Via Postumia Castellana, 2   tel. 04223730   www.bhrtrevisohotel.com

QUINTO VICENTINO

Dolce Idea   gelato   €, AIC
Via Vittorio Veneto, 31   tel. 348.4000241 www.facebook.com/GelateriaDolceIdea

RECOARO TERME

La Linte   restaurant   €€, AIC
Via Roma, 19   tel. 445.75566   www.ristorantelalinte.it

ROMANO D'EZZELINO

Al Pioppeto   restaurant   €€-€€€, AIC
Via Barbarigo, 13   tel. 0424570502

Dalla Mena   inn, restaurant   €€, AIC
Via Valle S. Felicita, 14   tel. 042436481
Notes: Closed Mondays.

RONCADE

Pasqualino 90   restaurant, pizzeria   AIC
Via Roma, 48   tel. 0422708377

ROSOLINA MARE

Chiosco Bar Bagno Tamerici   bar   €, AIC
Via Trieste, 140   tel. 426.68424   www.bagniferro.it

Fiorella   restaurant, hotel   €€, AIC
Via Trieste, 17   tel. 0426.68010   www.albergofiorella.it

ROVIGO

Re Artù
Via Petrarca, 20
Notes: DS pizza point. Closed at lunch.

pizzeria
tel. 042533330

€, AIC

S. GIULIANO - VENEZIA

Russott Hotel Venezia
Via Orlanda, 4

hotel, restaurant
tel. 0415310500

€€€€, AIC
www.russotshotels.com

S. PIETRO IN CARIANO

Agriturismo Fioravante
Via Don C. Biasi, 7

B&B
tel. 0457701317

AIC
www.agriturismofioravante.it

S. ZENO DI COLOGNOLA AI COLLI

La Fenice
Via Cesare Battisti
Notes: Closed Mondays.

pizzeria, osteria
tel. 0456152686

€-€€, AIC

S. ZENONE DEGLI EZZELINI

Ezzelino
Via Marconi, 55
Notes: DS pizza point. Closed Mondays.

hotel, restaurant, pizzeria
tel. 0423964070

€€, AIC

SACCOLONGO

Il Console
Via Roma, 4
Notes: Closed Tuesday-Saturday at lunch.

restaurant
tel. 0498016648

AIC
www.ilconsole.com

SALZANO

Belfiore
Via Roma, 234
Notes: DS pizza point. Closed Wednesdays.

pizzeria
tel. 041437010

€, AIC
www.belfiorehotel.it

SAN BONIFACIO

Mychef San Lorenzo Ovest
A4 Padova - Brescia

mychef
tel. 340.1674815

€, AIC
www.mychef.it

SANDRIGO

La Colombara
Via Chiesa, 7/a fraz. Lupia
Notes: Closed Mondays, Tuesdays at lunch.

restaurant, pizzeria
tel. 0444750767

€€€-€€€€, AIC

SCHIO

da Beppino
Località Ceresara, 1

restaurant
tel. 0445670139

€€€, AIC

Il Fornino
Via Pio X, 223/A

pizzeria
tel. 445.672939

€, AIC
www.ilfornino.it

Il Piacere

gelato (€, AIC)

Via Batt. Val Leogra, 79/d

SEDICO

Ristorante Alla Stanga
Via La Stanga, 24

restaurant
tel. 043787611

€€€, AIC
www.ristoranteallastanga.it

SELVAZZANO DENTRO

Senza Spiga
Via Brentella, 25

bar, tavola calda/fredda
tel. 49.630915

€, AIC
www.senzaspiga.it

SETTIMO DI PESCANTINA

Settimo Cielo restaurant, pizzeria €€, AIC
Via Bernardi 1 tel. 45.6703207 www.pizzeriasettimocielo.net

SOAVE

Autogrill Scaligera autogrill €, AIC
A4 Brescia - Padova tel. 45.7610398

SOTTOMARINA DI CHIOGGIA

Grom gelato €, AIC
Lungomare Adriatico ai Bagni Clodia tel. 41.5542931 www.grom.it

Hotel Le Tegnùe hotel AIC
Via Lungomare Adriatico, 48 tel. 41.4917 www.hotelletegnue.it

SOVIZZO

Da Manfron restaurant €€€, AIC
Via Alfieri, 44/46 tel. 0444551960 www.ristorantemanfron.it

SPINEA

All'Antico Graspo d'Uva pizzeria €€, AIC
Via Roma, 32 tel. 041992759
Notes: Closed Tuesdays.

TAGLIO DI PO

Osteria La Pioppa restaurant €-€€€€, AIC
Via Milite Ignoto, 99 tel. 0426660440
Notes: Closed Sundays.

TESSERA VENEZIA

Airest Culto Caffè & Cioccolato "Cultino" fast food €, AIC
Aeroporto Venezia "Marco Polo"- via L.Broglio, 8 tel. 041.2603871-2 www.airest.com

Airest Ristorante L'Orto fast food €, AIC
Aeroporto Venezia "Marco Polo"- via L. Broglio, 8 tel. 041.2603871-2 www.airest.com

THIENE

Gelat. Artig. Vale gelato (€, AIC) Via Divisione Julia, 45

TORREGLIA

La Griglia restaurant €€, AIC
Via S. Daniele, 39 tel. 0495211158
Notes: Closed Tuesdays.

TREVISO

Albergo Alla Scoa hotel
Borgo Treviso, 196 tel. 0423723712
Notes: GF dishes available on request.

Conca d'Oro bar, tavola calda, bakery €, AIC
Via T. Salsa, 351/G tel. 0422420623 www.pasticceria.com

Ezzelino Hotel hotel, restaurant
Via Marconi tel. 0423969448 www.hotelezzelino.com

Grigio Perla pizzeria €, AIC
Via S. Ambrogio da Fiera, 3/b tel. 0422541456

Grom gelato (€, AIC) P.zza del Quartiere Latino, 16

TRICHIANA

Alla Lanterna B&B AIC
Via Casteldardo, 50/A tel. 437.555469

La Pollùce	B&B	AIC
Via Confos, 79	tel. 437.757536	www.pollucebedandbreakfast.it

VERONA

Ai Glicini	restaurant, pizzeria	€€, AIC
Via Centro, 235	tel. 045584100	www.pizzeriaaiglicini.it

Fata Zucchina	restaurant	€€, AIC
Via Don Carlo Steeb, 25	tel. 045597897	www.sucabaruca.com

Gelat. Artig. Oasi	gelato (€, AIC)	Via L. Prina
Maracanà	gelato (€, AIC)	P.le Olimpia, 36/a

Quinto Miglio	pizzeria	€€, AIC
Via Valpantena, 62/a	tel. 45.550361	www.quintomiglio.it

VERONELLA

Prima o poi	pizzeria	€, AIC
Via O. Fontana	tel. 0442480130	

VICENZA

Antico Guelfo	restaurant	€€, AIC
c.da Pedemuro S. Biagio, 92	tel. 0444547897	www.anticoguelfo.it

Gelateria Brustolon	gelato (€, AIC)	Contrà Ponte Pusterla, 23

Giorgio e Chiara	pizzeria	€, AIC
Via Cà Balbi, 377	tel. 0444911004	www.giorgioechiara.it

Gocce di bio	gelato (€, AIC)	Strada di Saviabona, 97b

Ristorante Il Querini da Zemin	restaurant	€€€, AIC
V.le del Sole, 142	tel. 0444552054	

VIGOROVEA

Papillon	pizzeria	€, AIC
Via Trieste, 1	tel. 0499701891	

VILLAFRANCA DI VERONA

Il Gargano	restaurant	€€€€, AIC
Via della Pace, 137	tel. 0456301800	www.ristoranteilgargano.com

La Filanda	osteria	€€-€€€, AIC
Via Nino Bixio, 370	tel. 0456303583	www.osterialafilanda.com

VITTORIO VENETO

Europa	pizzeria	€, AIC
Via Dalmazia, 120	tel. 043859890	

Pizzeria Ristorantino Da Pietro	pizzeria	€, AIC
Via S. Antonio da Padova, 18	tel. 438.912419	

ZOVENCEDO

Ca' Martina	pizzeria	€, AIC
Via Croce, 18	tel. 444.893177	

MILAN AND LOMBARDIA

PLACES IN MILAN TO BUY
GLUTEN-FREE FOOD PRODUCTS

EsseMon.ga

Viale Regina Giovanna 34
Viale Zara 123
Viale Piave 38/B
Via Cagliero 14/a
Via Jenner ang.
Viale Cassala 22
Via Trilussa 24
Via Pezzotti
Via Morgantini 15   Via Monte Rosa
Via Losanna 20/22   Via Forze Armate
Via Feltre
Via Bergamo 10
Viale Papiniano 27   Via Mac Mahon 128
Via Solari, 29
Via Ripamonti 181

Viale Ungheria 12
Viale Vigliani 59
Via Amoretti 4/6
Viale Certosa 59
Via Legnone 3
Via Washington 55
Via Suzzani 221
V.Pellegrino Rossi 33

Via die Missaglia 61/A
piazza Ovidio

Via Morgantini 15

Ipercoop Bonola
Ipercoop La Torre
Ipercoop Piazza Lodi

c/o C.c. Bonola-Via Quarenghi 23
Via B. Gozzoli 130
Via Colletta 46b

Pam
Via Foppa 33
Viale Olona 1/3

Via Inganni 87
Via Archimede 8

PLACES IN MILAN TO GET GUARANTEED GLUTEN-FREE GELATO
(SPONSORED BY ITALIAN CELIAC SOCIETY)

Bar Gelateria Top del Gelato   C.so di Porta Romana, 92
Frozen Gelateria   C.so Porta Ticinese, 96/98
Grom   Via Alberto da Giussano, 1
Grom   C.so di Porta Ticinese, 51
Grom   C.so Buenos Aires, 13
Grom   C.so XXII Marzo, 5
Grom   V. S.ta Margherita, 16
Grom   P.zza Argentina, 6
Grom   Piazza Gae Aulenti, 8
Il Gelato Ecologico   Via Ravizza, 5
L'Isola   Via Forze Armate, 50
Pinguino Blu   Via Paolo Sarpi, 2

HOTELS IN MILAN LISTED ALPHABETICALLY

Best Western Hotel City
Corso Buenos Aires 42/5   tel. 02 2952 3382   www.hotelcitymilano.it
Notes: Stazione Centrale.

Best Western Hotel Galles
Piazza Lima 2   tel. 02 204 841   www.hotelcitymilano.it
Notes: Buenos Aires.

Boscolo Exedra Milano
Corso Matteotti 4 -6   tel. 02 7767 9611   www.milano.boscolohotels.com
Notes: Centro Storico.

Carlton Hotel Baglioni
Via Senato 5   tel. 02 77 077   www.baglionihotels.com
Notes: Centro Storico.

Carlyle Brera Hotel
C.so Garibaldi 84   tel. 02 2900 3888   www.hotelcarlyle.com
Notes: Moscova.

Crowne Plaza Hotel Milan City
Via Melchiorre Gioia 73   tel. 02 6671 7715   www.crowneplazamilan.com
Notes: Business district (Sondrio).

Doria Grand Hotel Milano
Viale Andrea Doria 2   tel. 02 6741 1411   www.doriagrandhotel.it
Notes: (Business district) Corso Buenos Aires.

Doubletree by Hilton Milan
Via Ludovico di Breme 77   tel. 02 928 831   www.dtmilan.com
Notes: Certosa.

Grand Hotel Puccini
Corso Buenos Aires 33   tel. 02 2952 1344   www.grandhotelpuccini.com
Notes: Stazione Centrale.

Grand Visconti Palace
Viale Isonzo 14   tel. 02 540 341   www.grandviscontipalace.com
Notes: Porta Romana.

Hotel Ambasciatori
Galleria del Corso 3   tel. 02 7602 0241   www.ambasciatorihotel.it
Notes: Centro Storico.

Hotel Ariston
Largo Carrobbio 2   tel. 02 7200 0556   www.aristonhotel.com
Notes: Centro Storico.

Hotel Berna Milan
Via Napo Torriani 18   tel. 02 677 311   www.hotelberna.com
Notes: Stazione Centrale.

Hotel Capitol Milano
Via Cimarosa Domenico 6   tel. 02 438 591   www.hotelcapitolmilano.com
Notes: Centro Storico.

Hotel Manzoni
Via Santo Spirito 20   tel. 02 7600 5700   www.hotelmanzoni.com
Notes: Centro Storico.

Hotel Mercure Milano Centro
Piazza Oberdan 12   tel. 02 2940 3907
www.accorhotels.com/gb/hotel-5705-mercure-milano-centro/index.shtml
Notes: Porto Venezia.

Hotel Pierre Milano
Via De Amicis 32   tel. 02 7200 0581   www.hotelpierremilano.it
Notes: Business district.

Hotel Principe di Savoia
Piazza della Repubblica 17   tel. 02 623 01
www.dorchestercollection.com/en/milan/hotel-principe-di-savoia
Notes: Moscova.

Meliá Milano
Via Masaccio 19   tel. 02 44 406
www.melia.com/en/hotels/italy/milan/melia-milano/index.html
Notes: Fiera.

NH Grand Hotel Verdi
Via Melchiorre Gioia 6   tel. 02 62 371
 www.nh-hotels.com/hotel/nh-milano-grand-hotel-verdi
Notes: Moscova.

Novotel Linate/Novotelcafé
Via Mecenate, 121   tel. 02507261   www.novotel.com

Novotel Milano Nord/Novotelcafé
V.le Suzzani,13   tel. 02641151   www.novotel.com

Milano (A. Komorowski)

RESTAURANTS AND BAKERIES IN MILAN
(AIC = participates in the Associazione Italiana Celiachia program)

Autogrill Milano - Duomo Store	autogrill	€, AIC
Via U. Foscolo nr. 1	tel. 2.86331911	
Bar Ted One	bar, tavola calda	€, AIC
Via Solferino, 32	tel. 0206575260	
Notes: Closed Sundays.		
Be Bop	restaurant, pizzeria	€-€€, AIC
Viale Col di Lana, 4	tel. 028376972	
Cantina Piemontese	restaurant	€€€€, AIC
Via Laghetto, 2	tel. 02784618	www.cantinapiemontese.it
Capoverde	restaurant, pizzeria	€, AIC
Via Leoncavallo, 16	tel. 0226820430	
Cook Window	restaurant, pizzeria	€, AIC
via Amatore Sciesa, 18	tel. 0255186997	www.cookwindow.it
Da Hakim	pizzeria	€, AIC
Via Vallazze, 74	tel. 0270630315	
Doris Diner	restaurant	AIC
Viale Sarca, 336/F	tel. 0287250184	
Eco Hotel La Residenza	hotel, restaurant	AIC
Via Scialoia, 3	tel. 2.6461646	www.ecohotelresidenzamilano.it
Guyot	restaurant, wine bar	AIC
Via Arnaldo da Brescia, 3	tel. 0287237103	www.tavernaguyot.com
Notes: Garibaldi.		

Il Giorno Bistrot c/o Hotel Hermitage hotel, restaurant   €€€, AIC
Via Messina, 10   tel. 2.31817
www.fedegroup.it/ristorante/ristorante-il-giorno-bistrot

Il Grissino	restaurant, pizzeria	€€, AIC
Via Legioni Romane 37	tel. 024046141	www.algrissino.it
Notes: Bande Nere.		
Il Papiro	pizzeria/restaurant	€, AIC
Via F.lli Bressan, 9	tel. 022579589	www.pizzeriaristoranteilpapiro.it
Notes: Villa San Giovanni.		
Il Piccolo Padre	restaurant, pizzeria	€, AIC
Via Cenisio, 54 (da Via Princ.Eugenio)	tel. 023494906	www.ilpiccolopadremilano.com
Notes: Monumentale.		
Il Piccolo Principe	restaurant, pizzeria	€€, AIC
Via Pelizza da Volpedo, 16	tel. 2.498275	www.ilpiccolopadremilano.com
Notes: Fiera.		
Isa e Vane	restaurant, bar	€€€, AIC
Via Perugino, 1	tel. 2.36515288	www.isaevane.com
Notes: Porta Vittoria.		
Kitchen Ristorante	restaurant	€€€, AIC
Via Neera, 40	tel. 0284895749	www.kitchenristorante.com
Notes: Navigli.		

La Basilicata   restaurant, pizzeria   €, AIC
Via E. De Marchi, 44   tel. 0266987892
Notes: Turro Gorla Greco. DS pizza point. Closed Mondays.

La Rosa dei Venti   restaurant   €€€, AIC
Via Piero della Francesca,34   tel. 02347338   www.ristorantelarosadeiventi.it
Notes: Monumentale.

La Tellina   restaurant, pizzeria   €, AIC
Via Palanzone, 26   tel. 0266108063
Notes: Bicocca.

Le Specialità   restaurant, pizzeria   €€€-€€€€, AIC
Via P. Calvi, 29   tel. 027388235   www.ristorantelespecialita.com
Notes: Porta Vittoria. Many GF choices. Very accommodating staff.

Lepontina   restaurant, pizzeria   €€€, AIC
Via Lepontina, 8   tel. 2.39820772   www.residencelepontina.it
Notes: Garibaldi.

Mychef Aeroporto Linate   mychef   €, AIC
Viale Forlanini   tel. 2.7383742   www.mychef.it

Mychef Centro Direzionale San Siro   mychef   €, AIC
Via Caldera, 21   tel. 2.40910101   www.mychef.it

Mychef Politecnico di Milano-Facol tà Ingegneria   mychef   €, AIC
P.zza L. da Vinci, 32   tel. 2.2666681   www.mychef.it

Mychef Self Service Corso Italia   mychef   €, AIC
Corso Italia   tel. 2.8812831   www.mychef.it

Osteria dei 5 Sensi   restaurant   €€€-€€€€, AIC
Via Cicco Simonetta, 17   tel. 0258102650   www.osteriadei5sensi.com
Notes: Centro Storico. Closed Saturdays at lunch and Mondays.

Out of Gluten   bakery, pasta shop, sandwich shop   €€, AIC
Via San Michele del Carso, 13   tel. 2.433004   www.facebook.com/outofgluten/info
Notes: Washington.

Panta Rei Club   restaurant, pizzeria   €€€-€€€€, AIC
Viale Pasubio, 14   tel. 026597370   www.pantareiclub.com
Notes: Moscova.

Pasticceria Navotti Senza Glutine   cupcake shop   €€, AIC
Via Paisiello, 7   tel. 2.29401244
www.facebook.com/pasticceria.navotti.senzaglutine

Peperino Pizza & Grill   pizzeria   €€€, AIC
Viale F. Crispi, 1   tel. 0263793078   www.peperinopizza.it
Notes: Moscova.

Petit Paradis   pizzeria   €€, AIC
Via Fezzan, 3   tel. 2.471378   www.ristorantepetitparadis.com
Notes: Washington.

Rigolo   restaurant   €€€€, AIC
Via Solferino, 11 ang. L.go Treves   tel. 02804589   www.rigolo.it
Notes: Moscova.

Splendini & Co.   bakery   €, AIC
Via Pietro Custodi, 1   tel. 2.87066449   www.splendini.it
Notes: 100% gluten-free.

Trattoria Casa Fontana 23 Risotti restaurant €€, AIC
P.zza Carbonari, 5   tel. 026704710   www.23risotti.it
Notes: Garibaldi. Closed Saturdays at lunch and Mondays.

THE REST OF LOMBARDIA
ABBIATEGRASSO
Riti e Conviti restaurant, pizzeria €€-€€€, AIC
Galleria Mirabello, 10   tel. 2.945247   www.ritieconviti.com

AGNOSINE
Da Nicola restaurant, pizzeria €, AIC
Via G. Marconi, 94   tel. 03065896145

ALBESE CON CASSANO
Al Pesce Vela pizzeria €, AIC
Via Nazionale, 132   tel. 031426129   www.pescevela.it
Notes: DS pizza point. Closed Mondays.

ALBINO
Az. Agrituristica Monte Cura agritourism €€-€€€, AIC
Via Monte Cura, 6   tel. 035754745   www.montecura.it
Notes: Closed Monday-Thursday.

APRICA
Magie di zucchero bakery €-€€, AIC
Via Valtellina, 24   tel. 392.8383207

Stambèch pizzeria €, AIC
C.so Roma, 77   tel. 340.1642782

ASSAGO
Autogrill Carrefour Assago2 autogrill €, AIC
Viale Milanofiori   tel. 2.57701953

Autogrill Forum Palazzetto dello Sport autogrill €, AIC
Via G. Di Vittorio   tel. 2.45709966

AZZANO S. PAOLO
Artigel gelato (€, AIC) Via Cremasca, 34

BAGNATICA
Pizzeria al 18 pizzeria €, AIC
Via Papa Giovanni XXIII   tel. 035680406   www.pizzeriaal18.com

BARZIO
Rifugio Campelli restaurant, B&B €, AIC
Loc. Piani di Bobbio s.n.   tel. 0314910576   www.baiadipare.it

BELLAGIO
Salice Blu restaurant €€€€, AIC
Via per Lecco, 33   tel. 031950535   www.ristorante-saliceblu-bellagio.it

BELLANO
Villa Anita B&B AIC
Strada Nuova per Oro, 11   tel. 0341820225   www.villanita.lc.it

BERGAMO
Albergo 900 pizzeria €, AIC
Via Statuto, 23   tel. 035255210

Bombyx Inn B&B AIC
Via Lunga, 42   tel. 35.322786   www.bombyxbed.com

Byron Via Palma il Vecchio, 33	pizzeria tel. 035233477	€, AIC
Casa Chiara Via A. Balestra, 8	B&B tel. 035257733	AIC www.casachiarabeb.it/bed-breakfast
Charlot Via A. Fantoni, 4	restaurant, pizzeria tel. 35.213544	€€€€, AIC www.ristorantebernabo.it/it/index.asp
Grom V.le Papa Giovanni XXIII, 60	gelato www.grom.it	€, AIC
Le 5 Vie P.zza Pontida, 14	B&B tel. 035240141	AIC www.le5viebb.com
Osteria Risico Via Nullo, 7/a	restaurant tel. 340.8923518	€€, AIC www.osteriarisico.it

BIASSONO

| L'Officina dei Sapori
P.zza S. Francesco, 242 | restaurant
tel. 0392754029 | €€€€, AIC
www.lofficinadeisapori.com |

BINASCO

| Hosteria della Pignatta
Largo Loriga, 5
Notes: Closed Sundays. | restaurant
tel. 029054046 | €€€, AIC |

BOCCASERIO DI MONTODINE

| La Palazzina
S.P. Crema- Codogno, 591 | trattoria
tel. 373.667301 | €€, AIC
www.trattorialapalazzina.it |

BORGHETTO LODIGIANO

| La Locanda dei Sapori
Via XXV Aprile, 3
Notes: Closed Mondays. | restaurant, pizzeria
tel. 037180588 | €€€-€€€€, AIC |

BORMIO

| Rifugio Garibaldi
Località Passo dello Stelvio
www.facebook.com/rifugio.garibaldialladamello | restaurant, hotel
tel. 342.904312 | €€€, AIC |

BOVEZZO

| Al Pescatore
Via dei Prati, 19 | restaurant/pizzeria
tel. 0302711390 | €€, AIC
www.hotelimpero.it |

BRESCIA

Al Serbatoio Via G. Galilei, 4	restaurant, pizzeria tel. 30.38151	€€-€€€, AIC www.ristorantealserbatoio.com
Alergo Via Diaz, 30	bakery tel. 30.5236299	€, AIC www.alergo.it
Bierhaus Via Triumplina, 103	pizzeria tel. 0302005500	€, AIC
Castello Malvezzi Via Colle S.Giuseppe,1	restaurant tel. 0302004224	€€€€, AIC www.castellomalvezzi.it
Cormorano Via Salodini, 2	pizzeria tel. 30.394504	€, AIC www.misterimprese.it
Da Nicola via Duca degli Abruzzi, 27	restaurant, pizzeria tel. 0302425015	€€-€€€, AIC

Gentileria Via Levi Sandri, 3	gelato, bar tel. 339.5442535	€, AIC www.facebook.com/la.gentileria
I Silvani Via Triumplina, 86	restaurant, pizzeria tel. 0302040008	€, AIC
Il Piacere Viale Piave, 53 www.pizzaleggera.it/brescia/pizzeria.html	restaurant, pizzeria tel. 030362082	€€, AIC
Il Vicolo Corto Vicolo S. Agostino, 3	restaurant, pizzeria tel. 30.2808264	€€-€€€, AIC www.facebook.com/IlVicoloCorto
Impero Via Triumplina, 8	hotel, restaurant, pizzeria tel. 030381483	€-€€€, AIC
La Duchessa Via Montello, 28/c	restaurant, pizzeria tel. 0303384814	€-€€, AIC
Mamey Cafè Via Casazza, 5	bar, tavola calda tel. 30.2092315	€, AIC www.mamey.it
Mangiarè Via Valle Camonica, 16	pizzeria tel. 0303735869	€, AIC www.mangiare.brescia.it
Mille Gusti Via Lamarmora, 256	bakery, bar tel. 331.4384968	€, AIC
Novotel Brescia/Novotelcafé Via Montello, 28/c	hotel, restaurant tel. 0302286811	€€€-€€€€, AIC www.novotel.com
Osteria Molin del Brolo Via Cadorna, 14	osteria tel. 0303757507	€€€, AIC www.molindelbrolo.it
Possi Gelatieri	gelato (€-€€, AIC)	Via Triumplina, 245

BUCCINASCO

Baia Blu Via della Resistenza, 15/a	pizzeria tel. 2.48843729	€, AIC www.ristorantebuccinasco.it
Mamey Cafè Via Resistenza, 121	tavola calda, bar tel. 2.45716212	€, AIC www.mamey.it

BURAGO DI MOLGORA

Brianteo Hotel and Restaurant Via Martin Luther King, 3/5	hotel, restaurant tel. 0396080436	€€€, AIC www.brianteo.it

BUSTO ARSIZIO

Limin Viale Borri, 32	Chinese restaurant tel. 331.63919	€-€€, AIC www.limin.it

CADREZZATE

Miralago Via Mogno, 441	restaurant, pizzeria bar tel. 0331953284	€€, AIC www.miralagoweb.com

CALUSCO D'ADDA

Pizza Leggera Calusco Via Marconi, 1459	pizzeria tel. 35.791852	€, AIC www.calusco.pizzaleggera.it

CALVAGESE DELLA RIVIERA

L'Oasi del Chiese Via Basse Sopra, 1	pizzeria tel. 0306000060	€, AIC

9 Muse
Via G. Bruno, 42/a

CANNETO SULL'OGLIO
B&B
tel. 03358007601
AIC
www.9muse.it

Le Vigne
Via Vergani, 21
Notes: Closed Wednesdays.

CANTÙ
restaurant, pizzeria
tel. 031711088
€, AIC

Pizzeria Vecchia Napoli
via Fossano, 18
pizzeria
tel. 31.701256
€, AIC

Rossopeper oncino
via Como, 23
pizzeria
tel. 31.7073925
€, AIC
www.rossopeperoncino.org

CAPRIANO DEL COLLE
Gelatando
gelato (€, AIC)
Via Martiri Piazza Loggia, 2/4

CAPRIATE SAN GERVASIO
LeoBar
via Vittorio Veneto, 52
tavola calda, bar
tel. 2.9090169
€, AIC

CAPRINO BERGAMASCO
Agriturismo Villa Serica
Via Ombria, 2/a
agritourism
tel. 339.3818967
AIC
www.villaserica.it

CARATE BRIANZA
Ristorante Il Ritrovo
Via U. Bassi, 1 bis
restaurant
tel. 0362902287
€€€€, AIC
www.osteriadelritrovo.it

CARAVAGGIO
Giardino
C.ne Papa G.ni Paolo II, 24
restaurant
tel. 036350581
€-€€€, AIC
www.giardinoristorante.it

CARBONATE
Tourlè Pizza Club
p/le Miglio sn
pizzeria
tel. 345.1394803
€-€€, AIC
www.tourle.it

CARDANO AL CAMPO
Novotel Malpensa/Novotelcafè
Via al Campo
hotel, restaurant
tel. 0331266611
€€-€€€, AIC
www.novotel.com

CARONNO PERTUSELLA
Il Giaguaro
Via Bergamo, 444
pizzeria, restaurant
tel. 029650380
€€, AIC
www.ilgiaguaro.com

CASIRATE D'ADDA
La Vecchia Ruota
via R. Paladini, 18
pizzeria
tel. 036387200
€, AIC

CASORATE PRIMO
Orlandi Pasticceria
Piazza Mira, 3
bakery
tel. 2.9056384
€, AIC
www.orlandipasticceria.com

CASSANO MAGNAGO
Da Grillo
Via Galvani,15
restaurant
tel. 0331206830
€€-€€€, AIC
www.ristgrillo.it

Il Dolce Sogno
gelato (€, AIC)
Via Nenni, 7

Il Marchese del Grillo
Via Galvani,15
restaurant
tel. 331.20683
AIC
www.marchesedelgrillo.com/Ristorante

CASTANO PRIMO

A Modo Mio c/o C.C.le Castano
Via Adua ang. S.P. 34

restaurant
tel. 0331882797

AIC
www.amodomio.it

CASTEL D'ARIO

Trattoria Castello
Via di là dell'acqua, 8

restaurant
tel. 376.661565

AIC

CASTEL GOFFREDO

La Rotonda
Via Principe Amedeo, 2

pizzeria
tel. 0376770738

€, AIC

CASTELLANZA

Il Dolce Sogno

gelato (€, AIC)

Via Don Minzoni, 45

CASTIGLIONE OLONA

Elisir
Via C. Battisti, 3

pizzeria
tel. 0331824954

€, AIC

CASTIONE ANDEVENNO

Sisti
Via Margella, 41

restaurant, pizzeria
tel. 0342358310

€€, AIC
www.sisti1891.it

CAVA MANARA

Il Büus del Rat
Via Garibaldi, 88

pizzeria
tel. 0382554997

€, AIC
www.ilbuusdelrat.it

CAVARIA

The King
via IV Novembre, 402

pizzeria
tel. 331.735949

€€€, AIC
www.pizzeriatheking.it

CAZZAGO SAN MARTINO

Il Braciere
Via Rizzini, 38

restaurant
tel. 30.7254778   www.ristoranteilbraciere.net/home.html

€€, AIC

CERMENATE

L'Alambicco
Via Cavour, 13

pizzeria
tel. 31.774217   www.facebook.com/lalambicco.cermenate

€€, AIC

CERNUSCO LOMBARDONE

I Gelsi
Via S. Dionigi, 11

agritourism
tel. 39.990279

AIC
www.igelsi.com

CESANO BOSCONE

Le Betulle
Via delle Betulle, 11

pizzeria
tel. 2.4580282

€€, AIC
www.ristorantelebetulle.com

CESANO MADERNO

No Stop Il Giropizza
Via San Carlo Borromeo, 121

pizzeria
tel. 362.54199

€€, AIC
www.nostopilgiropizza.it

CHIESA IN VALMALENCO

Tremoggia
Via Bernina, 4

hotel
tel. 0342451106

€€€€, AIC

CINISELLO BALSAMO

A Modo Mio
Via De Amicis

restaurant
tel. 2.6125776

€€€, AIC
www.amodomio.it

Liberi dal glutine
Via XXV Aprile, 142

sandwich shop, bakery
tel. 2.61298704

€, AIC
www.liberidalglutine.com

Artigiana Gelati

Park Club
P.zza Cairoli, 26

Corona
Via Antonio Locatelli, 74

Ristorante Movida
Via Garibaldi, 3

Cremeria Bolla

In Centro
Via Cesare Cantù, 53

L'Antica Trattoria
Via Cadorna, 26

Locanda dell'Oca Bianca
Via Cadorna, 26

Osteria L'Angolo del Silenzio
V.le Lecco, 25

Al Grillo
Via Bevilacqua, 13

La Camilla
Via Dante, 267

Pomodoro & Basilico
Viale Italia, 31

Cascina Loghetto
Via Milano, 4

Ice Cream

Dordoni
Via Del Sale, 58

Grom

Al Vecchio Faggio
Via Garibaldi, 8

A Modo Mio
Via Gen. Lauger

Bobadilla Feeling Club
Via Pascolo, 34

CLUSONE
gelato (€, AIC)   P.za Uccelli, 22
CODOGNO
restaurant, pizzeria   €, AIC
tel. 037735153   www.parkclub.com

COLOGNO AL SERIO
pizzeria   €-€€€€, AIC
tel. 035896104
COMERIO
restaurant   €€€-€€€€, AIC
tel. 0332743240   www.ristorantemovida.it
COMO
gelato (€, AIC)   Via Boldoni, 6

pizzeria   €€, AIC
tel. 31.272692   www.pizzeriaincentro.com

restaurant   €€€€, AIC
tel. 031242777

inn, restaurant   €€€€, AIC
tel. 031025605   www.hotelocabianca.it

restaurant   €€-€€€€, AIC
tel. 0313372157
CONCESIO
restaurant, pizzeria   €-€€€, AIC
tel. 0302751408

CONCOREZZO
agritourism   €€€€, AIC
tel. 039647289   www.lacamilla.it

CORSICO
pizzeria   €€€, AIC
tel. 2.4511948   www.pomodoroebasilico.com

CREMA
agritourism   €€-€€€, AIC
tel. 0373230209   www.cascinaloghetto.it

gelato (€, AIC)   P.zza Giovanni XXIII, 26

CREMONA
restaurant, pizzeria   €€€€, AIC
tel. 037222703

gelato (€, AIC)   C.so Campi, 1 corner of via Cavour

CUASSO AL MONTE
trattoria   €€€€, AIC
tel. 0332938040
CURTATONE
restaurant   €, AIC
tel. 0376348065   www.amodomio.it

DALMINE
restaurant   €€€€, AIC
tel. 035561575

DAVERIO

A Modo Mio restaurant €, AIC
Via Dell'Industria, 1 tel. 0332947159 www.amodomio.it

DESENZANO DEL GARDA

Rose e Sapori restaurant €€€€, AIC
Lungo Lago C.Battisti, 89 tel. 0309144585 www.roseesapori.eu

DESIO

Bar Gelateria I Delfini gelato (€, AIC) Largo Primo Levi, 4

Charleston restaurant, pizzeria €€, AIC
Via Milano, 189 tel. 362.62708 www.ristorante-charleston.it

La Taverna restaurant, pizzeria AIC
Via Tripoli, 28 tel. 0362303329

DORNO

Autogrill Dorno autogrill (€, AIC) A7 Milano - Serravalle

ERBA

Acqua, Farina e Brace pizzeria €, AIC
V.le Lecco, 25 tel. 031610878

Tourlè Erba pizzeria €, AIC
via Cascina California, 2 tel. 348.9622384 www.tourle.it

FAGNANO OLONA

La Corte dei Sapori restaurant €€€, AIC
Via Cesare Battisti, 55 tel. 331.619076 www.lacortedeisapori.it

FALOPPIO

Borgonuovo restaurant, pizzeria €€-€€€€, AIC
Via Volta, 3 tel. 31.986163 www.ristoranteborgonuovo.com

FERNO

Mychef Aeroporto Malpensa Terminal 1 mychef €, AIC

GALLARATE

I Fontanili pizzeria €, AIC
Via Assisi, 103 tel. 0331772516

La Locanda Nord Est restaurant/pizzeria €€, AIC
Via Varese, 34 tel. 0331248355

GAMBOLÒ

Regina Margherita pizzeria €, AIC
C.so Vittorio Emanuele II, 52/b tel. 0381939554 www.pizzeriareginamargheritagambolo.it

GAVARDO

El Mamacita restaurant, pizzeria €-€€, AIC
Via A. Gosa, 164/f tel. 036534275

Giocabosco Parco Didattico tavola calda €, AIC
Via del Colle, 21 tel. 339.5631539 www.giocabosco.it
Notes: Funpark for kids.

Trattoria alle Trote restaurant/trattoria €€€€, AIC
Via Bariaga, 24 tel. 036531294

GAVIRATE

Vecchio Ottocento restaurant, pizzeria AIC
Viale Ticino, 33 tel. 0332735693

GERENZANO

L'Angelato gelato (€, AIC) Via C. Berra, 8

GEROLA ALTA

Albergo Pineta inn, restaurant €€€, AIC
Piana di Fenile, 5 tel. 03426901809

GRASSOBBIO

All'Angolo restaurant, pizzeria €-€€€€, AIC
Via Fornacette, 27 tel. 0354522111

GROSIO

Paradiso B&B AIC
Via Rovaschiera, 48/c tel. 03409655279 www.bbparadiso.it

GROSOTTO

Garni Le Corti B&B AIC
Via Patrioti, 73 tel. 342.848624 www.garnilecorti.it

GRUMELLO CREMONESE

Locanda San Martino agritourism €€-€€€, AIC
Str. Prov.le 47 - Cascina S. Martino, 1 tel. 03472878756
Notes: Closed Monday-Thursday.

GUSSAGO

Osteria dell'Angelo restaurant €€€€, AIC
Via Fontana, 25 tel. 0302770139 www.osteriadellangelo.it

IDRO

Da Arrigo inn, restaurant, pizzeria €, AIC
Via Trento, 39 tel. 0365823371 www.daarrigoristorante.it

ISEO

Mama's Pizza pizzeria €, AIC
Via Roma II tel. 0309822247

LACCHIARELLA

Il Mare Mosso restaurant, pizzeria €€, AIC
Via Vittorio Veneto, 15 tel. 2.90076673 www.pizzeriamaremosso.it
Notes: Italian-Chinese restaurant with GF pizza too.

LAINATE

Latenasca osteria €-€€, AIC
Via Mengato, 11 tel. 0293780995 www.latenasca.it

LAMBRUGO

Al Rustico da Luisa e Marco restaurant €€€€, AIC
Via S. Carlo, 3 tel. 031608125 www.ristorantealrustico.it

LECCO

Grom gelato (€, AIC) P.zza XX Settembre

Ricky e Alex gelato (€, AIC) Via Bovara, 15

LEGNANO

Gambero Rosso restaurant €, AIC
Via per Busto Arsizio, 37 tel. 0331450519

LENO

Oasi restaurant, pizzeria — AIC
Via Viganovo, 47 — tel. 0309067105 — www.oasileno.it

LENTATE SUL SEVESO

Trattoria al Murun trattoria — €, AIC
Piazza S. Vito, 22 — tel. 0362566034 — www.almurun.it

LISCATE

Gasoline Road Bar restaurant, pizzeria — AIC
Via Grandi, 5 — tel. 029587740 — www.gasolinemilano.it

LIVIGNO

Hotel Nevada hotel, restaurant, pizzeria — €€, AIC
Via Saroch, 35 — tel. 0342996551 — www.hnevada.it

LOCATE TRIULZI

La Corte del Moro restaurant, pizzeria — AIC
Via Vigentina, 8 — tel. 2.90428177 — www.ristorantelacortedelmoro.com

LODI

Agripizza pizzeria — €, AIC
Via Ada Negri, 20 — tel. 0371417017 — www.agripizzaitalia.eu

Calicantus Food pizzeria — €, AIC
Viale Agnelli, 27 — tel. 0371772043 — www.calicantuscafe.com

Isola Caprera restaurant — €€€-€€€€, AIC
Via Isola Caprera,14 — tel. 0371421316

LOVERE

Artigiana Gelati gelato (€, AIC) — Via Gregorini, 15

Barboglio bar-cafe — €, AIC
Via Marconi, 95 — tel. 035964571

Le Terrazze restaurant, pizzeria, bar — €€€, AIC
P.le Marconi, 4 — tel. 035983533 — www.ilristoranteleterrazze.it

LUMEZZANE

Sampei pizzeria — €, AIC
Via Madre Lucia Seneci, 26 — tel. 0308925772

MACLODIO

Il Pane di Anna sandwich shop, bakery — €, AIC
C.na Ciocchino Strada per Trenzano tel. 30.9780014 — www.ilpanedianna.it

MAGHERNO

Grotta Azzurra restaurant, pizzeria — €, AIC
Via Roma, 23 — tel. 0382966959

MALNATE

Osteria degli Angeli restaurant — €€€-€€€€, AIC
Via Brusa, 5 — tel. 0332427614 — www.osteriadegliangeli.net

MALONNO

King's Pizza pizzeria — €, AIC
Via Vallesabbia, 145 — tel. 0364635048

Regina Major
Via Vallesabbia, 145
Notes: Closed Tuesdays.

Alla Nuova Marasca
P.zza L.B. Alberti, 19/20

Grom

Dolci Tentazioni
Via Matteotti, 9/e

Mastro Marco
Lungolago Marconi, 1

Top 2000
Via Bardellina, 63

I Girasoli Cafè
Galleria Gandhi, 6

Fattoria Laghetto
Via Laghetto, 2

Dal Dosso Sala Mensa
Via Romero Mons. Oscar, 69

La Margherita
Via Santa Margherita, 6

Burger Club
Via Mentana, 24

L'Oasi del Celiaco
via Pavoni, 9/C

Bella Europa
Via Europa, 33/a

Marabù
Via Brescia, 179

Al Mulino
Via Al Molino, 18

Lo Sfizio
Via Milano, 11

MANERBIO
restaurant, pizzeria €-€€, AIC
tel. 0309380709 www.reginamajor.it

MANTOVA
trattoria €€€€, AIC
tel. 0376322620 www.nuovamarasca.it

gelato (€, AIC) Via Paolo Sarpi, 2

MARIANO COMENSE
gelato, bakery €, AIC
tel. 339.7346505 www.dolcitentazionisenzaglutine.it

MARONE
restaurant, pizzeria €€€€, AIC
tel. 30.9877885 www.mastromarco.eu

MARTIGNANAPO
pizzeria AIC
tel. 375.260121

MAZZO DI RHO
bar €, AIC
tel. 2.93900552 www.girasolicafe.altervista.org

MERATE
agritourism €€€-€€€€, AIC
tel. 399902283 www.fattorialaghetto.com

MONTICHIARI
restaurant €€€-€€€€, AIC
tel. 030961025 www.daldossosalamensa.com

restaurant, pizzeria €-€€€€, AIC
tel. 348.9115151 www.misterimprese.it

MONZA
bakery €€, AIC
tel. 39.2020129 www.burgerclub.it

tavola calda, grocery store €, AIC
tel. 39.9634374 www.oasidelceliaco.it

MUGGIÒ
pizzeria €, AIC
tel. 39.792892 www.ristorantebellaeuropa.com

NAVE
pizzeria €, AIC
tel. 30.2531563

NUVOLENTO
B&B AIC
tel. 338.9736532 www.bebalmulino.it

OGGIONO
pizzeria, bar €€, AIC
tel. 341.579557

Near Bellagio (D.Kraushaar)

OLGIATE OLONA

Giuseppe Verdi	restaurant, pizzeria	€-€€, AIC
Via Piave, 1	tel. 0331642129	

OLGINATE

La Locanda	restaurant, pizzeria	€-€€€€, AIC
Via S. Maria La Vite, 16	tel. 0341650506	www.ristorantelalocanda.com

OSIO SOPRA

Autogrill Brembo	autogrill (€, AIC)	A4 Milano - Brescia

OSTIGLIA

Maison del Celiaco	bakery, sandwich shop	€
Via Abetone Brennero 56	www.maisondelceliaco.it	

PALESTRO

Vecchio Mulino	restaurant	€€€, AIC
Via Umberto I, 99	tel. 384677105	

PAVIA

Locanda del Carmine	restaurant	€€€-€€€€, AIC
P.zza del Carmine, 7/A	tel. 038229647	
Pizza Leggera Pavia	pizzeria	€, AIC
Via Brambilla, 70/f	tel. 0382527429	www.pavia.pizzaleggera.it
Vecchia Pavia	trattoria, pizzeria	€, AIC
Via Mantovani, 3	tel. 038227178	www.vecchiapavia.it

PEGOGNAGA

Ca' Rossa	B&B	AIC
Str.Prov.le Est, 6	tel. 0376559072	

La Pastizzeria
Via Vittorio Veneto, 93

PEREGO
bakery   €, AIC
tel. 39.570325

Dadaumpa
Via S. Francesco, 33

PIOLTELLO
restaurant, pizzeria   AIC
tel. 0292590342

Baobab Lounge Cafè Pizzeria
Piazza Mercato, 7

PISOGNE
pizzeria   €, AIC
tel. 364880117   www.ristorantecucupizzeriabaobab.it

Il Cucu Osteria
P.zza Corna Pellegrini, 12/b

restaurant   €€€€, AIC
tel. 036486288

Il Poggio
Via Panoramica, 4

POGGI RIDENTI
restaurant   €€€€, AIC
tel. 0342380800

Pasticceria Alessandro
Via Pontesecco, 26

PONTERANICA
bakery   €, AIC
tel. 35.572167   www.pasticceriaalessandro.com

B&B La Marinella
Via Osteno, 29

PORLEZZA
B&B   AIC
tel. 344.72298   www.bblamarinella.com

Darna
via Osteno, 50

pizzeria   €, AIC
tel. 3334064833   www.darna.it

Brother and Sister
Via Milano, 55

POZZO D'ADDA
pizzeria   €, AIC
tel. 0290960850   www.barpizzeria.net

L'Altra Oasi
Via Garibaldi, 36

PRALBOINO
pizzeria   €, AIC
tel. 030954259

Due Lune
Via Al Palazzo, 6

PRATA CAMPORTACCIO
restaurant, pizzeria   €, AIC
tel. 034320633

Black Horse
Via Vittorio Veneto, 279

PRESEZZO
restaurant, pizzeria   €€, AIC
tel. 35.610247   www.blackhorsebg.it

Trattoria Al Fondaco
Via Padovani, 6

QUINZANO D'OGLIO
trattoria   AIC
tel. 30.992423   www.alfondaco.com

San Gottardo
via S. Gottardo, 23

RASA DI VARESE
pizzeria   €, AIC
tel. 0332224189 www.ristorantepizzeriasangottardo.it

Trattoria Da Vira
Via Bossi, 33

RESCALDINA
trattoria   AIC
tel. 331.465794

RHO

Autogrill Ristorante Bistrot Milano SS. del Sempione, 28 Fieramilano €, AIC

Dal Fluminese	restaurant	€€€€, AIC
Via Lura, 24	tel. 0293504592	www.dalfluminese.com
Notes: Closed Tuesdays.		

Pomerol restaurant/wine bar €€€€, AIC
Via Pomè, 3 tel. 029311019 www.pomerol.it

Trattoria Dodici Volte restaurant €€€-€€€€, AIC
Via Larga, 24 tel. 0293900460

Trattoria La Barca restaurant €€€€, AIC
Via Achille Ratti, 54 tel. 029303976 www.trattorialabarca.it

RIVOLTELLA DEL GARDA

Le Caravelle restaurant, pizzeria €, AIC
Via Papa Giovanni XXIII, 69 tel. 0309110198

RODIGO

Agriturismo Corte Canova B&B AIC
Strada Camignana, 5 tel. 03383932112 www.cortecanova.it

Corte Catenaccio restaurant, pizzeria €, AIC
Strada Francesca Est, 109/B 1 tel. 0376681003

RONCARO

Il Sorriso restaurant, pizzeria €€, AIC
Via Dell'Aia, 11 tel. 038294257 www.ristoranteilsorriso.it

SALA COMACINA

La Comacina restaurant €€€, AIC
Via Statale, 14 tel. 344.55035 www.ristorantelacomacina.it

SALICE TERME

Pizza Leggera Salice Terme pizzeria €, AIC
Via delle Terme, 129 tel. 038392753 www.salice.pizzaleggera.it

SALÒ

Antica Cascina San Zago restaurant €€€, AIC
Via dei Colli, 13 tel. 036542754 www.anticacascinasanzago.it

Il Lucaniere restaurant, pizzeria €€€, AIC
Via Bortollo Pollini tel. 365.521185 www.illucaniere.com

Pijei Osteria& Vineria restaurant, wine bar €€, AIC
Via Europa, 9 tel. 365.42111
www.facebook.com/pages/Osteria-PJ/210402645713014

PJ osteria €€€, AIC
Via Valle, 1 tel. 03654211

SAN DAMIANO AL COLLE

Trattoria Fugazza trattoria €€€€, AIC
Frazione Boffalora, 11 tel. 385.75183 www.latrattoriafugazza.it

SAN MARTINO IN STRADA

Witch Pub restaurant, pizzeria AIC
Via Vittorio Emanuele II 53 tel. 0371476078

SAN PELLEGRINO TERME

Orizzonte restaurant, pizzeria €€-€€€€, AIC
Via Vittorio Veneto, 8 tel. 345.23116

SAN ZENO NAVIGLIO

La Rocchetta pizzeria €€, AIC
Via Volta, 23/c tel. 30.3546623

SAREZZO

Ciar de Luna restaurant, pizzeria €-€€, AIC
Via Cimabue, 1 tel. 0308901491

SCHIGNANO

La Zoca di Strii agritourism €€€, AIC
Via S. Maria, 13 tel. 031819721 www.lazocadistrii.it

SEDRINA

B&B da Isa B&B AIC
Via Roma, 87/a tel. 345.6112 www.bed-and-breakfast.it

La Lanterna restaurant, pizzeria AIC
Via Roma, 85 tel. 345.6112 www.lalanternasedrina.it

SEGRATE

Biolunch pizzeria € - €€, AIC
Via C. Battisti, 51 tel. 0226928155

SEREGNO

Velò gelato, bar (€ - €€, AIC) Via Pacini, 20

SIRMIONE

Hotel du Lac hotel €€, AIC
Via XXV Aprile, 60 tel. 030916026

Hotel Riel Ristorante Pizzeria Al Braciere hotel, restaurant €€-€€€, AIC
Via San Martino, 2 tel. 0309905561 www.hotelriel.it

La Paul hotel, restaurant, pizzeria €-€€, AIC
Via XXV Aprile, 26 tel. 030916077 www.hotelapaul.it

Lisca pizzeria €€, AIC
Via Brescia, 41 tel. 30.9904191 www.ristorantisirmione.com/lisca

Mauro hotel €€, AIC
Via Lazzarini, 25 tel. 030919031

SOAVE DI PORTO MANTOVANO

Corte Casone B&B AIC
Strada Soana 17/a tel. 0376300545

SOLFERINO

La Speranza trattoria €€€, AIC
Via S. Martino, 6 tel. 0376854191 www.la-speranza.it

SOMMA LOMBARDO

Desiree pizzeria €€€, AIC
via Bellini, 14/C tel. 331251400 www.desiree.va.it

Mychef Aeroporto Malpensa Terminal 2 mychef €, AIC

SOMMALO MBARDO

Autogrill Milano Malpensa 2000 autogrill (€, AIC) Aeroporto Malpensa Terminal 1

SORICO

Il Beccaccino
Via Boschetto, 49
restaurant
tel. 034484241
€€€€, AIC
www.beccaccino.it

SOTTO IL MONTE GIOVANNI XXIII

La Taverna
Via Roncalli, 18
restaurant, pizzeria
tel. 035799599
€€€, AIC

STOCCHETTA

Risorgimento
Via Triumplina, 238
restaurant, pizzeria
tel. 0302008304
AIC

SULBIATE SUPERIORE

Agrit. Fondo Brugarolo
Via Manzoni, 15
agritourism
tel. 039623735
€€€, AIC
www.fondobrugarolo.it

TELGATE

Il Leone D'Oro
Via Roncalli, 18
hotel, restaurant, pizzeria
tel. 0354420803
€-€€€€, AIC
www.hotelleonedoro.it

TIGNALE

Al Torchio
Via Triumplina, 238
restaurant, pizzeria
tel. 0365760296
AIC
www.altorchiotignale.it

Apollo XI
Via Badiale, 4
restaurant, pizzeria
tel. 0365760293
€-€€, AIC

TIRANO

Vineria
Via XX Settembre, 25
restaurant
tel. 0342702116
€€, AIC
www.vineriatirano.com

TORRICELLA VERZATE

Più e Più
Piazzale Oltrepo, 1
restaurant, pizzeria
tel. 0383876327
€, AIC

TOSCOLANO MADERNO

Villa dei Roccoli
Via Sanico, 11
restaurant
tel. 0365541592
€€€-€€€€, AIC
www.ristorantevilladeiroccoli.com

TREZZO SULL'ADDA

Le Cave del Ceppo
Via Val Porto, 28
agritourism
tel. 2.90962295
AIC
www.lecavedelceppo.it

TROMELLO

Il Boss delle Balze
S.S. per Mortara, 21
pizzeria
tel. 038286401
€, AIC

URGNANO

La Rocca
Via Battisti, 132
www.facebook.com/pages/Pizzeria-la-Rocca/177027599023362
pizzeria
tel. 35.892838
€, AIC

VALMADRERA

Bar Baia
Via Parè, 29/a
pizzeria
tel. 341.207156
€, AIC
www.baiadipare.it

VANZAGO

Bigatt
Via S. Giovanni Bosco, 7
B&B
tel. 0240709422
AIC
www.bigatt.com

Al Vecchio Convento Via Montello, 8	**VARESE** restaurant tel. 0332261005	€€€€, AIC
Dolci Brividi	gelato (€, AIC)	C.so Matteotti, 2
Grom	gelato (€, AIC)	Piazza Montegrapp a, 13
La Vecchia Varese Via Ravasi, 37	restaurant tel. 332.287104	€, AIC www.lavecchiavarese.it
Montello Via Montello, 8	restaurant tel. 0332286181	€€€-€€€€, AIC
Osteria Caffè di Villa Giavazzi Via Don Giavazzi, 6	**VERDELLO** restaurant, bar tel. 35.4191159	€€-€€€, AIC www.villagiavazzi.it
A Modo Mio S.S. dei Giovi	**VERTEMATE** restaurant tel. 31.887349	€€, AIC www.amodomio.it
Al Salice Via Giovanni XXIII, 16	pizzeria tel. 31.90035	€€-€€€, AIC www.alsalice.com
Trattoria San Sebastiano Via per Rogorbello, 19	**VERVIO** restaurant, trattoria tel. 348.7147595	AIC
Casa del Parco dell'Adamello Via Nazionale, 132	**VEZZA D'OGLIO** hotel, restaurant tel. 036476165	€, AIC
Agorà Via Sacchetti, 1	**VIGEVANO** restaurant, pizzeria tel. 038184384	€, AIC
Fantasy V.le Commercio, 318	restaurant, pizzeria tel. 0381346650	€, AIC www.pizzeriafantasy.com
Geko Cafè C.so Torino, 299	restaurant, pizzeria tel. 381.329903	€€, AIC www.gekocafe.com
Primavera C.so Torino, 48	restaurant, pizzeria tel. 0381326415	€, AIC
Primavera Express Via Buozzi, 31	pizzeria tel. 038178464	€, AIC www.primaveraexpress.it
Le Coccinelle Via M. D'Azeglio, 5	**VILLA CORTESE** pizzeria tel. 0331430043	€, AIC
Agriturismo Belotti Via C. Battisti, 11	**VILLA DALEGNO DI TEMÙ** agritourism tel. 364.9185	€€, AIC www.agriturismobelotti.it
Al Ponte Via Nazionale, 63	**VILLA DI TIRANO** restaurant, pizzeria tel. 0342795703	€€, AIC
Stazzona Via Giambonelli, 10 fraz. Stazzona	B&B tel. 0342795538	AIC www.agristazzona.com

Il Veliero
Via Roma Nord, 290

VILLA POMA
restaurant/pizzeria
www.ristoranteveliero.net

€ - €€, AIC

La Sosta
V.le Brescia, 32

VILLANUOVA SUL CLISI
restaurant/pizzeria
tel. 0365374412

€, AIC

A Modo Mio
Via Tiziano Vecellio

VILLASANTA
restaurant
tel. 0392051369

€, AIC
www.amodomio.it

Le Tatin
Via Garibaldi, 40

bakery, sandwich shop
tel. 366.3198387

€, AIC
www.letatin.com

A Modo Mio Steak House
Via Torri Bianche, 16

VIMERCATE
restaurant
tel. 39.6084662

€€, AIC
www.amodomio.it

Pomodoro & Basilico
Via Burago, 28

restaurant, pizzeria
tel. 39.6614109

€€-€€€€, AIC
www.pomodoroebasilico.com

La Voglia Matta
P.zza della Repubblica, 14

ZANICA
pizzeria
tel. 35.672058

€€, AIC
www.pizzerialavogliamatta.it

Da Tonino
Via Pollini, 135

ZINASCO NUOVO
pizzeria
tel. 0382915110

€, AIC

GENOA, LIGURIA
AND THE ITALIAN RIVIERA

PLACES IN GENOA TO BUY GLUTEN-FREE FOOD PRODUCTS

Conad
Via Gaspare Murtola, 12
Via Giovanni Trossarelli, 1

Coop Liguria   Corso Aldo Gastaldi

Ipercoop   Via Romairone 10

Pam
Via Manuzio11
Via Don Giovanni Verità 6/R
Via Lagaccio 48/R

PLACES IN GENOA TO GET GUARANTEED GLUTEN-FREE GELATO (SPONSORED BY ITALIAN CELIAC SOCIETY)

Caffè Balilla   Via Cesarea, 121/R

Gelateria Artigianale Alfredo   Via Giovannetti, 83/R

Gelateria Rota   Via A. Manuzio, 20/R

Grom   Via S. Lorenzo, 81/83

Grom   Via S. Vincenzo, 53/r

Genoa (S.Amatangelo)
RESTAURANTS AND HOTELS IN GENOA
(AIC = participates in the Associazione Italiana Celiachia program)

GENOA

HOTELS

Boccascena	hotel	€€€€, AIC
Via C. Barabino, 62/r	tel. 0105740006	www.hotelboccascena.it
Helvetia	hotel	AIC
Piazza della Nunziata, 1	tel. 0102465468	www.hotelhelvetiagenova.it
Notes: Only GF breakfast.		
Il Vico	B&B	AIC
Vico del Dragone 4/6	tel. 339.5753845	www.ilvicogenova.it
Iris	hotel	AIC
Via G. Rossetti, 3	tel. 0103760703	www.hoteliris.it
Notes: Only GF breakfast.		
Novotel Genova City	hotel, restaurant	€€€, AIC
Via Cantore, 8 C	tel. 01064841	www.novotel.com
Quitocchilcieloconundito	B&B	AIC
Via Cesare Cabella, 11/12	tel. 0104071304	www.quitocchilcieloconundito.it
Veronese	hotel	AIC
Vico Cicala, 3	tel. 0102510771	www.hotelveronese.com

RESTAURANTS

Alla Tavola di Malqù	restaurant	AIC
Via Carloforte,8 R	tel. 010.6965049	
Antica Cantina i Tre Merli	restaurant	€€€, AIC
V. Dietro il Coro d. Maddalena, 26/R	tel. 0102474095	www.itremerli.it
Notes: Closed Sundays.		
Antica Osteria del Bai	osteria	€€€€, AIC
Via Quarto, 12	tel. 010387478	www.osteriadelbai.it
Notes: Closed Mondays.		

Bar Cose Buone   bar, tavola calda   €, AIC
Via Fereggiano, 43/r   tel. 010810834
Notes: Closed Sundays.

Bar Pizzeria I Due Fratelli   restaurant, pizzeria   €€, AIC
Via alla Chiesa di Prà, 71/73 n   tel. 010.6399944
www.facebook.com/pages/Bar-Pizzeria-I-Due-Fratelli/490571951014189

Cafè Rest.and More La Porcigna   tavola calda   €, AIC
Via Ronchi, 12   tel. 393.3363349   www.laporcigna.it

Caffetteria San Giorgio   bar   €, AIC
Via Colombo, 24/r   tel. 347.3994421

Castello Raggio   pizzeria   €, AIC
Via S. Giovanni D'Acri, 29/r   tel. 0108690494
Notes: Closed Saturdays and at lunch.

Gran Gotto   restaurant   €€€€, AIC
Viale Brigate Bisagno, 69 R   tel. 010564344   www.grangotto.com
Notes: Closed Saturdays at lunch and Sundays.

I Tre Merli Restaurant & Wine Bar restaurant   €€€-€€€€, AIC
Via Calata Cattaneo, 17 (ex Porto Antico Edif. Millo)   tel. 0102464416   www.itremerli.it

Il Focone   pizzeria   €, AIC
Via 5 Maggio N   tel. 0103773313

Il Focone/Centro Divert."La Fiumara" pizzeria   €, AIC
Via Operai, 1   tel. 010413999

iPizza   pizzeria   €, AIC
Via Bologna, 21r   tel. 010.4031409   www.facebook.com/ipizzapizzeria

J'Aime Les Crêpes   creperie   €, AIC
Stradone S. Agostino   tel. 0102465345   www.jaimelescrepes.eu
Notes: Closed Sundays.

Kapperi Cucina Medit. e Sushi   restaurant   €€€, AIC
V.co dei Lavatoi, 6/r   tel. 010869 6901   www.ristorantekapperi.it
Notes: Closed Mondays.

Kilt Express   pizzeria   €, AIC
Viale Brigata Bisagno, 8-10R   tel. 010580211   www.kilt-express.it

La Ola   pizzeria   €, AIC
Via Quinto, 14/r canc   tel. 0103202817   www.pizzerialaola.it
Notes: DS pizza point. Closed Mondays.

La Rose en Table Vino e Desinare restaurant   €€-€€€, AIC
L.re di Pegli, 79/R   tel. 010.4074156   www.laroseentable.it

Le Bistrot   bar   €, AIC
Via Porta degli Archi, 21/r   tel. 010590649
Notes: Closed Sundays.

Mychef San Ilario Nord   mychef   €, AIC
A12 Genova - Roma   tel. 010.3726387   www.mychef.it

Officine Senza Glutine   bakery, gastropub   €, AIC
Piazza De Caroli, 34R   tel. 348.4503260   www.officinesenzaglutine.it

Osteria dei Cacciatori   osteria, pizzeria   €€, AIC
Via Serra di Bavari, 15   tel. 0103450323   www.osteriadeicacciatori.it

Pacetti Antica Ostaria   restaurant   €€€ - €€€€, AIC
Via Borgo Incrociati, 22R   tel. 0108392848   www.ostariapacetti.com

Pizza Rò   pizzeria   €, AIC
Via Felice Cavallotti, 1a/R

Pizzeria Franco   pizzeria   €, AIC
Via G. B. Piovera, 22R   tel. 0106452255

Pockeat   gastropub   €, AIC
Via Colombo, 3-5RR   tel. 010.0985341   www.pockeat.it

Rossopomodor o c/o Centro Divertimenti Fiumara pizzeria   €€, AIC
Via Paolo Mantovani 62/4   tel. 10.460757   www.portoantico.rossopomodoro.it

Rossopomodoro (Porto Antico)   pizzeria   €€, AIC
Calata Molo Vecchio, 16-17-18 N   tel. 010.2466376   www.portoantico.rossopomodoro.it

Scabeccio   restaurant   €€€, AIC
Via D. Oliva, 42 R   tel. 0106591511

Teresa   restaurant   €€€€, AIC
P.zza Lido, 5/6 R   tel. 010.6973774   www.ristoranteteresa.com

Trattoria Alle Due Torri   trattoria   €€, AIC
Salita del Prione, 53 R   tel. 0102513637   www.alleduetorri.com
Notes: Closed Sundays.

Trattoria da Patan   restaurant   €€€, AIC
Via Oberdan, 157/R   tel. 010323897   www.patan.biz

Zeffirino   restaurant   €€€€, AIC
Via XX Settembre, 20/7   tel. 0105705939   www.zeffirino.com

THE REST OF LIGURIA
ALASSIO

Golfo Blu   pizzeria   €-€€, AIC
Via XX Settembre, 142   tel. 0182640492
Notes: Closed Tuesdays.

Hotel Ristorante Toscana   restaurant, hotel, bar   AIC
Via Flavio Gioia, 4   tel. 0182.640657   www.hoteltoscanaalassio.it

ALBENGA

Osteria e B&B del Tempo Stretto osteria, B&B   AIC
Regione Rollo, 40   tel. 0182.571387   www.osteriadeltempostretto.it

Planet Pizza   restaurant, pizzeria   €-€€, AIC
Via Del Roggetto, 2   tel. 018252024
Notes: Closed Mondays.

ALBISOLA SUP.

Isla Morada   restaurant, pizzeria   €-€€€, AIC
C.so Ferrari, 221   tel. 0194004372
Notes: Closed Wednesdays.

ALBISSOLA MARINA

Au Caruggiu   restaurant, pizzeria   €€, AIC
Via Isola, 12   tel. 019485252   www.pizzaworld.it

ARENZANO

Aranciamara   restaurant, pizzeria   €, AIC
Via Manni, 25   tel. 0109135095

Cremeria del Sasso   gelato   €, AIC
C.so Matteotti, 158 R   www.cremeriadelsasso.it

BADALUCCO

Il Ponte   restaurant   €€, AIC
Via Ortai, 3/5   tel. 0184408000   www.ristoranteilponte.it
Notes: Closed Wednesdays.

BONASSOLA

Hotel delle Rose   hotel   €€, AIC
Via Garibaldi, 8   tel. 0187813713   www.hoteldellerosebonassola.it

BUSALLA

Verdebasilico   restaurant, pizzeria   €, AIC
Via Milite Ignoto, 13/a, 13/b   tel. 0109642557

CAMOGLI

Locanda I Tre Merli   hotel, bar   AIC
Via Scalo, 5   tel. 0185776752   www.locandaitremerli.com
Notes: GF breakfast only.

Ristorante Rosa   restaurant   €€€€, AIC
Via Ruffini, 13   tel. 0185.773411   www.rosaristorante.it
Notes: Beautiful view.

CARCARE

Antico Borgo   gelato (€, AIC)   Via Roma, 44

CASARZA LIGURE

San Giovanni   restaurant   €€€€, AIC
Via Monsignore Podestà, 1   tel. 0185467244

Nervi (S. Amatangelo)

CASTELNUOVO MAGRA

Al Bacio   pizzeria   €, AIC
Via Aurelia, 235   tel. 0187676255   www.pizzeriaalbacio.it

Focacceria Cinquecento — restaurant, pizzeria — €€-€€€, AIC
Via Aurelia, 71 — tel. 0187693511 — www.focacceriacinquecento.it

CASTIGLIONE CHIAVARESE LOCALITÀ CAMPEGLI
Azienda Agricola Arca di Nenè — agritourism, pizzeria — €-€€, AIC
Via Arturo Rossi, 21 — tel. 3333128653 — www.agripizza.com

CAVI DI LAVAGNA
Pizzeria Ugo — pizzeria — €, AIC
Via Aurelia, 1935 — tel. 0185395762

Ziki Paki — pizzeria — €, AIC
Via Aurelia - Loc. Lo Scoglio — tel. 0185390285 — www.zikipaki.com

CELLE LIGURE
Albergo Gioiello — inn — €€, AIC
Via Lagorio, 24 — tel. 019990201 — www.albergogioiello.it

Torre — hotel, restaurant — €€-€€€, AIC
Via Aurelia, 20 — tel. 019993465 — www.hoteristorantetorre.it

CEPARANA
Vecchia Napoli — pizzeria — €, AIC
Via Genova, 69 — tel. 0187933669

CERIALE
Bar Noemi — bar-cafe — €, AIC
Lung.re A. Diaz, 55 — tel. 03455943306

CERIANA
Vecchia Fattoria — restaurant, pizzeria, inn, B&B — €-€€€, AIC
Via Armea Sud, 2006 — tel. 0184551742 — www.ristorantevecchiafattoria.com

CHIAVARI
Boccon Divino — restaurant — €€€€, AIC
Via Entella, 18 — tel. 0185362964
www.facebook.com/pages/Boccon-Divino/260945860669774

La Bitta — restaurant, pizzeria — €-€€€, AIC
C.so Garibaldi, 99 — tel. 0185.312963 — www.labitta.it

Pizzeria Verdi — pizzeria — €, AIC
C.so Dante, 70 — tel. 0185.303178 — www.pizzeriaverdi.com

CHIUSAVECCHIA
Le Giare — agritourism, restaurant, inn — €€-€€€, AIC
Via XX Settembre, 14 - Sarola — tel. 03493788253
Notes: Open only by reservation.

CISANO SUL NEVA
Peperoncino Rosso — pizzeria — € - €€, AIC
Via Pineta, 1 — tel. 018220853

COSSERIA
Le 4 Ruote — bar restaurant, pizzeria — €, AIC
Fraz. Lidora, 83M — tel. 019517328

DIANO MARINA
G.H. Diana Majestic — hotel, restaurant — €€€€, AIC
Via degli Oleandri, 15 — tel. 0183402727 — www.dianamajestic.com

Olympic — hotel — €€€€, AIC
P.zza Mazzini, 10 — tel. 0183498844 — www.hotelolympic.it

FINALE LIGURE

Hotel del Bambino-Villa Ada
Via Genova, 4
hotel
tel. 019601611
€€€, AIC
www.hoteldelbambino.it

Villa Italia
Via Torino, 111
inn
tel. 019690617
AIC
www.hotelvillaitalia.it

IMPERIA

Amelia
Via Carli, 6 Loc. Piani
pizzeria
tel. 0183780235
€, AIC

Dalla Padella alla Brace
Via Ospedale, 31
trattoria
tel. 0183294159
€€-€€€, AIC
www.dallapadellallabrace.com

Hotel Rossini al Teatro
P.zza Rossini, 14
hotel
tel. 018374000
AIC
www.hotel-rossini.it

Il Vascello
Via C. Colombo, 200
pizzeria
tel. 0183667269
€, AIC

U Fogu Acesu
Via Nino Siccardi,43
pizzeria
tel. 0183.667056
€, AIC
www.foguacesu.it

LA SPEZIA

Hosteria al Leon d'Oro
Via Baracchini, 16
restaurant
tel. 0187702295
€€, AIC
www.hosterialeondoro.it

Hotel Firenze E Continentale
Via Paleocapa, 7
hotel
tel. 0187.713200
AIC
www.hotelfirenzecontinentale.it

Il Lagora
P.zza Cesare Battisti, 38
pizzeria
tel. 018722242
€, AIC
www.pizzeriasopraillagora.it

La Bella Napoli
Via Gramsci, 175
pizzeria
tel. 0187714750
€, AIC
www.bellanapolionline.it

Parco del Colombaio
Via dei Pioppi, 1
restaurant
tel. 0187712336
€€, AIC
www.parcodelcolombaiolaspezia.it

Vesuvio
Via S. Bartolomeo,833
restaurant, pizzeria
tel. 0187520646
€, AIC

LAVAGNA

Il Gabbiano
Via S. Benedetto, 26
restaurant
tel. 0185390228
€€€, AIC
www.ristoranteilgabbiano.com

LE GRAZIE

Il Gambero
Via della Libertà, 143
restaurant
tel. 0187798023
€€-€€€, AIC

LERICI

B&B Al Lizzo
Località Tre Strade, 5
B&B
tel. 0187.970308
AIC
www.allizzo.it

La Rosa Canina
Loc. Monti Branzi, 16
agritourism
tel. 0187966719
€€-€€€, AIC
www.larosacanina.net

Ristorante da Paolino
Via Gerini, 50
restaurant
tel. 0187.967801
€€-€€€, AIC
www.ristorantepaolinolerici.it

LEVANTO

La Loggia
P.zza del Popolo, 7
restaurant
tel. 0187808107
€€€€, AIC

LOANO

Aurora
V.le Tito Minniti, 5
hotel, restaurant
tel. 019669992
€€, AIC

Da Rino Mare
Corso Roma, 64
pizzeria
tel. 019671278
€, AIC

La Buona Luna
Via Stella, 2
restaurant
tel. 019673239
€€€, AIC

Ristorante Piatti Spaiati - Le Marionette restaurant
Via Stella, 34
tel. 019670948
€€€-€€€€, AIC

Trattoria Matamà
Via Ghilini, 26
restaurant
tel. 019677459
€€€, AIC

MALLARE

All'Eremo
Via Santuario Eremita, 2 R
restaurant
tel. 019586402
€€, AIC

MELE

Mychef Turchino Ovest
A26 Genova - Gravellona
mychef
tel. 010.6319205
€, AIC
www.mychef.it

MONEGLIA

Moneglia/Pizz. La Pagoda
Via Figarolo Monte, 1
pizzeria
tel. 018549778
€-€€, AIC

Villa Edera
Via Venino,12
hotel, restaurant
tel. 018549291
€€-€€€€, AIC
www.villaedera.com

MONTEROSSO AL MARE

La Barcaccia
Via Molinelli, 6/8
restaurant
tel. 0187829009
€€-€€€, AIC

NEIRONE

Da Beppe
Via Banchella, 29
B&B
tel. 0185936011
AIC
www.dabeppe.it

NOLI

Pappus
gelato (€, AIC)
Via Colombo, 12

ORCO FEGLINO

Il Portico
Via S. Rocco, 34
restaurant
tel. 019699207
€€€, AIC

ORTONOVO

da Fiorella
Via per Nicola, 46
restaurant
tel. 018766857
€€-€€€, AIC
www.ristorantedafiorella.com

PIETRA LIGURE

Ca' di Trincia
Via Maglio, 2
agritourism
tel. 019615591
€€, AIC
www.caditrincia.it

Gelateria Papero
gelato (€, AIC)
Via Garibaldi, 32

Il Capanno
Via Cappelletta, 63 fraz. Ranzi
restaurant
tel. 019625198
AIC
www.ristoranteilcapanno.com

Villa Marina
C.so Italia, 221
hotel, restaurant
tel. 019615823
€-€€, AIC
www.hotelvillamarina.eu

RAPALLO

Best Western Tigullio Royal
P.zza IV Novembre, 3
hotel
tel. 0185273805
AIC
www.hoteltigullioroyal.it

Ciro
Via Mameli, 322
pizzeria
tel. 018551000
AIC

Hotel Canali
Via Pietrafraccia, 15
hotel
tel. 018550369
AIC
www.hotelcanali.com

L'Arca tra gli Ulivi
Salita al Pianello, 17/b
agritourism
tel. 018550890
€€-€€€, AIC
www.arcaulivi.it

RECCO

da O Vittorio
Via Roma, 160
Notes: Closed Tuesdays.
inn, restaurant
tel. 018574029
€€€-€€€€, AIC
www.daovittorio.it

La Giara
Via Cavour,79
hotel, reception hall
tel. 018574224
€€, AIC
www.hotel-lagiara.com

Lino
Via Roma, 70
Notes: Closed Mondays and Tuesdays at lunch.
restaurant
tel. 018574336
€€€-€€€€, AIC
www.ristorantedalinorecco.com

Vitturin 1860
Via dei Giustiniani, 50
restaurant
tel. 0185720225
€€€-€€€€, AIC
www.vitturin.it

RIALTO

La Ca' dell'Alpe
Via Alpe, 6
agritourism
tel. 019688030
€, AIC
www.agriturismofinaleligure.it

S. STEFANO D'AVETO

Groppo Rosso
Via Badinelli, 1
inn
tel. 018588054
€€, AIC

S. TERENZIO-LERICI

C'era una Volta
P.zza Cavallotti, 3
Notes: Closed Mondays and Tuesdays at dinner.
restaurant
tel. 0187971382
€€€, AIC

S.MARGHERITA LIGURE

da Paladini
Via Aurelia,95
trattoria
tel. 0185.261405
€€€, AIC
www.trattoriapaladini.it

Regina Elena
L.re Milite Ignoto, 44
hotel
tel. 0185287003
€€€€, AIC
www.reginaelena.it

SANREMO

Gluten Free
Piazza S. Siro, 15
sandwich shop, bakery, gastropub
tel. 329.4026810
€-€€, AIC

Grom
gelato (€, AIC)
C.so Garibaldi 3/4

Hotel Eveline Portosole
C.so Cavallotti, 111
hotel
tel. 0184503430
AIC
www.evelineportosole.com

Salsadrena
C.so Imperatrice, 45
Notes: Closed Wednesdays.
pizzeria
tel. 0184663754
€-€€€€, AIC
www.salsadrena.it

Victory Morgana Bay
C.so Trento Trieste, 16
restaurant
tel. 0184591620
€€€-€€€€, AIC
www.victorymorganabay.it

SANREMO FRAZ. VEREZZO

Tratt. del Ponte
Str. S. Antonio, 5

trattoria
tel. 0184559028

AIC

SARZANA

Arribabà
Via San Bartolomeo, 1

pizzeria
tel. 0187620533

€, AIC

Il Giardinetto del Mauri
Via dei Molini, 112

pizzeria
tel. 0187620333

€, AIC

SAVONA

Caffè Ligure
Via Astengo, 10-12 R

bar, tavola calda
tel. 349.3417893

€, AIC
www.caffeligure.mysupersite.it

Gelateria Cora

gelato (€, AIC)

C.so Vittorio Veneto, 33/R

Giardino del Sole
Via G. Bove, 61 r
www.hotelgiardinodelsolesavona.com

hotel, restaurant, pizzeria
tel. 019.8621773

€-€€€, AIC

Ristorante Barbarossa
Via Niella, 36R

pizzeria
tel. 019.8148042

€-€€, AIC
www.barbarossasavona.com

Sleek Burger Cafe
Via Montenotte, 58R

bar, tavola calda
tel. 19.808658

€€, AIC
www.sleekcafe.com

SESTRI LEVANTE

I Due Gabbiani
Via Nazionale, 500

restaurant, pizzeria
tel. 018543807

€-€€€, AIC

L'Albero del Pane
Via Sara, 47

pizzeria
tel. 0185480803

€, AIC

Pizzeria Dodo
Via Antica Romana Occidentale, 71

restaurant, pizzeria
tel. 0185459838

€, AIC

Ristorante Tigullio
Via Sara , 111

restaurant, pizzeria
tel. 0185.458291

AIC
www.ristorantitigullio.com

SPOTORNO

Gelateria Sagapò

gelato (€, AIC)

Viale Europa, 19

TERZORIO

Antichi Sapori
Strada per Pompeiana

restaurant, pizzeria
tel. 3357847010

€€€-€€€€, AIC
www.antichisapori-terzorio.com

VARAZZE

I Giardini di Marzo

gelato (€, AIC)

P.zza Dante, 28

VENTIMIGLIA

La Grotta
Passeggiata Oberdan, 23

restaurant/pizzeria
tel. 018433440

€, AIC

Le Due Lanterne
Pass. Oberdan, 37

pizzeria
tel. 0184.841749

€-€€, AIC

Angelo (J. Kelly)

PERUGIA, ASSISI AND UMBRIA
(AIC = participates in the Associazione Italiana Celiachia program)

PERUGIA

LODGING

B&B Nubes Alba Via G. Calderini 17	B&B tel. 393.6549889	AIC www.nubesalba.com
C'era una Volta B&B Str. San Marino, 6/i	B&B tel. 393.9871968	AIC www.ceraunavoltabeb.it
Mille Soli Str. Mugnano Poggio Montorio	B&B tel. 0753744885	AIC www.casalemillesoli.it

RESTAURANTS

Caffè di Roma P.zza Matteotti 31	bar tel. 75.5731752	€, AIC
Celimangiamo P.zza Umbria Jazz 1	sandwich shop, bakery, rotisserie tel. 75.5001573	AIC
E'nonè Corso Cavour, 61	restaurant, wine bar tel. 75.572195	AIC
Etruscan Chocohotel Via Campo di Marte, 134	hotel tel. 75.5837314	AIC www.chocohotel.it
Hotel Giò Wine e Jazz Area via R. D'Andreotto	hotel, restaurant tel. 75.57311	AIC www.hotelgio.it
Ilgo Hotel-I Girasoli Via Agostino di Duccio, 1	inn, restaurant tel. 0755736641	€€€, AIC www.hotelilgo.com
La Botte Via Volte della Pace, 31	restaurant tel. 75.5722679	AIC www.ristorantelabotte.com

La Casina Rossa Via Pievaiola, 246	restaurant tel. 75.5149524	AIC www.lacasinarossa.it
La Luna Nel Pozzo Via Settevalli, 838 - Loc. Pila	restaurant, pizzeria tel. 0755287839	AIC www.lalunanelpozzo.biz
Lago Verde Str. Cappuccinelli 20/D	restaurant tel. 75.46291	AIC
Les Crè Fantastique P.zza Danti (Pozzo Etrusco)	creperie, pizzeria tel. 3925742917	€-€€, AIC
L'Officina Borgo XX Giugno, 65	restaurant tel. 75.5721699	AIC www.l-officina.net
Lupi Cafè Via Brunamonti 4 b/c/d	bar tel. 75.96613	€-€€, AIC www.facebook.com/cafelupi
Mediterraneo Via Piccolpasso 149	restaurant, pizzeria tel. 75.5002451	€€, AIC www.mediterraneopastaepizza.it
Osteria di Pinocchio Via Tazio Nuvolari, 19	restaurant, pizzeria tel. 75.5052591	€€, AIC www.osteriapinocchio.it
Osteria il Gufo Via della Viola 18	restaurant tel. 75.5734126	€€, AIC www.osteriailgufo.wordpress.com
Pian di Marte - Ospitalità rurale Località Pian di Marte 9	hotel, restaurant tel. 75.845342	AIC
RossoPomodoro Via della Valtiera 181 (C. Com Collestrada) tel. 75.397201	pizzeria	€-€€, AIC www.rossopomodoroperugia.it
S. Martino RO.ME. Via Pontani, 15	restaurant tel. 0755053366	€, AIC
Sotto Sopra Settevalli strada 834	pub tel. 75.5270675	€, AIC www.sottosopraperugia.it
Trattoria del Borgo Via della Sposa 23/A	restaurant tel. 75.572039	AIC www.trattoriadelborgoperugia.it
Tuttotesto C.so Garibaldi, 15	restaurant, creperie tel. 0755736666	€, AIC
Villa Taticchi-Agrit. Il Covone Str. Fratticciola, 2	restaurant agritourism tel. 075694503	€€-€€€, AIC www.villataticchi.it
Zero7Cinque Strada Bellocchio S. Faustino, 54	restaurant, pizzeria tel. 0755058294	€€€€, AIC www.zero7cinque.it
Cioccolato Augusta Perusia	gelato (€, AIC)	Via Pinturicchio, 2
Gelateria Veneta	gelato €, AIC	P.zza Italia
Grom	gelato €, AIC	Via Mazzini, 31
Gel Art. La Terrazza	gelato (€, AIC)	Via Mastrodicasa 107
Menchetti	gelato (€, AIC)	Strada Trasimeno Ovest

PERUGIA- LOC. PONTE VALLECEPPI

Pegaso-Hotel Vega   hotel, restaurant, pizzeria   €€, AIC
Strada Bellocchio S. Faustino, 54   tel. 0756929534 www.hotelvegaperugia.com
Notes: Closed Mondays.

THE REST OF UMBRIA
AMELIA

Scoglio dell'Aquilone restaurant, hotel €€-€€€€, AIC
Via Orvieto 23 tel. 744.982445 www.scogliodellaquilone.it

ASSISI

LODGING
Alla Madonna del Piatto B&B AIC
Via Petrata 37 tel. 075.8199050 www.incampagna.com

B&B I Nidi B&B AIC
Fraz. San Gregorio 42 tel. 075.8038123 www.assisionline.com/inidi

B&B Le Tortorelle B&B AIC
Via della Conciliazione, 18 tel. 338.3504883 www.assisi-letortorelle.com

Chiara B&B AIC
Via Pietro Uber, 10 tel. 3384387238

RESTAURANTS
Agrit. Tordoni Daniela agritourism €€, AIC
Via del Paduletto, 24 tel. 0758065810 www.valledelsubasio.it
Notes: Closed Mondays.

Le Silve di Armenzano/ Romantik Hotel restaurant, hotel AIC
Loc. Armenzano 89 tel. 75.8019 www.lesilve.it

Millematti pizzeria €-€€, AIC
Via Assisiana 43 tel. 75.8064175

Valle del Subasio agritourism AIC
Via del Paduletto, 24 tel. 75.806581 www.valledelsubasio.it

ASSISI - SANTA MARIA DEGLI ANGELI

Starbene senza glutine restaurant, pizzeria, Pan AIC
Via della Repubblica 8 A tel. 75.8043627

Villa Cherubino restaurant AIC
Via P. d'Italia, 39 tel. 75.8040226

AVIGLIANO UMBRO

La Tenuta dei Ciclamini agritourism €€€-€€€€, AIC
Loc. Casa Pancallo, 3 tel. 074493431

Le Bandite Country & Relax B&B AIC
Voc. Suffragio, 5 www.lebanditecountryrelax.com

BASTIA UMBRA

Pane e Ciliegie restaurant catering €€-€€€€, AIC
Via S. Lucia, 34 tel. 0758004959 www.paneeciliegie.it

Villa Rabasco hotel, restaurant €€€, AIC
Strada Assisiana, 147 - Bastiola tel. 0758010011

CASALINA

Country House L'Antico Forziere restaurant €€€, AIC
Via della Rocca, 2 tel. 0759724314 www.anticoforziere.it

CASCIA

Agriturismo Baldassari agritourism, restaurant, pizzeria AIC
Loc. Avendita tel. 743.755086 www.agriturismocascianorcia.it

CASTIGLIONE DEL LAGO

H. Aganoor/R. La Cantina Via Vitt. Emanuele, 91	hotel, restaurant tel. 0759652463	AIC www.hotelaganoor.it
Isola Polvese Loc. Isola Polvese	restaurant tel. 0759659545	AIC
La Pigra Tinca Via Divis. Partigiani Garibaldi	restaurant tel. 0759652480	€-€€, AIC

CENERENTE

Poggio del Sole Str. Forcella, 49/a	restaurant, pizzeria tel. 075690752	AIC
Relais Poggio del Sole Str. Forcella, 49/a	restaurant, pizzeria, hotel tel. 75.690752	AIC

CITTÀ DI CASTELLO

Artcafè Gel. Cremì	gelato (€, AIC)	C.so Vittorio Emanuele 31/b
BomBarolo Piazza Pertini 1	restaurant, pizzeria tel. 75.8511097	AIC
Caffe' Magi Piazza Gabriotti 9/B	restaurant tel. 333.8610403	AIC
Con e Senza Via P. della Francesca	tavola calda, bar tel. 075 8520903	€-€€, AIC
Il Sesto Canto Piazza Giovanni XXIII	restaurant, pizzeria tel. 75.8553251	AIC
Molenda Loc. S. Paterniano Voc. Monini, 10	B&B tel. 0758521416	AIC www.molenda-bedandbreakfast.com
Tankard Via Luca della Robbia, 21 - C. Comm.le Le Fonti	pizzeria	AIC tel. 75.8554495
Trattoria Pappa e Ciccia Via del Popolo 16	restaurant tel. 075.8521386/380.7817333	AIC
Uomini di Mare Via R. De Cesare 8	restaurant, pizzeria tel. 075.85569909	€-€€, AIC www.ristoranteuominidimare.it
Villa San Donino Località San Donino	hotel, restaurant tel. 75.8578108	AIC www.hotelvillasandonino.it

CORCIANO

Al Borgo Via Collesi, 1	B&B tel. 393.7659437	AIC www.laportadicorciano.it
L'arte del Gelato P.zza dei Caduti, 6	bar tel. 75.6978867	€-€€, AIC

DERUTA

Country House L'Antico Forziere Casalina	restaurant tel. 75.9724314	AIC www.anticoforziere.it

ELLERA DI CORCIANO

Best Wester Golf Hotel Quattrotorri Via Corcianese,26 0	hotel, restaurant tel. 75.5171722	, AIC
Revolution Via Juri Gagarin 1	restaurant, pizzeria tel. 75.7974465	AIC

Revolution Restaurant
Via Juri Gagarin

restaurant, pizzeria
tel. 0755170367

€, AIC

FERENTILLO

Ai Tre Archi
S.S. Valnerina 29

restaurant, pizzeria
tel. 744.780004

AIC

Piermarini
Via F. Ancaiano, 23
Notes: Closed Mondays.

restaurant
tel. 0744780714

€€-€€€€, AIC

Vecchio Mulino Monterivoso
Case Sparse, 5

hotel, restaurant, pizzeria
tel. 0744780772

€-€€€€, AIC

FIGHILLE

L'Isola Che Non C'è
Loc. Petriolo

restaurant, pizzeria
tel. 0758593336

AIC

FOLIGNO

Delfina Palace Hotel
Via Romana Vecchia

hotel, restaurant
tel. 74.2692911

AIC
www.delfinapalacehotel.it

Maison del Celiaco
Via Monte Acuto, 53

bakery, sandwich shop
www.maisondelceliaco.it

€

MeTeMagno TVB
P.zza don Minzoni, 1-3

restaurant
tel. 74.2620452

AIC

Voglia di Pizza
Giacomini, 44

pizzeria
tel. 0742342371   www.vogliadipizzaglutenfree.com

€-€€, AIC

FOLIGNO - TREVI

Ristozoo
Via Popoli snc

restaurant, pizzeria
tel. 742.679099

AIC

FOSSATO DI VICO

De Gusto
Via del Rigo 26

restaurant, pizzeria
tel. 75.9190113

AIC

GIOVE

Mychef Giove Est
Al Roma - Milano

mychef
tel. 744.99293

€, AIC
www.mychef.it

GUALDO CATTANEO- S.TERENZIANO

Il Buongustaio
Piazza Vittorio Emanuele

restaurant
tel. 0742.930033/347.3661689

AIC

GUALDO TADINO

Da Clelia
Via G. Matteotti, 80 e Loc.Valsorda

restaurant
tel. 075913261

AIC

GUBBIO

Agriturismo Villa Dama
Loc. Torre dell'Olmo

agritourism, restaurant
tel. 75.925613

AIC

Alla Balestra
Via della Repubblica, 41
Notes: Closed Tuesdays.

restaurant, pizzeria
tel. 0759273810

€-€€€€, AIC

Aquilone (Campi Scuola)
Str. di Vignoli 3 - Torre Calzolari

agritourism
tel. 75.9271105

AIC

Piede (J. Roglieri)

Contessa S.S. Contessa 10	restaurant, pizzeria tel. 75.9277256	AIC
Dulcis in Fundo Corso Garibaldi 2	restaurant, pizzeria tel. 75.9273376	AIC
Faro Rosso Fraz.Montanal do 69	agritourism, restaurant tel. 75.925801	AIC
Hotel dei Consoli Via dei Consoli, 59	hotel, restaurant tel. 75.9220639	AIC
Hotel Sporting Via Bottagnone	hotel, restaurant tel. 75.9220753	AIC
L'Arte Golosa	gelato (€, AIC)	Via Europa, 63- Fraz. Cipolleto
Locanda del Gallo Loc. S. Cristina	agritourism tel. 75.9229912	AIC
Parco Coppo Monte Ingino	restaurant, pizzeria tel. 75.9272755	AIC
San Benedetto Piazza Empedocle	restaurant, pizzeria tel. 75.9220489	AIC
San Francesco e il Lupo Via Cairoli, 24	restaurant, pizzeria tel. 0759272344	AIC

MERCATELLO

Locanda le Noci   agritourism, restaurant   AIC
Vocabolo Molinella, 1   tel. 75.8783271   www.locandadellenoci.it

MONTECASTRILLI

Relais dei Principi   restaurant, pizzeria   AIC
Via dello Scalo, 9   tel. 744933244

MONTEFALCO

L'Alchimista   restaurant, wine bar   AIC
Piazza del Comune 14   tel. 742.378558

MONTORO - NARNI

Villa Pina B&B   B&B   AIC
Str. Castelluccio Amerino 5   tel. 366.9361468   www.villapinaumbria.it

NARNI

Grano e Sale   pizzeria   €-€€, AIC
Via Flaminia Ternana, 145   tel. 0744715519   www.granoesale.it

Il Gattamelata   restaurant   AIC
Via Pozzo della Comunità   tel. 744.717245

Il Parco dei Cavalieri   restaurant, pizzeria   AIC
Strada Flaminia Ternana 510   tel. 744.744399

La Rocca   restaurant, hotel   AIC
S.S. Flaminia Ternana, 508   tel. 744.744521

Tenuta Marchesi Fezia   restaurant, pizzeria, B&B   AIC
Loc. San. Bartolomeo - Narni Scalo   tel. 744.750324   www.tenutamarchesifezia.com

ORVIETO

Antica Cantina (Osteria delle Donne) restaurant   AIC
Piazza Monaldeschi 18   tel. 0763.344746/329.6509966

PIEGARO

Millenovecento Pub   restaurant, pizzeria, pub   AIC
Loc. Canneto 109 -Castiglion Fosco   tel. 75.835208   www.millenovecentopub.com

PIETRALUNGA

Bio Agrit./ Fatt. Didattica La Cerqua agritourism   AIC
Via San Salvatore   tel. 75.9460283   www.cerqua.it

La Cima   agritourism, restaurant   AIC
Vocabolo Fontinelle   tel. 75.9460272   www.agriturismolacima.it

PONTE S. GIOVANNI

Le Olive   B&B   AIC
Via A. Manzoni, 391   tel. 3282646821

SAN GIUSTINO

Green   restaurant, pizzeria   AIC
Loc.Uliano 3   tel. 75.8560391

Il Covo del Contrabbandie re   restaurant, pizzeria   AIC
Via della Repubblica   tel. 75.8560427

Il Dongione   restaurant   AIC
Via Largo Crociani, 6   tel. 75.856567

Starbene San Giustino   sandwich shop   €-€€, AIC
Via G.O Bufalini 13   tel. 3667312229

SAN SISTO

Caffè La Rosa bar €, AIC
Viale S. Sisto 188 tel. 75.5289792

SAN TERENZIANO

Alla Casella restaurant €€-€€€€, AIC
Via Collazzone, 11/2 tel. 074298989

SANGEMINI

Il Colle restaurant AIC
Viale Garibaldi 6 tel. 744.630428

Meeting Coffee gelato (€, AIC) Via Ternana, 1/c

Soc. Agric. Vallantica restaurant, wine bar €€€€, AIC
Loc. Valle Antica, 280 tel. 0744243454

SELCILAMA - SAN GIUSTINO

Il Musicista restaurant, pizzeria AIC
Voc. Osteriaccia 1 tel. 75.85835

SIGILLO

Taverna del Gobbo restaurant AIC
Via Petrelli 16/A tel. 366.5940225

SPELLO

Borgo della Marmotta agritourism AIC
Loc. Poreta, 1 tel. 0743274137 www.leterrediporeta.it

Caffè Porta Consolare gelato (€, AIC) P.zza Kennedy, 7/8

SPOLETO

Gi.Gio's restaurant, pizzeria, tavola calda, bar AIC
V.le Trento e Trieste 147/a tel. 743.221161

H Clitunno/Rist. S. Lorenzo inn €€-€€€€, AIC
P.zza Sordini, 6 tel. 0743223340
Notes: Closed Tuesdays.

La Ginestra pizzeria €-€€, AIC
Loc. Pompagnano tel. 743.4701

Le Logge restaurant, pizzeria AIC
V.le Martiri della Resistenza, 51 tel. 0743225225

Ristogiocando/ Italgonfiabili restaurant, pizzeria AIC
Via U. La Malfa 21 - Loc. Madonna di Lugo tel. 348.5595253

Ristorante del Mercato restaurant AIC
Piazza del Mercato 29 tel. 743.45325

S. Pietro restaurant, pizzeria AIC
Loc. S. Pietro tel. 074346788
Notes: DS pizza point. Closed Tuesdays.

Taverna La Lanterna restaurant AIC
Via della Trattoria, 6 tel. 74349815

Trattoria il Capanno restaurant AIC
Torrecola di Spoleto tel. 0743.54119/3358237537

SPOLETO - CASTEL RITALDI

Locanda di Rovicciano restaurant AIC
Via la Penna 9 tel. 743.51679

TAVERNELLE DI PANICALE

Break Bar — gelato, bar (€, AIC) — Via della Resistenza 21

Mr Over — restaurant, pizzeria — AIC
Via Palladio — tel. 75.832732

TERNI

Agrit. Fontana della Mandorla — agritourism — AIC
Str. Fontana della Mandorla 112 — tel. 744.40071

Andrea — gelato (€, AIC) — Via Mancini, 6

Antico Ponte del Toro — hotel, restaurant, resort — AIC
Via Ponte del Toro 23 — tel. 744.67636

Best Western - Garden Hotel - Rist.Melograno hotel, restaurant — AIC
Viale Bramante 4 — tel. 0744.300375/300041

Cassiopea MMX — restaurant — AIC
Strada di Miranda 55 — tel. 744.279058

Country House Il Pozzo — restaurant, pizzeria — AIC
Strada di Collescipoli, 190 — tel. 74.4813069

Grilli Pasticceria & Food — restaurant, pizzeria — AIC
Via dei Gonzaga 26 — tel. 744.3046

H. del Lago Piediluco - Rist. la Ginestrella hotel, restaurant — AIC
Str. del Porto, Piediluco 71 — tel. 744.36845

Il Forno di Babette — sandwich shop, bakery — €-€€, AIC
Via G. di Vitalone 41 — tel. 744.082921

La Briciola di Pani — bakery — €, AIC
Via Mentana 25 — tel. 744.275579

La Clessidra — restaurant, wine bar — AIC
Via Masaccio 24/28 — tel. 744.433611

Livingstone Pub — pub, pizzeria — €, AIC
Viale Cesare Battisti, 69 — tel. 0744409746 — www.livingstonepub.it

Lu Somaru — restaurant — AIC
Via Cesare Battisti 106 — tel. 744.304787

Pantarhei — restaurant, pizzeria — AIC
Via Cavour 50/52 — tel. 0744.1980941

Placebo — restaurant — €€, AIC
Via Cavour 45 — tel. 744.401216 — www.placeboterni.it

TODI

Le Scalette — restaurant — €€, AIC
Via delle Scalette,1 — tel. 75.8944422 — www.ristorantelescalette.it

TODI - FRAZ. COLLEVALE NZA

H. La Collina di Collevalenza — hotel, restaurant — AIC
Viale Madre Speranza 117 — tel. 75.8870034 — www.lacollinadicollevalenza.com

TORRICELLA-MAGIONE

Caravelle — pizzeria — €-€€, AIC
Via del Lavoro, 59 — tel. 075843330

TRESTINA - UMBERTIDE

Pizza Time   pizzeria   €€, AIC
Fr. Verna - Loc. Banchetti snc   tel. 75.9410448

TUORO SUL TRASIMENO

La Tosca   B&B   AIC
Via Mercato, 14   tel. 075825312

UMBERTIDE

Agrit. Vegetariano/V egano Le Tortorelle agritourism, restaurant   AIC
Fraz. Molino Vitelli, 180   tel. 75.9410949   www.letortorelle.it

Casagrande   restaurant, pizzeria   €€€, AIC
Via Madonna del Moro 30B   tel. 75.9413014

Il Vecchio Granaio   pizzeria   €€€, AIC
Voc. Busternan- Calzolaro 44   tel. 75.9302322   www.ilvecchiogranaio.com

L'Arte del Caffè   bar   €, AIC
Piazza Carlo Marx, 10   tel. 366.3507839

Tankard   pizzeria   €€, AIC
Via R. Morandi - Centro Comm. Fratta   tel. 75.9415388   www.tankard.it

VALFABBRICA

Ca' Mazzetto   agritourism   €€, AIC
Voc. Camazzetto, 22   tel. 0759029409

Ferrara (M. Roglieri)

BOLOGNA AND EMILIA-ROMAGNA
(AIC = participates in the Associazione Italiana Celiachia program)
BOLOGNA

America Graffiti fast food c/o area commerciale Le Piazze sandwich shop €, AIC
Via Pio La Torre,11 c/o area Commericale Le Piazze   tel. 51.705404 www.americagraffiti.it

Bar Pasticc. Ornielli	bar-cafe	€, AIC
Via Battindarno, 354	tel. 0510950461	
Due Lune	restaurant, pizzeria	AIC
Via Nino Bertocchi, 1	tel. 051567569	www.ristoranteduelune.it
La Spiga Amica	bakery	€, AIC
Via Petrarca, 13/2 G	tel. 800601675	www.laspigaamica.it
Master Beer	pub, restaurant, pizzeria	€-€€, AIC
Via Andrea Costa, 158	tel. 051.6140523	www.masterbeer.net
Notes: Gluten-Free menu.		
Novotel Bologna Fiera	hotel, restaurant	€€-€€€, AIC
Via Michelino, 73	tel. 051637771	www.novotel.it
Palazzo Trevi	B&B	AIC
Via Frassinago, 31	tel. 051580230	www.palazzotrevi.it
Pantera Rosa 1 (via C.Tomba)	restaurant, pizzeria	€, AIC
Via Cleto Tomba, 14 A	tel. 0515870544	
Pantera Rosa 2 (via Guelfa)	pizzeria bar	€-€€, AIC
Via Guelfa, 74	tel. 0516011069	
Notes: DS pizza point. Closed Mondays and at lunch.		
Pantera Rosa di Via Zanardi	pizzeria	€-€€, AIC
Via Francesco Zanardi, 189/D	tel. 051.6341538	
Ristorante La Capriata	restaurant	€€-€€€, AIC
Corte Isolani n. 1/E	tel. 51.236932	www.lacapriata.it

| Star Bene Senza Glutine | bar, desserts | € |
| Via Angelo Ruffini 6/G/h | tel. 350/5143504 | www.starbenesenzaglutine.it |

Capo Nord	gelato (€, AIC)	Via Murri, 39
Gelateria Iglù	gelato (€, AIC)	Via F. Barbieri, 66/a
Grom	gelato (€, AIC)	Via Massimo D'Azeglio, 13

Carrefour	food store	Via Marilyn Monroe, 2/9
Esselunga	food store	Via Guelfa 13
Esselunga	food store	Via Emilia Ponente 72
Ipercoop	food store	Via M.E. Lepido 184
Ipercoop	food store	Via Beverara 50
Pam	food store	Via Marconi 28/A

THE REST OF EMILIA-ROMAGNA
AGAZZANO

Fricandò il Ristolocale	restaurant	€€€€, AIC
P.zza Europa, 26	tel. 3406970402	
Notes: Closed Wednesdays.		

ANZOLA DELL'EMILIA

| I Salici | agritourism, B&B | €-€€€, AIC |
| Via Suor Orsola Donati, 108 | tel. 051739418 | |

BAGNACAVALLO

| Gelateria Mambo | gelato (€, AIC) | Via Mazzini 58 |

BAGNO

| Villabagno | agritourism | €€€-€€€€, AIC |
| Via Lasagni, 29 | tel. 0522343188 | |

BELLARIA

| Aurea | hotel | €€€€, AIC |
| L.re Colombo, 21 | tel. 0541345665 | |

Club Hotel Angelini	hotel	€€€€, AIC
Via Pirano, 3	tel. 0541345001	
Notes: Closed October-March.		

BELLARIA IGEA MARINA

| Albergo Serenità | B&B | AIC |
| Via Fratelli Cervi, 3 | tel. 0541.346541 | |

| Capitan Bagati | restaurant, pizzeria | €€€, AIC |
| Viale Pinzon,10 | tel. 0541340034 | www.capitanbagati.it |

| Imperiale | hotel | €€€€, AIC |
| Via Panzini, 73 | tel. 0541344122 | www.nellyhotels.com |

| Taverna da Bruno | restaurant, pizzeria | €€€-€€€€, AIC |
| Via Panzini, 150 | | |

Villa Lucia	B&B	AIC
Via Ovidio, 31	tel. 0541331428	
Notes: Closed October-March.		

BERTINORO

| Autogrill Bevano Est | autogrill | €, AIC |
| A14 Ancona - Bologna | tel. 0543.440813 | |

| Autogrill Bevano Ovest | autogrill | €, AIC |
| A14 Bologna - Ancona | tel. 0543.440822 | |

BORGO VAL DI TARO

La Bottega del Chisolino	restaurant, pizzeria, bar	€€, AIC
Via Torresana, 4	tel. 525.90522	

www.facebook.com/pages/LA-BOTTEGA-DEL-CHISOLINO/41398950965

CÀ DI LUGO - LUGO

Osteria del Tempo Perso	restaurant, pizzeria	€, AIC
Via Fiumazzo, 176	tel. 054573069	

CADELBOSCO SOPRA

Gelateria K2	gelato (€, AIC)	Via Matteotti n.2/d

CADEO

Relais Cascina Scottina/R.Ant.Ost.della Pesa hotel, restaurant		€€€€, AIC
Str. Del Riglio - Loc. Scottina	tel. 0523504232	www.osteriadellapesa.it

CALDERARA DI RENO

Itaca	restaurant, pizzeria	€-€€€, AIC
Via Roma, 81/a	tel. 051720383	www.pizzeriaitaca.it

CAMPAGNOLA EMILIA

Toro Blanco c/o Multiristorante La Bussola Spanish restaurant/pizzeria		€ - €€, AIC
Via Reggiolo, 22	tel. 0522663508	www.ristorante-labussola.it

CAPRARA CAMPEGINE

Il Porto	restaurant	€€-€€€, AIC
Via Nenni, 2/b	tel. 0522676625	
Notes: Closed Sundays.		

CARPI

Cortina	gelato (€€, AIC)	Via Maiella, 29
Notes: They also have crêpes.		
Il Delfino	pizzeria, tavola calda	€, AIC
Via Don L.Sturzo,36	tel. 59.65186	www.pizzeriaildelfino.com/la-pizzeria
Sapori di Carpi	gastropub	€€-€€€, AIC
Via Aldo Moro, 6 - 6/B	tel. 59.694124	www.saporidicarpi.it

CASALECCHIO DI RENO

Autogrill Cantagallo	autogrill	€, AIC
A1 Bologna - Firenze	tel. 51.593864	

CASALGRANDE

Gianni	restaurant, pizzeria	€€€, AIC
Via del Bosco, 14	tel. 0536823379	www.gianniristorante.it
Notes: Closed Monday-Tuesday.		

CASTEL DI CASIO

La Prossima	agritourism restaurant, pizzeria	€-€€, AIC
Via Prostima, 2	tel. 053442572	www.laprossima.com

CASTEL MAGGIORE

La Barattina	restaurant	€€-€€€, AIC
Via S. Giuseppe, 19	tel. 51.705734	www.ristorantelabarattina.it

CASTELLARANO

L'Angolo	gelato (€, AIC)	Via Respighi, 9

CASTIGLIONE DEI PEPOLI

Mychef Roncobilaccio Est	mychef	€, AIC
A1 Firenze - Milano	tel. 534.9795	www.mychef.it

L'Anfora
Via Rossini, 16

Pizza e Pasta
Via Largo della Pace, 3/5

Tradizioni di Famiglia
Via Mazzini, 38

Pizz'Osteria da Mazza
Via Ausa, 138

Borgomarina

Ca' D'oro
Viale Italia, 92

Gli Angeli
Via Capinera, 20

Re Sale e Regina Salina
L.re D'Annunzio, 26

Dolce Paradiso

I Girasoli
Via Emilia Levante, 2223

Il Portico
Via Rio Maggiore, 57

Zero Farina
Via Ravennate, 2846

Al Cenacolo
V.le Trento, 68
Notes: Closed Tuesdays.

Bagno Piscina 4 Venti
Via Ferrara spiaggia di levante
Notes: At the beach.

Cà Nostra
Corso Garibaldi, 60
www.miositoweb.com/ristorante-cesenatico

Globus
Via Dante, 1

Hotel Vera
Via Ippolito Nievo, 2

Il Jelato di Jessica

Antica Pieve
Via Maestri del Lavoro, 16

CATTOLICA
agritourism,restaurant, pizzeria   €€€-€€€€, AIC
tel. 0541953702

pizzeria   € - €€, AIC
tel. 0541831166   www.pizzascuola.com

gastropub   € - €€, AIC
tel. 346.3673842   www.tradizionidifamiglia.it

CERASOLO DI CORIANO
restaurant, pizzeria   €-€€, AIC
tel. 0541759060   www.cerasoloausa.net

CERVIA
gelato (€, AIC)   Via Nazario Sauro, 92

hotel   AIC
tel. 054471939   www.hotelcadoro.net

B&B   AIC
tel. 339.4830281   www.bebgliangeli.it

restaurant, pizzeria   €€, AIC
tel. 0544970442   www.emmehotels.com

CESENA
gelato (€, AIC)   V.le Giacomo Matteotti, 124

restaurant, pizzeria   €-€€, AIC
tel. 0547303737   www.ristoranteigirasoli.it

restaurant, pizzeria   €-€€€€, AIC
tel. 0547.333039   www.ilportico-ristorante.com

bakery   €, AIC
tel. 329.5780105

CESENATICO
restaurant, pizzeria   €-€€€€, AIC
tel. 0547672820   www.ristorantealcenacolo.com

tavola calda, bar   €, AIC
tel. 547.75567   www.bagno4venti.com

restaurant, pizzeria   €€, AIC
tel. 0547.481522

hotel   €€€€, AIC
tel. 0547680700   www.nellyhotels.com

hotel, B&B   AIC
tel. 054780342   www.hotelvera.info

gelato (€, AIC)   Viale Carducci, 46/A

COLOMBARO DI FORMIGINE
restaurant, pizzeria   €€, AIC
tel. 059553040

COMACCHIO

Al Ponticello   B&B   AIC
Via Cavour, 39   tel. 0533314080   www.alponticello.it

COPPARO

La Dolce Vita   bar   €, AIC
P.zza del Popolo, 29   tel. 0532.863715   www.dolcevitapasticceria-fe.com

CORREGGIO

Star Bene Senza Glutine   bar, desserts   €
Corso Mazzini 25/B   tel. 340.6525284   www.starbenesenzaglutine.it

COTINGNOLA

Ponte di Ferro   pizzeria   € - €€, AIC
Via Madrara, 1   tel. 0545992464   www.pontediferro.net

CROCE DI MONTECOLOMBO

Villa Leri   hotel, restaurant   €€€€, AIC
Via Canepa, 172   tel. 0541985262   www.villaleri.it

FAENZA

Gelateria OK   gelato (€, AIC)   Via F.lli Rosselli, 6/2

Jack   restaurant, pizzeria   AIC
Via Firenze, 561   tel. 054643071

Self service Bontavola   restaurant   AIC
Piazzetta Carlo Zauli,1   tel. 546.21722

FAIDELLO-FIUMALBO

Albergo K 2   hotel, restaurant, bar   €€€-€€€€, AIC
Via Giardini, 281   tel. 053673913

FANANO

Lo Chalet   restaurant, pizzeria   €, AIC
Via Giardini, 281   tel. 053668442

FARNETA DI MONTEFIORINO

Al Ciocco   hotel, restaurant   €€, AIC
Via Palloncino, 2   tel. 0536974018   www.alciocco.com
Notes: Closed Monday and month of November.

FERRARA

Albergo Annunziata   hotel   AIC
P.za Repubblica, 5   tel. 0532201111   www.annunziata.it

Astra Hotel   hotel   AIC
Viale Cavour, 55   tel. 0532206088   www.astrahotel.info
Notes: Will serve GF breakfast only.

Carlton   hotel   AIC
Via Garibaldi, 93   tel. 0532211130   www.hotelcarlton.net

Dolcemela   B&B   AIC
Via Sacca, 35   tel. 0532769624   www.dolcemela.it

Le Stanze di Torcicoda   B&B   AIC
Vicolo Mozzo Torcicoda,9   tel. 0532.1993033   www.lestanze.it

Locanda Borgonuovo   B&B   AIC
Via Cairoli, 29   tel. 0532211100   www.borgonuovo.com

Bella Napoli restaurant, pizzeria €, AIC
Via M.Boiardo 5 tel. 0532205015
Notes: DS pizza point. Closed Wednesdays.

L'Orlando restaurant €, AIC
Via Aldighieri, 3 tel. 0532.202693 www.lorlando.it

Grom gelato €, AIC
P.zza Trento e Trieste www.grom.it

FIDENZA

Il Tondino agritourism €€-€€€, AIC
Via Tabiano, 58 tel. 052462106

Sanafollia restaurant €€-€€€, AIC
Via B. Bacchini, 23

FILO

Antica Trattoria Vallone restaurant, pizzeria €€-€€€, AIC
Via Porto Vallone, 11 tel. 0532.802050 www.trattoriavallone.it

FINALE EMILIA

Pasta per Celia bakery €, AIC
Via Stazione, 1 tel. 346.4006185

FIORENZUOLA D'ARDA

Autogrill Arda autogrill €, AIC
A1 Milano - Bologna tel. 0523.985311

FOCOMORTO

F.lli Rizzieri 1969 gastropub €, AIC
Via Ponte Ferriani,1 tel. 532.65092 www.1969macelleriarizzieri.com

FONTANELICE

Agriturismo La Taverna agritourism €€-€€€, AIC
Via Casolana, 53 tel. 054292714
Notes: Closed Monday-Wednesday.

FONTANELLATO

Scacciapensie ri restaurant, pizzeria €€-€€€, AIC
Loc. Cannetolo, 25 tel. 0521.821350 www.villascacciapensieri.it

FONTEVIVO

L'Abbazia B&B AIC
Via P. P. Pasolini, 19 tel. 0521672472

FORLI

Del Corso restaurant, pizzeria €-€€, AIC
Corso della Repubblica, 209 tel. 054332674

Dolce Ro gelato (€, AIC) Corso Giuseppe Garibaldi, 61

Hotel della Città hotel, B&B AIC
Corso della Repubblica,117 tel. 054328297 www.hoteldellacittà.it

Hotel Masini hotel AIC
C.so Garibaldi, 28 tel. 054328072

Los Locos restaurant, pizzeria €-€€, AIC
Via dell'Appennino, 697 tel. 0543480735

Mangia Pizza
Via dell'Appennin o, 287
pizzeria
tel. 0543.405212
€, AIC

Piada 52
Via Dragoni, 52
restaurant
tel. 340.3712548
€, AIC
www.piada52.it

Ristorante Tennis Villacarpena
Via Brando Brandi, 69
restaurant
tel. 0543.402344
AIC
www.facebook.com/pages/Ristorante-Tennis-Villa-Carpena/507753002569209
Notes: Restaurant within a tennis village.

SGlab
Via Nazario Sauro, 5-7
bakery
tel. 0543.092812
€, AIC
www.sglabforli.it
Notes: Everything is gluten-free.

FORLIMPOPOLI

America Graffiti Fast Food
Via Emilia per Forlì, 1387
sandwich shop
tel. 0543744945
€, AIC

FORMIGINE

Gelateria Alaska
gelato (€, AIC)
Via S. Antonio, 8/D 8/E

Harlow
Via Quattro Passi, 21
restaurant, pizzeria
tel. 0595750204
€, AIC
Notes: DS pizza point. Closed Tuesdays for dinner.

FORNOVOTARO

Ristorante Bel Sit
Via Nazionale, 167
restaurant
tel. 0525400243
€€€, AIC
www.ristorantebelsit.net

FUNO DI ARGELATO

C'è pizza per te 2
Via Galliera, 112
pizzeria
tel. 051.8659415
€, AIC

GAIANO

Chantilly
gelato (€, AIC)
Via Nazionale, 26

GAZZOLA

La Locanda
Loc. Tuna, 48
restaurant
tel. 0523978103
€€€-€€€€, AIC
www.trattorialocanda.pc.it
Notes: Closed Thursdays.

GUASTALLA

La Mandragola
Via Sacco e Vanzetti, 2/g
restaurant
tel. 0522219810
€€€€, AIC
Notes: Closed Monday-Tuesday.

GUIGLIA

Locanda del Parco
Via Fondovalle, 3892
restaurant
tel. 059.795920
€€-€€€€, AIC
www.locandadelparco.com
Notes: Everything is gluten-free.

IGEA MARINA

Internazionale
V.le Pinzon, 72
hotel
tel. 0541331447
€€€€, AIC
www.internazionalehotel.net
Notes: Closed October-April.

Missouri
Via Tibullo, 28
hotel
tel. 0541331730
€€€€, AIC
www.hotelmissouri.net

IMOLA

Milana
Via della Milana, 21
pizzeria
tel. 054242200
€, AIC

Pit Stop
Via Pisacane, 69/d

restaurant, pizzeria
tel. 054228884

€-€€€, AIC
www.pitstoppizzeria.it

LEMIGNANO DI COLLECCHIO

Timeout
Via Spezia, corner of Via Antolini

restaurant, pizzeria
tel. 0521804503

€ - €€€€, AIC
www.ristorantetimeout.it

LIDO ADRIANO

Bar Blue

gelato (€, AIC)

V.le Virgilio, 56/58

LIDO DI SAVIO

Ai Pioppi
Via Marina, 5

restaurant
tel. 0544948000

€€-€€€€, AIC

LIDO ESTENSI

Bagno Astra
Via Spiaggia, 13

restaurant bar
tel. 0533327953

€€€-€€€€, AIC

Logonovo
Viale delle Querce, 109

B&B
tel. 0533327520

AIC
www.hotellogonovo.it

Mammamia

gelato (€, AIC)

Viale Carducci 116

LIDO POMPOSA COMACCHIO

Gelateria K 2

gelato (€, AIC)

P.zza Trento e Trieste

LONGIANO

Borgonovo
Via A. Moro, 1
Notes: Closed Tuesdays.

inn, restaurant, pizzeria
tel. 054757357   www.ristorantealbergoborgonovo.com

€-€€€€, AIC

LUGO

Tatì
V.le degli Orsini, 5

pizzeria
tel. 054525901

€, AIC

MARINA ROMEA

Boca Barranca
Viale Italia, 301
Notes: At the beach.

pizzeria
tel. 0544.447858

€-€€, AIC
www.bocabarranca.it

MARZABOTTO

Agrit. Rustico La Quercia
Via Quercia, 22

agritourism
tel. 0516775397

€-€€, AIC
www.lallegroturismo.it

MEDICINA

Il Murello
Via Fiorentina, 3780
Notes: Closed Monday-Thursday

agritourism
tel. 0516962054

€€, AIC
www.agriturismoilmurello.it

Paggio Simone
Piazza Garibaldi, 30/31

bakery
tel. 51.850828

€, AIC
www.paggiosimone.it

Pizzissima Italia
Via Argentesi, 24/c
www.it-it.facebook.com/pizzissimaitaliasrl

pizzeria
tel. 051.0343968

€, AIC

MILANO MARITTIMA

Hotel Fenice
Via XVII Traversa, 9
www.alberghimilanomarittima.com/ita/hotel-fenice-milano-marittima

hotel
tel. 0544.994325

AIC

MIRAMARE DI RIMINI

Albergo Sabrina
V.le Tirrenia, 7
Notes: Closed October-March.
hotel
tel. 0541372213
€€€€, AIC

Hotel Carlo
Via Regina Margherita,72
hotel
tel. 0541.372477
AIC
www.hotelcarlo.it

La Dolcetteria
Via Oliveti, 68c/70
bakery
tel. 333.9572725
€, AIC

MIRANDOLA

Il Gelatino
gelato (€, AIC)
Piazza della Costituente, 29

MISANO ADRIATICO

I Due Fratelli
Via Scacciano, 15
restaurant, pizzeria
tel. 0541606363
€-€€€€, AIC

L'Angelo Azzurro
S.S. Adriatica, 11
restaurant, pizzeria
tel. 0541615341
AIC

Morotti
Via Gabriele D'Annunzio, 17
hotel
tel. 0541.615560
AIC
www.hotelmorotti.it

MODENA

Anissa
Via Mar Mediterraneo, 6
pizzeria
tel. 059252392
€-€€, AIC

Caffè con tè
Via Baccelli, 46/48
restaurant, tavola calda, bar
tel. 340.5530867
AIC
www.caffeconte.com

Fusorari cibi&viaggi
P.le Torti, 5
restaurant
tel. 0594270436
AIC

Grom
gelato (€, AIC)
Largo di Porta Bologna, 40

La Moretta
tel. 380.6950313
gelato (€, AIC)
www.gelaterialamoretta.it
V.le Martiri della Libertà,18/A

La Scintilla
gelato (€, AIC)
Via Giardini, 306-308

Le Macine
Via P. Giardini, 739
pizzeria
tel. 059344646
€, AIC
www.lemacineristorante.it

Le stelle di Adua
Via Biagio Pascal, 123
Notes: Everything gluten-free.
bakery
tel. 059.8756288
€, AIC
www.lestellediadua.com

Osteria Stallo del Pomodoro
Largo Hannover, 63
restaurant, wine bar
tel. 059214664
€€€€, AIC

Pisano
gelato (€, AIC)
Via Pisano, 40/44

Raphael Caffè
Via Vignolese, 92
tavola calda
tel. 347.1807136 www.facebook.com/raphaelcafemodena
€, AIC

Slurp
gelato (€, AIC)
V.le Trento Trieste, 50

Star Bene Senza Glutine
Via Vignolese 870
bar, desserts
tel. 59.374047
€
www.starbenesenzaglutine.it

Starbene senza glutine caffè
Via Vignolese, 870/A
bar, tavola calda
tel. 59.374047
€, AIC
www.starbenesenzaglutine.mo.it

MONTE COLOMBO

I Muretti   agritourism, B&B   €€€, AIC
Via Sarciano, 5   tel. 0541985146   www.imuretti.net

MONTECCHIO EMILIA

La Grattugia   restaurant   €€€, AIC
Via Montegrappa, 30   tel. 0522871520
Notes: Closed Thursdays.

MONTECENERE DI LAMA MOCOGNO

Bacio del Cimone - Prosciutteria restaurant   €, AIC
Via Torre, 5   tel. 053641662

MONZONE DI PAVULLO

Casa Minelli   agritourism   €€, AIC
Via per Montecenere, 30   tel. 053641580

NONANTOLA

La Bodeguita   restaurant, pizzeria   €-€€, AIC
Via Costa, 6/1   tel. 059546858

Pizza Matta   pizzeria   €, AIC
Via Mavora, 4/2   tel. 59.547786

PARMA

Al Petitot   restaurant, pizzeria bar   €€-€€€, AIC
Via P. Torelli, 1/a   tel. 0521235594

Celì   sandwich shop, gastropub   €, AIC
Via Jenner, 2/D   tel. 0521.710272   www.senzaglutineparma.it

Gelateria Due di Fiori   gelato (€, AIC)   Via G. Sidoli, 33/d

Gelateria OK   gelato (€, AIC)   Via Valenti, 1/c

Grom   gelato (€, AIC)   Via XXII Luglio, 3

Il Cortile   restaurant   €€-€€€, AIC
Borgo Paglia, 3   tel. 0521285779
Notes: Closed Sundays.

La Vela   pizzeria   €, AIC
Via Montanara, 85   tel. 0521.962478
www.facebook.com/pages/La-Vela-Ristorante-Pizzeria/164960630187276

Mychef San Martino Est   mychef   €, AIC
Al Milano - Napoli   tel. 0521.604248   www.mychef.it

Officina Gastronomica   sandwich shop, bakery   €, AIC
Via Pò, 9   tel. 0521.967327   www.officinagastronomicaparma.net

Star Bene Senza Glutine   bar, desserts   €
Via Braglia 1/D   tel. 521.240554   www.starbenesenzaglutine.it

PAVULLO NEL FRIGNANO

Da Martino   restaurant, pizzeria   €, AIC
Via Fondovalle Panaro, 39   tel. 053648062

PIACENZA

Buon per te - Bontà fresche di Nonna Luisa bakery   €, AIC
Via Millo, 51/53   tel. 0523.1998789   www.buonperte.com

Cone Island   gelato (€, AIC)   Via Farnesiana 8/c

Il Grillo   pizzeria   €, AIC
Emilia Parmense,58   tel. 0523.593393   www.pizzeriailgrillo.it

Ludoteca Jungle Village   bar   €, AIC
Via Emilia Parmense, 21   tel. 366.7131308   www.junglevillagepc.com
Notes: For little kids.

Pausa Caffè   bar   €, AIC
Via P. Cella, 51   tel. 348.5639011
www.facebook.com/pages/Pausa-Caff%C3%A8/515601301833273

Pizzeria Bella Napoli   pizzeria   €, AIC
Via Emilia Pavese,98   tel. 0523480038   www.bellanapolipiacenza.it

Trattoria del Borgo   restaurant   €€€ - €€€€, AIC
Via Trebbia, 22   tel. 0523484176   www.tdb-trattoriadelborgo.it

PIANORO

Il Poggiolo   agritourism, B&B   €€-€€€, AIC
Via Gorgognano, 4   tel. 0516510208

PIEVE DI CENTO

Minelli   restaurant/pizzeria   €€ - €€€, AIC
Via Ponte Nuovo, 21   tel. 05175466   www.ristorantepizzeriaminelli.it

PODENZANO

I Cucinieri   bakery   €, AIC
Via Roma, 65   tel. 0523.070266   www.icucinieripiacenza.com

PORTO GARIBALDI

Gelateria del cuore   gelato (€, AIC)   Piazza tre Agosto, 1/A

PUIANELLO

Il Pomodorino   pizzeria   €, AIC
Via C. Marx, 29/B   tel. 0522880374

PUNTA MARINA TERME

Bagno Vela   restaurant   €€-€€€, AIC
Lungomare C. Colombo, 24   tel. 0544438789   www.bagnovela.it

Bar Centrale   tavola calda, bar   €, AIC
Viale dei Navigatori, 29   tel. 0544.437244

H. Ambra/Rist. Eulalia   hotel, restaurant, pizzeria   €-€€, AIC
V.le delle Ondine, 11   tel. 0544437108   www.ristoranteeulalia.it

Pizzeria Cento Pizze   pizzeria   €, AIC
Via delle Nasse, 21   tel. 0544.437321   www.centopizze.com

QUARTO DI GOSSOLENGO

Molto Pizza   restaurant, pizzeria   €-€€, AIC
Via Terracini, 10   tel. 0523557132

RAVENNA

Al 45   restaurant   €€-€€€, AIC
Via Paolo Costa, 45   tel. 0544.212761   www.al45.it

America Graffiti Fast Food c/o Cinema City sandwich shop   €, AIC
Viale Secondo Bini, 11   tel. 0544.461097   www.americagraffiti.it

Cine Pizza Via Secondo Bini, 7	pizzeria tel. 0544.464251	€, AIC
Cube Via Masotti, 2	hotel tel. 0544464691	€€€€, AIC
Il Brigantino Via Marconi, 57	restaurant, pizzeria tel. 0544402598	€€, AIC www.ilbrigantino.org

REGGIO EMILIA

Ad Bed and Breakfast Via Scaruffi, 14/3	B&B tel. 3358155624	AIC
Anna & Ricca C.so Garibaldi, 2	B&B tel. 0522432719	AIC
Piedigrotta 2 Via Emilia Ospizio, 50	restaurant, pizzeria tel. 0522.552637	€-€€, AIC www.nuovapiedigrotta.it
Star Bene Senza Glutine Via F.lli Cervi n. 130/c	bar, desserts tel. 0522/082224	€ www.starbenesenzaglutine.it
Twiga Via Fratelli Cervi, 40/b	pizzeria tel. 0522791029	€, AIC
West Pacific	gelato (€, AIC)	Via Kennedy, 17/h

REGGIO EMILIA-CANALI

La Razza Via Monterampino, 6	agritourism tel. 0522599342	€€€, AIC

RENAZZO-CENTO

La Pergola Via Tassinari, 30	restaurant, pizzeria tel. 051909124	€, AIC

Notes: DS pizza point. Closed Mondays and at lunch.

RICCIONE

22 Garibaldi Home Via Garibaldi, 22	B&B tel. 0541.600683	AIC www.riccionebedandbreakfast.com
Bouganville Via Virgilio, 28/30	restaurant, pizzeria tel. 0541692622	€-€€€, AIC www.ristorantebouganville.it
California Burger Via Bellini, 9	sandwich shop tel. 3425755353	€, AIC
Cremeria Vanilla	gelato (€, AIC)	Viale Dante, 114/A
Niagara V.le Tasso, 40	hotel tel. 0541648664	AIC www.hotelniagara-riccione.it

Notes: Closed October-Easter.

Nuovo Fiore	gelato (€, AIC)	Viale Ceccarini, 1
Sirena Passeggiata Goethe, 10	restaurant tel. 0541660416	€€-€€€€, AIC

Notes: Closed October-Easter.

Trieste Via Manzoni, 7/9	hotel tel. 0541646352	AIC www.hoteltriestericcione.com

RIMINI

Bikini V.le Cristoforo Colombo, 4	hotel tel. 054125700	AIC

| **Corallo** | hotel, restaurant | AIC |
| V.le Vespucci, 46 | tel. 0541390732 | www.hotelcorallorimini.com |

| **Da Biagio** | osteria, pizzeria | €-€€€€, AIC |
| Via Circon.ne Meridionale, 28 | tel. 0541782403 | |

| **Fratelli La Bufala** | restaurant | € - €€, AIC |
| Via Caduti di Nassirya | tel. 0541380639 | www.fratellilabufala.eu |

| **Grom** | gelato (€, AIC) | P.zza Cavour, 11 |

| **La Brocca** | pizzeria, restaurant | €, AIC |
| via Caduti di Marzabotto, 11 | tel. 0541770796 | www.labroccarimini.com |

| **La Piazzetta** | gelato (€, AIC) | Via Saffi, 4 |

| **Matiss** | restaurant, pizzeria | €-€€€, AIC |
| Via Della Fiera, 103 | tel. 0541776060 | |

RONCOLE VERDI

| **Le Roncole** | restaurant, B&B | €€-€€€, AIC |
| Via della Processione, 179 | tel. 0524930015 | |

S. ANDREA BAGNI

| **Andrea's** | restaurant, pizzeria | €, AIC |
| Via Circonvallazione, 51 | tel. 0525431818 | |

S. EGIDIO

| **La Rocchetta** | agritourism | €€€-€€€€, AIC |
| Via Rocca, 69 | tel. 0532725824 | |

S. GIOVANNI IN MARIGNANO

| **Party Pizza** | pizzeria | €, AIC |
| Via Galleria Marignano, 12 | tel. 0541955065 | |

SAN CARLO

| **La Pace Bar Pizzeria Trattoria** | restaurant, pizzeria, trattoria, bar | AIC |
| Via Statale, 63 | | |

SAN GIORGIO PIACENTINO

Il Pallino Rosa	bakery	€, AIC
Via Firenze, 16	tel. 348.3465567	
www.facebook.com/pages/Pallino-Rosa-pasta-fresca-senza-glutine/439591816083341		

| **Val di Luce** | restaurant, pizzeria | €-€€, AIC |
| Godi di San Giorgio Piacentino | tel. 0523.530100 | www.ristorantevaldiluce.it |

SAN GIOVANNI IN MARIGNANO

| **Star Bene Senza Glutine** | bar, desserts | € |
| Via Della Resistenza, 22 | tel. 541.97459 | www.starbenesenzaglutine.it |

SAN GIOVANNI IN PERSICETO

| **La Fattoria** | pizzeria | €, AIC |
| Via Crevalcore 84 - loc. Amola | tel. 051827072 | |

SAN GIUSTINO

| **Star Bene Senza Glutine** | bar, desserts | € |
| Via Ottavio Giovanni Bufalini, 13 | www.starbenesenzaglutine.it | |

SAN MAURO PASCOLI

| **Bio Pizza** | pizzeria | €, AIC |
| P.zza Giorgi, 29 | tel. 0541818413 | |

SANTA MARIA DEGLI ANGELI - ASSISI

Star Bene Senza Glutine
Viale della Repubblica n. 8/a

bar, desserts
tel. 075/8043627

€
www.starbenesenzaglutine.it

SANTARCANGELO DI ROMAGNA

Bio Pizza
Via Emilia, 3009

pizzeria
tel. 0541.624820

€, AIC

Vicolo di Brused
Via Battisti, 23

osteria
tel. 0541.622990

€, AIC
www.biopizza.org

SANTERNO

Vecchiacanala
Via Canala, 355

restaurant
tel. 0544417245

€€€€, AIC

SANT'ILARIO D'ENZA

Gusto&Sapore
Via della libertà, 22

pizzeria
tel. 0522.902268

€, AIC

Portami via
Via della libertà, 23

bakery
tel. 0522.472731

€, AIC
www.portamivia.net

SASSUOLO

Aragosta
Via Pia, 183

restaurant, pizzeria
tel. 0536805153

€-€€€€, AIC

Harlow Sassuolo
Via Ancora, 378

pizzeria
tel. 0536806422

€, AIC
www.pizzeriaharlow.it

SAVIGNANO SUL RUBICONE

Sweet Line

gelato (€, AIC)

P.zza Giovanni XXIII, 8

SESTOLA

Al Poggio
Via Poggioraso, 88

hotel, restaurant
tel. 053661147

€€-€€€, AIC

TAGLIATA DI CERVIA

Ranch
Viale Italia, 368

restaurant
tel. 0544987355

€€€-€€€€, AIC

TOSCANELLA DI DOZZA

Millevoglie
Via 1° Maggio, 12

pizzeria
tel. 0542673509

€, AIC

UMBERTIDE

Star Bene Senza Glutine
Via Fratta, 44

bar, desserts
tel. 392.1010452

€
www.starbenesenzaglutine.it

VERGATO

Gelateria artigianale Le Streghe

gelato (€, AIC)

Galleria I Maggio, 91

VIGNOLA

Cucinando
Via della Pace, 127

bakery, deli
tel. 59.765563

€, AIC
www.cucinandoavignola.com

L'Artigiano

gelato (€, AIC)

Via N. Bruni,166

VILLA VERUCCHIO

Kiosko il Vincanto
Via Aldo Moro, 105

café, bar
tel. 0541.676717

€, AIC

Nuovo Tarabacco
Via Casale, 340

pizzeria
tel. 0541.670672

€, AIC

Pizzeria Osteria De Sgrazjid   restaurant, pizzeria   €, AIC
Via Casale, 392-396   tel. 0541.670279
www.pizzeriaosteriadesgrazjid.it/ristorante.php

VISERBA DI RIMINI

Aurora   hotel   €€€€, AIC
Via Dati, 182   tel. 0541738337   www.haurora.it
Notes: Closed November-April.

VISERBELLA

Cadiz   hotel   €€€€, AIC
Via S. Cenci, 1   tel. 0541721713   www.hotelcadiz.it
Notes: Closed October-March.

ZOLA PEDROSA

C'è Pizza Per Te   pizzeria   €, AIC
Via Risorgimento, 432/8c   tel. 051756905
Notes: Closed Mondays, Sunday lunch.

Nuovo Parco dei Ciliegi   restaurant, pizzeria   €€, AIC
Via Gessi, 2   tel. 051750759   www.parcodeiciliegi.it
Notes: DS pizza point. Closed Tuesdays.

ZOLA PREDOSA

Mychef La Pioppa Ovest   mychef   €, AIC
A14 Bologna - Taranto
tel. 051.6160273   www.mychef.it

Bicicletta (M. Roglieri)

NAPLES AND CAMPANIA

Neopolitan water buffalo make the best mozzarella (U. Benninger)

(AIC = participates in the Associazione Italiana Celiachia program)

NAPOLI

Al Pruneto Discesa Coroglio, 101/102	restaurant, pizzeria tel. 081.7690744	AIC
Arcobaleno di Sapori Via G. Tropeano, 28/30	sandwich shop, bakery tel. 081/7704881	€, AIC
Birrzeria Re Carlo Larghetto S. Antonio Abate, 1	restaurant, pizzeria tel. 081.19979725	AIC
F.lli Pellone Via G.Leopardi, 239 Notes: Closed Mondays.	pizzeria tel. 0815934602	€, AIC
Holiday Inn Naples Centro Direzionale Isola, E/6	hotel, restaurant tel. 0812250111	€€ www.holidayinn.com/Naples
Hotel delle Terme di Agnano Via Agnano Astroni, 24	hotel, restaurant tel. 0817622180	€€ www.hoteltermeagnano.com
La Bufalina Via U. Masoni, 31	pizzeria tel. 081.7518890	€, AIC
La Caraffa Via Piave, 41/47	pizzeria tel. 0816403030	€, AIC
La Ruota Via Nicola Rocco, 16/18	pizzeria tel. 081.7805678	€, AIC

La Taverna di Bacco Via Sementini, 28/32	restaurant, pizzeria tel. 0815466119	€€, AIC www.latavernadibacco.com
Mama. Eat (2 locations) Via E. Alvino, 118 Via Manzoni, 6A/8 Notes: Closed Mondays and at lunch.	restaurant, pizzeria, pub tel. 081.5787833 tel. 0817148696	AIC
Mammina Via Partenope, 15/18	restaurant, pizzeria tel. 081.2400001	AIC
Mascagni Via Mascagni, 42/48	restaurant, pizzeria tel. 081.5602900	AIC
Menhir Via Giotto, 14,16,18 Notes: Closed Mondays at dinner, Sundays at lunch.	pub tel. 0815566945	€, AIC
Oliva da Concettina ai Tre Santi Via Arena alla Sanità, 7/b	pizzeria tel. 081.290037	€, AIC
Pizzazzà Via Michelangelo Caravaggio, 33	pizzeria tel. 081.7146941	€, AIC
Pizzeria La Ruota Via Nicola Rocco, 16/18	pizzeria tel. 0817805678	€, AIC www.pizzerialaruota.com
Rosso Pomodoro Napoli Centro Piazza Trieste e Trento, 7/8	pizzeria tel. 081.412791	€, AIC
Royal Continental Via Partenope, 38	hotel, restaurant tel. 0812452068	€€€-€€€€, AIC www.royalcontinental.it
Siani Senza Glutine Via Domenico Fontana 47/a	bakery tel. 081.5585332	€, AIC
Siani senza Glutine V.le Kennedy, 333	sandwich shop, bakery tel. 081.18901965	€, AIC
Sorbillo Via dei Tribunali, 38 Notes: Closed Sundays.	pizzeria tel. 0810331009	€, AIC www.sorbillo.eu
Gelat. Del Gallo Notes: Closed Wednesdays.	gelato (€, AIC)	Via A.C. De Meis, 60/62
Gelateria Della Scimmia **Gelatosità**	gelato (€, AIC) gelato (€, AIC)	P.zza Carità, 4 Via Mario Fiore, 2/a

THE REST OF CAMPANIA
CAPACCIO

Oleandri Via Poseidonia, 177	resort, hotel tel. 828.8518	AIC www.oleandriresort.com

S. GIORGIO

Italian Bakery Via Europa, 6	bakery tel. 345.71361	€, AIC

SAN GIORGIO

Tutto Senza Via Giovanni XXIII,	bakery tel. 81.36554	€, AIC

ACERRA

Gelatosità
Via A. De Gasperi, 30

gelato (€, AIC)

Via A. Diaz, 7/9

Primavera
restaurant, pizzeria
€-€€, AIC
tel. 0816588002

Totò e i Sapori
Via S. Gioacchino, 73

pizzeria
€, AIC
tel. 081.5206424

ACQUAVELLA DI CASALVELINO

Spina Rossa
Loc. Pantaleo

agritourism
€€, AIC
tel. 3406007508

ACQUAVENA DI ROCCAGLORIOSA

U' Trappitu
Via Del Mare, 51

restaurant, pizzeria
AIC
tel. 0974.980167

AFRAGOLA

Pachà
Via Cinque Vie, 24

crêperie
€, AIC
tel. 3278856811
www.cornetteriapacha.it

Rosso Pomodoro
Via S. Maria La Nova

pizzeria
€, AIC
tel. 081.3198509

AGROPOLI

Anna
Via S.Marco, 28-32

restaurant, pizzeria, inn
€€€-€€€€, AIC
tel. 0974823763

B&B Anna
Via S. Marco, 32

B&B
AIC
tel. 0974823763
www.affittacamereanna.it

AIELLO DEL SABATO

La Locandina
Via Ternana, 1/c

restaurant, pizzeria
€€, AIC
tel. 0825666620
www.villacalvo.it

AIROLA

Antovin
Via Caudisi, 11

restaurant, pizzeria
€, AIC
tel. 0823711439
www.ristorantepizzeriaantovin.com

ALBORI DI VIETRI SUL MARE

Il Cavaliere dei Conti
Via Case Sparse

agritourism
€€€, AIC
tel. 089210791
www.ilcavalieredeiconti.it

AMALFI

Hotel La Bussola
Via Lungo Mare dei Cavalieri, 16

hotel, restaurant
€€-€€€, AIC
tel. 089871533
www.labussolahotel.it

Hotel Santa Caterina
S.S. Amalfitana, 9

hotel, restaurant, pizzeria
€€€€
tel. 089871012
www.hotelsantacaterina.it

AMOROSI

La Piana
Via Telese, 296

hotel, restaurant, pizzeria
€€, AIC
tel. 0824970177

ANACAPRI

Hotel Bella Vista
Via Orlandi 10

hotel/restaurant
tel. 0818371463
www.bellavistacapri.com
Notes: GF breakfast. Restaurant will serve GF food.

La Rondinella
Via Orlandi 295

caprese/pizza
€€
tel. 0818371223
Notes: GF pasta. Reservations recommended.

ARIANO IRPINO

La Pignata in Bellavista
C.da Sterda, 19

restaurant, pizzeria
tel. 0825.872433

AIC
www.ristorantelapignata.it

ATENA LUCANA

Locanda San Cipriano
Via Serroni snc

restaurant, pizzeria
tel. 0975.511447

AIC
www.locandasancipriano.it

ATRIPALDA

Blueorange
Via Roma, 110

restaurant, pizzeria
tel. 0825627339

€€, AIC

AVELLINO

Cose da Mat
Via Circumvallazione, 118

bakery
tel. 0825.781815

€, AIC

Hotel de la Ville
Via Palatucci,20

hotel, restaurant
tel. 0825.780911

AIC
www.hoteldelavilleavellino.it

Mangiamoci su
Via Luigi De Nitto snc c/o Città Ospedaliera   tel. 0825.31097
www.facebook.com/mangiamocisuavellino

restaurant, pizzeria

AIC

Mastrogio'
C.so Umberto I, 71

tavola calda
tel. 0825.460367

AIC

Springfield
Via C. Colombo, 31

pizzeria
tel. 3490626515

€, AIC

The Happy Chef
Circumvallazione, 118/f

sandwich shop
tel. 08253199

€, AIC
www.happychef.it

Vecchia Fontana
C.so Umberto I, 32

restaurant, pizzeria
tel. 0825.756209

AIC

AVERSA

Da Mimmo
Via S. di Giacomo,52

pizzeria
tel. 081.8903016

€, AIC

Gastrò
Via Torrebianca, 78

pizzeria
tel. 0818905591

€, AIC
www.gustogastro.it

Il Magnifico
Via Filippo Saporito, 102

osteria
tel. 0815002093

€-€€, AIC

Infinity
V.le della Libertà, 156

sandwich shop
tel. 333.2288397

€, AIC

Punto Pizza
Piazza V. Emanuele, 50

restaurant, pizzeria
tel. 0818903920

€, AIC

Smile Gel
Notes: Also has crêpes.

gelato(€, AIC)

P.zza Vittorio Emanuele, 35

BACOLI

Baios - Il Gabbiano
Via Cicerone, 21

hotel, restaurant
tel. 081868796

€€€-€€€€, AIC

Cala Moresca
Via Faro, 44

hotel, restaurant
tel. 0815235595

€-€€€, AIC
www.calamoresca.it

BAGNOLI

Gennaro 2
Via Lucio Silla, 35

restaurant, pizzeria
tel. 0816100855

AIC

BARONISSI

I Love Pizza
Via T. Sanseverino, 51
pizzeria
tel. 089953360
€, AIC

BARRA

Scusate il Ritardo
Via Bartolo Longo, 249
restaurant, pizzeria
tel. 081.5961829
AIC

BATTIPAGLIA

Arienzo
V.le Primo Baratta, 14
bakery
tel. 0828.1994139
€, AIC

Centro Congressi San Luca
Via S.S. 18 - Km. 76, 5 M.no Braggio
hotel, restaurant, pizzeria
tel. 0828342533
€€, AIC
www.sanlucahotel.it

La Fabbrica dei Sapori
Via Spineta, 84/C
pizzeria
tel. 0828630021
AIC

Pizza Art
Via Rosario, 47
restaurant, pizzeria
tel. 08281840582
€-€€€, AIC
www.pizzaart.eu

Pizza e Sfizi
Via Silvio Pellico, 7
pizzeria
tel. 333.2518793
€, AIC

Positano
Via Amerigo Vespucci, 1
pizzeria
tel. 0828371285
€, AIC

Tenuta Marrandino
Via Fosso Pioppo, 5
pizzeria
tel. 0828.047059
€, AIC

Victoria
Via M. Ripa, 14
pizzeria
tel. 0828.302587
€, AIC

BELLONA

Cotton Hill
Via Nazionale Triflisco, 3
restaurant, pizzeria
tel. 0823960617
€€€, AIC
www.cottonhills.it

BELTIGLIO DI CEPPALONI

Zanzibar
Via Roma
bar
tel. 0824.46770
€, AIC

BENEVENTO

Da Claudio
C.da S. Chirico
restaurant, pizzeria
tel. 082429374
€, AIC
www.daclaudio.it

BOSCO DI SAN GIOVANNI A PIRO

La Locanda di Romeo
Via Provinciale, 33
hotel, restaurant
tel. 0974980004
€€-€€€, AIC
www.romeo-bosco.com

BRACIGLIANO

La Taverna dei Briganti
V.le Springfield Mass, 10
restaurant, pizzeria
tel. 3293490990
€€€, AIC

CAPACCIO PAESTUM

TraleSpighe
Via Nazionale S.S. 18, 119/121
bakery
tel. 0828.821544
€, AIC

CAPACCIO SCALO, PAESTUM

La Basilica Cafè
Via Magna Grecia, 881
pizzeria
tel. 828811301
€, AIC
www.labasilicacafe.it

CAPODICHINO

Autogrill Aeroporto Napoli Capodichino Autogrill   €, AIC
Via dell'Aeroporto di Capodichino   tel. 081.5993220

CAPODRISE

Marconi   bakery, sandwich shop   €, AIC
Via Greco, 1   tel. 338.1179570
www.facebook.com/pages/Pizzeria-Marconi-Celiachia-/184108851601979

Novotel Caserta /Novotelcafé   hotel, restaurant   €€€€, AIC
SS. 87 Sannitica km. 22,600   tel. 0823826553   www.novotel.com

CAPRI

Gelateria Buonocore Raffaele   gelato (€, AIC)   Via Vitt. Emanuele, 35
Notes: Closed Tuesdays.

Punta Tragara   hotel/restaurant
Via Tragara 57   tel. 0818370844   www.hoteltragara.com
Notes: GF breakfast, dinner with advance notice. Closed Nov. – Mar.

Villa Brunella   hotel/seafood restaurant
Via Tragara 24   tel. 0818370122   www.villabrunella.it
Notes: closed Nov.-March.

CARDITO

Appost' Accussi'   pizzeria   €, AIC
Via P. Donadio, 262   tel. 081.8345496

Charlot   gelato (€, AIC)   P.za Madonna d. Grazie, 9

CASALNUOVO DI NAPOLI

Hotel Rea/Rist. Convivio   hotel, restaurant, pizzeria   €€€, AIC
Via Nazionale delle Puglia, 62   tel. 0818421263   www.hotelrea.it

La Sequoia   restaurant, pizzeria   AIC
V.le dei Ligustri, 13   tel. 0818429851

Mister Pizz   restaurant, pizzeria   AIC
Via Napoli, 49   tel. 081.3441610

CASAVATORE

Pizzeria Iorio   pizzeria   €, AIC
G. Marconi, 123/125   tel. 081.7382626

Tutta 'Nata Storia   pizzera, trattoria   AIC
Via Locatelli, 34   tel. 081.0120973

Un Mondo Senza Glutine   bakery   €, AIC
Via Locatelli, 25/27   tel. 081.0401278

CASELLE IN PITTARI

La Pietra Azzurra   restaurant, pizzeria   €, AIC
Via Caporra, 64   tel. 0974988779   www.ristorantelapietrazzurra.it

CASERTA

Alba   gelato (€, AIC)   P.zza Cattaneo, 7

Antica Hostaria Massa   restaurant, pizzeria   AIC
Via Mazzini, 55   tel. 0823.456527

Dogana Golosa   restaurant   €-€€€€, AIC
S.S. Sannitica Km.113 loc. Vaccheria   tel. 0823301508   www.doganagolosa.it

Embè
Via Tescione, 173

restaurant/pizzeria
tel. 08231543751

€€€, AIC
www.embediscopub.it

Zero Glutine
Via Ricciardelli , 48

bakery
tel. 0823.1970249

€, AIC

CASERTAVECCHIA

Caserta Antica
Via Tiglio, 75

B&B
tel. 0823371158

AIC
www.hotelcaserta-antica.it

La Castellana
Via Tescione, 174

restaurant
tel. 08231540497

€, AIC

La Tana del Lupo
Via Lupara, 1

restaurant, pizzeria
tel. 0823371333

€€, AIC
www.allatanadellupo.it

CASORIA

Graffe & Co
Via S. Salvatore, 1

creperie
tel. 392.6603805

€, AIC

Juancarlos
Via D. Colasanto, 32/34

pizzeria, pub
tel. 0815844868

€, AIC

Pizzeria Carducci
Via Giosuè Carducci, 19

pizzeria
tel. 081.7573311

€, AIC

CASTEL SAN GIORGIO

Salerno Food
Via Palmiro Togliatti, 11

bakery
tel. 081.5162518

€, AIC

CASTELLAMMARE DI STABIA

Il Mago dello Spiedo
Via Annunziatella, 7

pizzeria, sandwich shop
tel. 0818704064

€, AIC

Monzu'
Via E. De Nicola, 35

restaurant, pizzeria
tel. 081.8721022

AIC

Re Di Pi...zze
Via Bonito, 45

bakery
tel. 334.9746551

€, AIC

CASTELNUOVO CILENTO

Anna dei Sapori
Via S. Venere, 1 Fraz. Velina

agritourism
tel. 0974.63928

AIC
www.annadeisapori.it

CASTELVENERE

Fattoria Ciabrelli
Via Sannitica

agritourism
tel. 0824940565

€€, AIC
www.ciabrelli.it

CASTIGLIONE DEL GENOVESI

Il Riccio
Via V. Genovesi

restaurant, pizzeria
tel. 089881641

€€-€€€, AIC

CAVA DE' TIRRENI

Alba Chiara
Via L. Palmentieri, 1

restaurant, pizzeria
tel. 089.2960099

AIC

Caffetteria Remo
Via Vittorio Veneto, 282

bar
tel. 089.340059

€, AIC

Made in Italy
C.so Mazzini, 111

restaurant, pizzeria
tel. 089345248

AIC
www.madeinitalycava.it

Montecaruso Hotel
Via S. Felice,snc S.Lucia

hotel, restaurant, pizzeria
tel. 089467817

€€-€€€€, AIC
www.montecaruso.it

CERASO

La Petrosa
Via Fabbrica, 25

agritourism
tel. 097461370

€€-€€€, AIC
www.lapetrosa.it

Osteria del Notaro
Via Isca, 19

restaurant, pizzeria
tel. 097461294

€, AIC
www.cilentohouse.it

CERCOLA

Del Pino
Via Don Minzoni, 225

restaurant, pizzeria
tel. 0817331145

€-€€€€, AIC
www.gruppoleonessa.it

CIMITILE

Maidomo
Via Enrico De Nicola, 24

restaurant, pizzeria
tel. 081.19532820

AIC

CIRCELLO

Antica Trattoria Bacco
C.so Municipio, 121/a

restaurant, pizzeria
tel. 0824937720

€€, AIC
www.anticatrattoriabacco.com

CONCA DELLA CAMPANIA

Agriturismo La Palombara
Via I° Novembre, 149

agritourism
tel. 0823923580

€€€, AIC
www.lapalombara.com

CUSANO MUTRI

Mastrillo
Via Giocagni,15

restaurant, pizzeria
tel. 0824862205

€€, AIC

DRAGONEA DI VIETRI SUL MARE

Il Limoneto
Via Raccio, 3

restaurant, pizzeria
tel. 089.210358

AIC

ERCOLANO

Gianni Al Vesuvio
Via Vesuvio, 10

restaurant, pizzeria
tel. 0817395684

€€€, AIC
www.giannialvesuvio.com

Le Nuvole Restaurant
Via Roma, 45

restaurant
tel. 0817322002

€€€, AIC

Villa Signorini Relais
Via Roma, 43

hotel, restaurant
tel. 0817776423

AIC
www.villasignorini.it

FELITO

L'Occhiano
Loc. Difesa Lombi

pub, pizzeria
tel. 0828945255 www.ristorantepizzerialocchiano.com

€€-€€€, AIC

FISCIANO

Belvedere
Via Del Centenario, 82

restaurant, pizzeria
tel. 089878996

€€€, AIC

Rosso Pomodoro
Via Faraldo, 11/23

restaurant, pizzeria
tel. 089.826081

AIC

FOGLIANISE

La Tripolina
Via Roma, 15

pizzeria
tel. 0824.871481

€, AIC

FORIO D'ISCHIA

Bosco Hotel
Via San Gennaro, 46

hotel, restaurant
tel. 081909132

AIC
www.hotelalbosco.it

Da Leopoldo
Via Scannella, 12 - Loc. Panza

restaurant, pizzeria
tel. 081907086

AIC

Hotel Terme Castaldi
Via Monterone, 70

hotel
tel. 081997101

€€€€, AIC
www.hotelcastaldi.com

Villa La Cesa
Via Parroco D'Abundo, 129

B&B
tel. 081907512

AIC
www.appartamenticesaischia.com

FORIO-PANZA ISCHIA

La Forastera
Via Forte, 31

restaurant, pizzeria
tel. 081907281

€€, AIC

FRATTAMAGGIORE

Black Burger
Via V. Emanuele, 167

pub
tel. 339.3525163

AIC

PalaPizza
Via Vittoria, 36

pizzeria
tel. 081.8322040

€, AIC

Gastrò
Via Veneto 38/44

pizzeria
tel. 0818804936

€, AIC

Il Rustichiere
Via Padre Mario Vergaro, 10/12

restaurant, pizzeria
tel. 0818804693

€€, AIC

Pinguino Reale

gelato (€, AIC)

Via Padre Mario Vergara, 201

FRATTAMINORE

Da Ciro
Via F. Turati, 40

restaurant, pizzeria
tel. 081.8363181

AIC

FRIGENTO

Fontana Madonna
C.da Fontana Madonna

agritourism
tel. 082544647

€€, AIC
www.fontanamadonna.it

Le Delizie Steakhouse
Via Pagliara, 156

restaurant, pizzeria
tel. 0825440357

€€, AIC

FURORE

Hostaria di Bacco
Via Giovan Battista Lama, 9

hotel, restaurant
tel. 089.830360

AIC

GIFFONI SEI CASALI

Al Vecchio Rifugio
Via Malche, 64

restaurant, pizzeria
tel. 089880141

€€-€€€, AIC
www.alvecchiorifugio.it

Popilia
Via Serroni, 45

restaurant
tel. 089880129

€-€€€, AIC

Villa Regina
Via Serroni, 45

B&B
tel. 089880129

AIC

GIUGLIANO IN CAMPANIA

Alexander Pizza
Via Casacelle, 50/Parco Regina

pizzeria
tel. 0813307010

€, AIC

La Capricciosa
Via Degli Innamorati, 149

pizzeria
tel. 081.5069936

€, AIC

Lido Varca d'Oro
Via Orsa Maggiore
Notes: Self-service.
restaurant, pizzeria, tavola calda €, AIC
tel. 0815091214

Nick
Via Ripuaria, 304
pub, sandwich shop €, AIC
tel. 081.3347517

GRAGNANO

Ai Giardini dei Cesari
Via Pass.ta Archeol.ca Varano
gelato €, AIC
tel. 081.8710234

L'Angelo Rosso
Via Cappella della Guardia, 23
restaurant/pizzeria €€, AIC
tel. 0818794132   www.langelorosso.it.gg

GROTTAMINARDA

A Tempo Perso
Via Valle snc
pizzeria €, AIC
tel. 0825.426204

Villa Sant'Andrea
Ctr Sant'Andrea snc
restaurant, pizzeria AIC
tel. 334.9864853

GROTTOLELLA

La Cantinella
Via della Repubblica, 14
restaurant, pizzeria €€, AIC
tel. 0825671077   www.lacantinella.av.it

MADDALONI

A'ddo' Napulitano
Via Napoli, 80/86
restaurant, pizzeria €-€€€, AIC
tel. 0823402642   www.addonapulitano.it

MAIORI

Al Mare Restaurant e Bar
Via G. Capone, 63
restaurant, pizzeria bar €€-€€€, AIC
tel. 3089852668

Casa Mariannina
Via Scala Santa, 1
B&B AIC
tel. 089.853609   www.casamariannina.com

La Casa d'Amare
Via Orti, 40
B&B AIC
tel. 089.851743   www.lacasadamare.it

Meublè Casa Mannini
Via Casa Mannini, 2
B&B AIC
tel. 331.6261044   www.casamanninimaiori.it

Pensione Vittoria
Via F. Cerasuoli, 4
B&B AIC
tel. 089877652   www.hotel-vittoria.it

MARANO

Adde' Figliole
Via Giovanni Falcone, 36
pizzeria €, AIC
tel. 08119255102

MARINA DI CAMEROTA

La Locanda di Romeo
Via Lungo Mare Trieste
restaurant, pizzeria €€, AIC
tel. 0974551143   www.romeo-bosco.com

Villaggio Alberg. Da Pepè
Via delle Sirene, 41
village restaurant €€€€, AIC
tel. 0974932461   www.villaggiodapepe.net

MASSA LUBRENSE

Emilia
Via Reola, 12
restaurant, pizzeria €€-€€€, AIC
tel. 0818080643

Hotel Piccolo Paradiso
P.zza Madonna della Lobra, 5
hotel, restaurant €€, AIC
tel. 0818789240   www.piccolo-paradiso.com

META

Tico Tico
Via Caruso, 3

restaurant, pizzeria
tel. 0815321837

€€, AIC

MIRABELLA ECLANO

Villa Assunta
Via Capo di Gaudio, snc

restaurant
tel. 0825.476169

AIC

MOIANO

Dal Guappo
Via Nuova S.Pietro, 69

restaurant, pizzeria
tel. 0823711225

€, AIC

Stella Maiuri
Via Nuova S.Pietro, 69

agritourism
tel. 3392050508

€€, AIC

MOLINARA

That's Amore
C.da Gregaria, 97

restaurant, pizzeria
tel. 0824994059

€€€, AIC
www.thatsamoremolinara.it

MONTANARO DI FRANCOLISE

Camelot
Via Passaro e Romano, 61

restaurant, pizzeria
tel. 335.1852822

AIC

MONTESARCHIO

Il Castello
Via Vitulanese, 188

hotel, restaurant
tel. 0824834690

€€, AIC

MONTEVERDE

Al Giardino
Via Fontana, 4

restaurant, pizzeria
tel. 3805453055

€, AIC
www.algiardino.eu

MONTORO INFERIORE

La Cantina dell'Arte
Via Risorgimento, 53

restaurant
tel. 08251728820

€€, AIC
www.lacantinadellarte.com

MONTORO SUPERIORE

Arco di Magliano
Via Magliano

restaurant, pizzeria
tel. 0825523515

€€€, AIC

MUGNANO DEL CARDINALE

Dell'Ulivo
Via dell'Uguaglianza, 3

restaurant, pizzeria
tel. 0818257650

€€, AIC
www.ristorantepizzeriadellulivo.it

NAPOLI - MARIANELLA

Club Degli Amici
Via E. Scaglione, 242

pizzeria
tel. 081.5853576

€, AIC

NAPOLI-POSILLI PO

La Gaiola
V.le Virgilio,1

restaurant, pizzeria
tel. 081.3653180

AIC

Rosiello
Via S. Strato,10

restaurant
tel. 081.7691288

AIC

NAPOLI-RIVIERA DI CHIAIA

Umberto
Via Alabardieri,30/31

restaurant, pizzeria
tel. 081.418555

AIC

NAPOLI-SAN GIOVANNI A TEDUCCIO

Le Ancelle
Via Ferrante Imparato, 25
pizzeria, trattoria
tel. 3772462733
€, AIC

NAPOLI-VOME RO

Bier Garten
Via Mattia Preti, 10/a-b
pub
tel. 081.5568932
€, AIC

Ciao Piada
Via Massimo Stanzione, 14/I
pub
tel. 081.19178942
€, AIC

NAPOLI-VOMERO

Gorizia
Via Albino Albini, 18/20
pizzeria
tel. 0815604642
€, AIC
www.pizzeriagorizia.it

NOCERA INFERIORE

Antico Borgo
Via Vescovado, 49
Notes: Closed Mondays.
restaurant, pizzeria
tel. 081920114
€€€, AIC

L'Uliveto
Via Poggio San Pantaleone snc
agritourism
tel. 081.928400
AIC
www.agriturismouliveto.it

Madison
Via Isaia Gabola, 53
Notes: Closed Mondays.
restaurant, pizzeria
tel. 0815153622
€, AIC

Rist. Pizz. Nocera
Via Marcello De Luca, 29
restaurant, pizzeria
tel. 0968.938090
AIC

Y Cabrera
Via Martinez Y Cabrera, 18/24
restaurant, pizzeria
tel. 081.0486961
AIC

NOCERA SUPERIORE

Caramari
V.le del Santuario, 7
restaurant, pizzeria
tel. 0815143740
€€, AIC

L'Angolo del Gusto
Via Indipendenza, 68
restaurant, pizzeria
tel. 081.19505245
AIC

Luna Galante
Via Santacroce, 13
Notes: Closed Mondays.
restaurant
tel. 0815176065
€€€-€€€€, AIC

Madison Nocera Superiore
Via Croce Mallone, 82
pizzeria
tel. 081.0201667
€, AIC

NOLA

Braciami Ancora
Vulcano Buon Isola Amalfi
restaurant, pizzeria
tel. 335.7362926
AIC

NOVI VELIA - VALLO DELLA LUCANIA

La Chioccia D'Oro
Via Pietra dei Correnti
restaurant
tel. 0974.70004
AIC

NUSCO

Hotel Colucci
Via Passaro, 11
hotel, restaurant
tel. 082764071
€€, AIC
www.hotelcolucci.it

OTTAVIANO

Maxi'o
Via Papa Giovanni XXIII, 14
pizzeria pub
tel. 0818278900
AIC

PADULA

La Certosa
Viale Certosa, 41

hotel, restaurant
tel. 097577046

€€, AIC
www.certosa.it

PAGANI

La Botte
Via A. Califano, 14/16

pizzeria
tel. 0815155440

€, AIC

PALINURO

Pizzeria Degli Amici dal 1973
Via Indipendenza, 166

pizzeria
tel. 3475506376

€, AIC

Villaggio Arco Naturale Club
Via Arco Naturale snc

resort, hotel, restaurant
tel. 0974.931157

AIC

PELLEZZANO

Taverna Antica Filanda
Via Filanda, 8
Notes: Closed Mondays.

restaurant, pizzeria
tel. 089481578

€€, AIC

PELLEZZANO - COPERCHIA

Il Girasole
P.zza Giovanni Paolo II, 8

pizzeria
tel. 089.566540

€, AIC

PIANA DI MONTE VERNA

Agriturismo Le Ghiandaie
Via Polizzano, 2

agritourism
tel. 0823861216   www.agriturismoleghiandaie.net

€€, AIC

PIANO DI MONTORO INFERIORE

La Botte
Via Ferrovia, 3

restaurant, pizzeria
tel. 3473206241

AIC

PIMONTE

Il Trifoglio
Via Piano, 24

restaurant, pizzeria
tel. 349.3856341

AIC

PISCIOTTA

Villaggio La Maree
Via Fossa della Marina, 25

resort, restaurant
tel. 0974.973242

AIC

POLLA

Santa Chiara
Via Annia

restaurant, pizzeria
tel. 0975391470

€€, AIC
www.ristoranteschiara.com

POMPEI

Osteria Da Peppino
Via Duca d'Aosta, 39
Notes: Closed Tuesdays.

restaurant
tel. 0818504821

€€-€€€€, AIC

Pompeo Magno
Via S. Abbondio, 155

restaurant, pizzeria
tel. 0818598050

€€, AIC
www.pompeomagno.it

PONTECAGNANO

La Basculla
Via Roma, 25

pizzeria
tel. 089849030

€, AIC
www.labasculla.com

La Regina Scalza
Via Tevere, 18

pizzeria
tel. 089.848156

€, AIC

Motiè
P.zza Risorgimento, 9

pizzeria
tel. 089.383114

€, AIC

Primavera pizzeria €, AIC
Via Dei Navigatori tel. 3395068161

PORTICI

Gelateria del Gallo gelato (€, AIC) P.zza S. Ciro, 24/26
Gelateria del Gallo gelato (€, AIC) Via Libertà, 115

La Locanda della Regina restaurant, pizzeria AIC
C.so Garibaldi, 89 tel. 081.482792

Pizza Verace pizzeria €, AIC
Via Gravina, 12 tel. 081.7769095

Pizzeria Vesuvio pizzeria €, AIC
Via B. Croce, 44 tel. 081475728

POSITANO

Da Bruno restaurant
Corso Colombo, 157 (up the hill from the main street) tel. 08 9875392
Notes: GF Pasta. English spoken.

Hotel Villa Gabrisa restaurant
Via Pasitea, 227 tel. 089811498 www.villagabrisa.it

Il Fornillo restaurant €€€
Via Pasitea 266 tel. 08 9811954
Notes: English spoken. GF pasta.

Le Tre Sorelle restaurant €€
Del Brigantino 27-31 (across from beach) tel. 089 875452
www.ristorantetresorelle.it
Notes: GF pasta. English spoken.

POZZUOLI

A' Ninfea restaurant AIC
Via Provinciale Lucrino Averno, 1 tel. 081.8042925

Anema e Cono gelato (€, AIC) C.so Umberto I, 59

La Cucina degli Amici restaurant €€€, AIC
C.so Umberto I, 17 tel. 0815269393 www.lacucinadegliamici.it

Menhir pub (€, AIC) Via Pendio S. Giuseppe, 13

PRAIANO

La Cala delle Lampare restaurant €€€€, AIC
Via Campo, 5 tel. 089874333

Tritone hotel €€€€, AIC
Via Campo, 5 tel. 089874333 www.tritone.it

Locanda Costa Diva hotel, restaurant
via Roma, 12 tel. 089 813076 www.hotelspraiano.com

QUARTO

L'Arcadia restaurant €€€€, AIC
Via Cuccaro, 29 tel. 0815873802 www.arcadiaristorante.it

RAVELLO

Al Ristoro del Moro restaurant €€€-€€€€, AIC
Via della Repubblica, 10 tel. 089857901 www.alristorodelmoro.it
Notes: Closed Tuesdays.

Hotel Graal hotel, restaurant €€€-€€€€, AIC
Via della Repubblica, 8 tel. 089857222 www.hotelgraal.it

Gluten-Free Italy by Region

Hotel Rufolo Via San Francesco, 1	hotel, restaurant tel. 089.857133	AIC www.hotelrufolo.it
Parsifal Via Gioacchino d'Anna	hotel, restaurant tel. 089857144	€€, AIC www.hotelparsifal.com
Villa Giordano Via Trinità, 14	inn, restaurant tel. 089857255	€€€€, AIC www.giordanohotel.it
Villa Maria Via Santa Chiara, 2	hotel, restaurant tel. 089857255	€€€€, AIC www.villamaria.it

S. ANGELO - ISOLA D'ISCHIA

Casa Giuseppina Via G. di Iorio, 7- Succhivo	hotel, restaurant tel. 081907771	€€, AIC wwwischiacasagiuseppina.com
Romantica Via Ruffano,11	hotel tel. 081999216	

S. ANGELO D'ISCHIA

Hotel Ferdinando Via Fondolillo, 4	hotel tel. 081999269	AIC

S. GIORGIO DEL SANNIO

Ricci Park Hotel Via Vitulanese, 188	hotel, restaurant, pizzeria tel. 0824338461	€-€€€, AIC

S. GIOVANNI A PIRO - SCARIO

Palazzone Loc. Palazzone snc	agritourism tel. 0974.986530	AIC

S. GIUSEPPE VESUVIANO

Sicilia Via Masseria Perillo, 6	sandwich shop tel. 335.1442316	€, AIC

S. MARZANO SUL SARNO

L'Oasi della Pizza Via Gramsci, 123	pizzeria tel. 3313880076	€, AIC

Notes: DS pizza point. Closed Tuesdays.

S. SEBASTIANO AL VESUVIO

Funiculì Via Figliola, 12	restaurant, pizzeria tel. 0815742627	€, AIC www.funiculifunicula.it

S.AGATA DÈ GOTI

Antico Borgo P.zza Trieste, 9	restaurant/pizzeria tel. 0823717389	€€, AIC www.ristoranteanticoborgo.org
Ape Regina C.da Palmentana	agritourism tel. 082395668	€€€, AIC www.agriturismoaperegina.it
Biancaneve e i Sette Nani Ctr Castrone, 25	agritourism tel. 0823.953181	AIC www.lafattoriadibiancaneve.it
Il Girasole Via Macere, 5	agritourism tel. 349761239	€-€€, AIC
Eden Via S. M. Scozzese, 5	agritourism tel. 0823.953027	AIC
Normanno	gelato (€, AIC)	Via Roma

S.MARTINO SANNITA

Agorà
Via Chiesa, 79
agritourism
tel. 0824337422
€-€€, AIC

SALA CONSILINA

Strapizzami
Via S. Antonio
pizzeria
tel. 3277607619
€, AIC

Villa delle Acacie
Contrada Sagnano
agritourism
tel. 0975545076
€, AIC
www.agriturismovilladelleacacie.it

SALERNO

Al Campetto
Via Sant'Angelo di Ogliara
pizzeria
tel. 089281640
€, AIC

Arienzo
Via A. Guglielmini, 7/9
bakery
tel. 089.797729
€, AIC

Bar Castorino
Via Del Carmine, 23
bar
tel. 089.226891
€, AIC

Bar Pedro
Via Ventimiglia, 41
bar
tel. 089.756364
€, AIC

Brera
Via Lungo Mare Clemente Tafuri, 1
restaurant
tel. 0897042027
AIC

Caffè Da Totò
Via Generale A. Diaz, 39
bar
tel. 089.220057
€, AIC

Celiafree
Via XX Settembre, 29
bakery
tel. 089.725402
€, AIC

Cico's
Via Picarelli, 70 loc. Pastena
restaurant, pizzeria
tel. 3207645154
AIC

Ciripizza
Via F. Conforti, 16-18
pizzeria
tel. 089.8426800
€, AIC

Grand Hotel Salerno
L.re Clemente Tafuri, 1
hotel, restaurant, B&B
tel. 0897041111
€€-€€€€, AIC
www.grandhotelsalerno.it
Notes: this hotel has five restaurants.

Il Giardino degli Dei
Via S. Eustachio, 44/48
pizzeria
tel. 089301127
€, AIC

La Bodeguita
Via Silvio Baratta, 16
restaurant, pizzeria
tel. 089.9956212
AIC

La Tombola
Via S. Marano, 5
restaurant, pizzeria
tel. 089229589
€€, AIC

Line Restaurant Cafè
C.so Vittorio Emanuele, 176
bar, tavola calda
tel. 089.241713
€, AIC

Novotel Salerno Est Arechi
Via Generale Clark, 49
hotel, restaurant
tel. 089.9957111
AIC
www.novotel.com

Trattoria del Padreterno
P.zza Flavio Gioia, 12
trattoria
tel. 089.239305
AIC

SAN GENNARELLO DI OTTAVIANO

Pathos
Via Giugliani, 43
restaurant, pizzeria
tel. 081.8274183
AIC

SAN GIORGIO A CREMANO

Pizzeria Galante Tutino pizzeria €, AIC
Via A. Gennaro Galante, 22 tel. 081.472566

Tutto Gelato gelato (€, AIC) Via Pittore, 188

SANTA MARIA CAPUA VETERE

La Loggetta restaurant, pizzeria AIC
P.zza Mazzini, 13 tel. 0823.898417

SANT'ANASTASIA

La Dolce Vita pizzeria €, AIC
Via Romani, 68 tel. 0815303418
Notes: Closed Wednesdays.

SANT'ANTONIO ABATE

Caruso restaurant, pizzeria €€, AIC
Via Scafati, 251 tel. 0818735743

SAPRI

Lucifero restaurant, pizzeria AIC
Trav. C.so Garibaldi, 6 tel. 0973603033

SAVIANO

The Drugstore pub €, AIC
C.so Garibaldi, 79 tel. 347.3465396

SCAFATI

B&B Il Fauno B&B AIC
Via Domenico Catalano, 97 tel. 3349332434 www.bbfauno.it

Il Bugigattolo restaurant, pizzeria AIC
Via D. Catalano, 68 tel. 081.8636297

Il Giardinetto osteria, pizzeria €€€, AIC
Via A. Manzoni, 56 tel. 0818599335 www.ristoranteilgiardinetto.com

Serafino restaurant, pizzeria AIC
Via Buccino, 28/30 tel. 0818638330

SOLOPACA

Masseria del Procaccia agritourism €€, AIC
Via Procaccia, 1 tel. 0824971366

SOMMA VESUVIANA

Gelatopoli gelato (€, AIC) Via Aldo Moro, 22/24

International Restaurant restaurant, pizzeria €€€, AIC
Via Aldo Moro, 182 tel. 0818997052
Notes: Closed Wednesdays.

Locanda del Cavaliere restaurant, pizzeria €, AIC
Via Santa Maria del Pozzo, 2 tel. 0815317444

Rose Rosse restaurant AIC
Via S.Maria a Castello, 93 tel. 0818931364 www.restaurantroserosse.it
Notes: Closed Tuesdays.

Villa La Sorgente restaurant AIC
Via S. Maria delle Grazie a Castello, 127 tel. 081.8932597

SORRENTO

Bar Syrenuse
Piazza Tasso Via Sant'Antonino, 14
Notes: gluten-free menu.
bar
tel. 818 075582
€€
www.barsyrenusesorrento.it

Hotel Conca Park
Via degli Aranci, 13 bis
hotel, restaurant
tel. 0818071621
AIC
www.concapark.com

Hotel Michelangelo
C.so Italia, 275
hotel
tel. 0818784844
www.michelangelohotel.it

I Giardini di Tasso
Via Santa Maria della Pieta 30
restaurant
tel. 08 18074145
€€€

Il Buco Ristorante
2a rampa Marina Piccola, 5 (Piazza S.Antonino)
restaurant
€€€€
www.ilbucoristorante.it

La Fenice
Via degli Aranci, 11
Notes: Closed Mondays.
restaurant, pizzeria
tel. 0818781652
€€, AIC

La Residenza
Via Rota, 1
hotel, restaurant
tel. 0818774698
€€€€
www.laresidenzasorrento.it

Old Taverna
Via Fuoro, 23
Notes: Gluten-free menu.
restaurant
tel. 0818781442
www.oldtavernasorrentina.it

Parco dei Principi
Via Rota, 1
hotel, restaurant
tel. 0818784644
€€€€
www.hotelparcoprincipi.com

Ristorante Ruccio
Piazza Marinai d'italia 33, Sorrento Peninsula
restaurant
tel. 08 18074069
€€€
www.ristoranteruccio.com

Villa Rubinacci
Via Correale, 25
restaurant, pizzeria
tel. 0818073357
€-€€€€

SPERONE

Golosità
C.so Umberto I, 70/72
creperie
tel. 338.7525964
€-€€, AIC

SQUILLE DI CASTEL CAMPAGNANO

L'Ape e il Girasole
Loc. Selvanova
agritourism
tel. 0823.1764551
AIC

STELLA CILENTO

I Fornari
Loc. Fornari, 2
agritourism, B&B
tel. 0974909204
€€, AIC

STRIANO

Il Golosone
Via Palma, 458
restaurant, pizzeria
tel. 081.5137063
AIC

TELESE TERME

L'Orso Bianco
gelato (€, AIC)
Via G. Tanzillo, 13/15

TERZIGNO

Il Cratere
Via Panoramica, 124
restaurant, pizzeria
tel. 0815299090
€€, AIC

Palm Garden
C.so A. Volta, 262
restaurant, pizzeria
tel. 0815298956
€€€, AIC
www.ristorantepalgarden.com

TEVEROLA

Il Magnifico
Via Roma, 161/163

osteria
tel. 0815048251

€-€€, AIC

TORRE DEL GRECO

Franco
Via Nazionale, 410

restaurant, pizzeria
tel. 0818471970   www.ristorantepizzeriafranco.com

€-€€, AIC

La Smorfia
Via E. De Nicola, 57

pizzeria
tel. 081.8492558

€, AIC

TORRECUSA

Rosso Pomodoro
Zona Industriale Torre Palazzo

pizzeria
tel. 0824.876217   www.rossopomodoro.com

€, AIC

TORRETTE DI MERCOGLIANO

Pink Panther
Via Nazionale, 160

restaurant, pizzeria
tel. 082568236473

€€, AIC

TORRIONE - SALERNO

Celiamix
P.zza M. Ricciardi, 9

tavola calda, bar
tel. 089.754718

€, AIC

TRAMONTI

Al Valico di Chiunzi
Via Chiunzi, 91

restaurant, pizzeria
tel. 089.876165

AIC

Costiera Amalfitana
Via Falcone, 21 - fraz. Pietre

restaurant, pizzeria, agritourism   €-€€, AIC
tel. 089856192   www.costieraamalfitana.it

VALLESACCARDA

Oasis Sapori Antichi
Via Provinciale, 8

restaurant
tel. 082797021

€€€€, AIC

VICO EQUENSE

Nonna Rosa
Via Privata Bonea, 2
Notes: Closed Wednesdays, Sunday nights.

restaurant
tel. 0818799055

€€€€, AIC
www.osterianonnarosa.it

Sale e Pepe
Via Filangieri, 87

pizzeria, sandwich shop
tel. 3398142500

€, AIC
www.salendpepe.com

VIETRI SUL MARE

Il Principe e la Civetta
Via Mazzini, 135

restaurant
tel. 897632201

€€€, AIC
www.ilprincipeelacivetta.com

La Fattoria
Via Iaconti 2/a (Dragonea)

restaurant
tel. 089210518

€€€, AIC

L'Argonauta c/o California Beach restaurant
Via G. Pellegrino

€€€, AIC

VOLLA

Leonessa
Via R. Sanzio

hotel, restaurant
tel. 0817748916

€€€€, AIC
www.hotelleonessa.com

Uomini in piazza (M. Roglieri)

BARI AND PUGLIA
(AIC = participates in the Associazione Italiana Celiachia program)

BARI

Al Capriccio	pizzeria	€€, AIC
Via G. Capruzzi, 36	tel. 80.553108	www.alcapriccioristoepizza.it
Corte di Torrelonga	reception hall	€€€€€, AIC
Strada Torrelonga, 10	tel. 0805461876	www.corteditorrelonga.it
Da Bari Napoli	pizzeria	€, AIC
Via Piccinni 187/189	tel. 0809905452	

Notes: DS pizza point. Closed Saturdays and Sunday at lunch.

Est	restaurant	€€, AIC
Via Toma, 81	tel. 80.9904796	www.vineriaest.it
Frulez	restaurant	€€, AIC
P.zza Umberto I, 14	tel. 80.5239827	www.frulez.it
Galu	pizzeria	€, AIC
Vle Papa Giovanni XXIII, 16/18	tel. 0805614739	

Notes: Closed Wednesdays, and everyday at lunch.

Il Braciere	restaurant	€€€-€€€€, AIC
Via S. Visconti, 29	tel. 0805239638	

Notes: Closed Sundays, month of August at lunch.

La Tana	pizzeria	€, AIC
Via Giovanni Amendola, 29	tel. 80.5559574	
Le Veronique	pizzeria	€€, AIC
Via Hahnneman, 4	tel. 0805461822	

Notes: Closed Sundays.

Lido S. Francesco alla Rena Via Verdi, 59/61	pizzeria tel. 0805341542	€€, AIC
Opera Prima Via Pietro Nenni, 9/7 Notes: Closed Mondays, month of August.	pizzeria tel. 0805024244	€, AIC
Pic Nic Via Pietro Colletta, 36 Notes: Closed Mondays.	restaurant, pizzeria tel. 0805615131	€€€, AIC www.ristorantepicnic.it
Sheraton Nicolaus Hotel Via C.A. Ciasca, 27	hotel, restaurant tel. 0805682111	€€€, AIC
Taverna Pane e Vino Via Re David, 14 Notes: Closed June-September.	restaurant tel. 0805566187	€-€€, AIC www.tavernapaneevino.it
Villa Romanazzi Carducci Via Capruzzi,326	hotel, restaurant tel. 80.54274	AIC www.villaromanazzi.it
Zonno Ricevimenti Molo S. Nicola, 5 Notes: Closed Mondays and month of August.	restaurant tel. 0805212470	€€€€, AIC
Pasticceria Portoghese **Piccinni** **Yogo Land 2**	gelato (€, AIC) gelato (€, AIC) gelato (€, AIC)	Via G. Modugno, 29/d Via Piccinni, 131 C.so Vitt. Emanuele, 9

BARI-PALESE

Vittoria Parc Hotel Via Nazionale, 10/f	hotel tel. 0805306300	€€€, AIC www.vittoriaparchotel.com

BARI-S.SPIRITO

La Tana dell'Artista Lung. Cristoforo Colombo 212/d Notes: Closed Tuesdays.	pizzeria tel. 0805331682	€€, AIC

ACQUAVIVA DELLE FONTI

Villa dei Fiori Prov.le 127 per Santeramo in Colle	restaurant, pizzeria tel. 080769293	€€€, AIC
Gelateria Pastore	gelato (€, AIC)	Via Roma, 40

ALBEROBELLO

La Chiusa di Chietri S.S. 172 dei Trulli Km.29, 800	hotel, restaurant, reception hall tel. 0804325481	€€-€€€€, AIC www.lachiusadichietri.it
La Foggia Via Don F. Gigante, 4 Notes: DS pizza point. Closed Mondays.	restaurant, pizzeria tel. 0804325927	€-€€€€, AIC

ALBERONA

Da Liberato Loc. Fornaci	restaurant tel. 881.592368	€€, AIC www.ristorantedaliberato.it
La Villetta Via Minerva, 12	restaurant tel. 881.592042	€€, AIC

ALLISTE

Antica Terra P.zza Municipio, 14	B&B tel. 0833599389	AIC

Cafè dei Napoli	gelato (€, AIC)	P.zza Municipio, 11
	ALTAMURA	
Gelat. Cenzino Notes: Closed Thursdays.	gelato (€, AIC)	V.le Martiri, 79
Tre Archi Via San Michele, 28 Notes: Closed Wednesdays.	restaurant, pizzeria tel. 0803115569	€€€-€€€€, AIC www.trearchi.it
	ANDRIA	
Assapora Via Piero della Francesca, 95	tavola calda tel. 883.892911	€, AIC
Imperiale Via L. Bonomo, 11 Notes: DS pizza point. Closed Sundays.	pizzeria tel. 0883557717	€, AIC
La Puglia in Tavola Via Castel del Monte, 23	store, restaurant tel. 883.545788	€, AIC www.lapugliaintavola.it
Officina del Gelato Via Vaglio, 28	gelato tel. 393.0008656	€, AIC www.officinadelgelato.eu
	ARADEO	
Antica Tenuta Cornacchia Contrada Spina Notes: Closed Tuesdays.	restaurant tel. 0836552902	AIC
Araknos Via Bosco ang. Via Grandi, 148	pizzeria tel. 836.552965	€€, AIC www.araknosrestaurant.it
Villa Silmona Contrada Tre Masserie	B&B tel. 3284182714	AIC www.villasilmona.it
	ARPINOVA-FOGGIA	
Posta Bassi Via Manfredonia, km 196,200 Notes: DS pizza point. Closed Mondays.	agritourism, pizzeria tel. 0881700155	AIC www.postabassi.it
	ASCOLI SATRIANO	
Il Tramonto Via Stazione, 20 Notes: Closed Mondays.	restaurant, pizzeria tel. 0885662393	€, AIC
	AVETRANA	
Il Balconcino Via Piave, 13	restaurant, pizzeria tel. 389.81737	€, AIC www.ilbalconcino2011.it
Masseria La Grottella Via Ariosto, 42 Notes: Closed Mondays.	restaurant reception hall tel. 0999707452	AIC
	BARLETTA	
Al Duomo Via Duomo, 29 Notes: Closed Wednesdays.	restaurant, pizzeria tel. 0883332816	€€€€, AIC
Al Pomodorino Via Cialdini, 47	pizzeria tel. 0883880273	€€ - €€€, AIC www.ilpomodorino.it
Antica Cucina Via Milano, 73	restaurant tel. 088352171	AIC

Bagno 27	restaurant	€€, AIC
Vicinale delle Salinelle, 24/26 - Lit. di Ponente	tel. 883.510197	www.bagno27.com

Calici di Bacco	restaurant, pizzeria	€€, AIC
Via Cialdini, 7	tel. 883.765858	www.calicidibacco.it

Crèpes à Porter	crêperie	€, AIC
Via Duomo, 3	tel. 3497190791	

Dolce Amore	gelato (€, AIC)	Via Imbriani, 10

Ginevra	restaurant	€€€-€€€€, AIC
Litoranea di Ponente	tel. 0883532262	www.ristoranteginevra.com
Notes: Closed Mondays.		

Guardami	pizzeria	AIC
V.le Regina Elena, 33	tel. 883.347177	

Il Brigantino	restaurant, pizzeria	€€€-€€€€, AIC
V.le Regina Elena, 19	tel. 0883533345	

Madness Caffè	bar	€€, AIC
C.so Garibaldi, 131	tel. 883.885805	

Nuovo Centaro	restaurant, pizzeria	€€, AIC
Via Andria, 30	tel. 330902812	
Notes: Closed Wednesdays.		

Public House Clarence	pizzeria	AIC
Via Cialdini, 8	tel. 883.891393	www.publichouseclarence.it

Taverna Brancaleone	osteria	€€€€, AIC
Via Antonio di Gilio, 4	tel. 0883390622	

Tenuta San Francesco	hotel, restaurant	AIC
S.S. 16 Km 736	tel. 883.639001	www.tenutasanfrancesco.it

Veleno Fish Restorart	restaurant	€€€€, AIC
Via Cialdini, 21	tel. 0883532880	
Notes: Closed Wednesdays.		

BISCEGLIE

Borgo Antico	pizzeria	€, AIC
Via La Marina, 49	tel. 3474144322	

Casale San Nicola	hotel, restaurant	AIC
Carrara Reddito La Notte	tel. 80.3961901	www.casalesannicola.it

Fermata Facoltativa	pizzeria	€, AIC
Carrara Le Coppe, 2	tel. 0803986055	
Notes: Closed Mondays.		

Gelat. Cavour	gelato (€, AIC)	Via Cavour, 53/55

Il Gelatiere	gelato (€, AIC)	Via G. Bovio, 67/69

La Fontana	pizzeria	€, AIC
P.zza Vittorio Emanuele, 27	tel. 3478851430	
Notes: Closed Mondays.		

La Piccola Botte	trattoria, pizzeria	€€-€€€, AIC
Via G. Bovio, 200	tel. 0803922627	

BITONTO

Arcobaleno	pizzeria	AIC
Via Dante, 43	tel. 082919099	

Garden Plaza
Via Abbaticchio, 2/6
Notes: Closed Mondays.

restaurant, pizzeria
tel. 0809903180

€-€€€, AIC

Gizero
Via Carlo Rosa, 12,14,16

restaurant, pizzeria
tel. 0802473798

€€, AIC

La Dolce Vita
Via Togliatti, 106

restaurant, pizzeria
tel. 0803718509

€-€€€, AIC

Lo Spuntino
Via G. Matteotti, 176

pizzeria
tel. 80.3752422

€€, AIC

BITRITTO

Petit Roy
C.so Mazzini, 34

pizzeria
tel. 080631339

€€, AIC

BRINDISI

Forum Cafè
Via Lanzillotti, 3 c/o Tribunale

bar
tel. 831.435413

€, AIC

Ge Yo'
C.so umberto, 8

ice cream, crêpes
tel. 831.560406

€, AIC

Gruit
Via Carmine, 120

restaurant, pizzeria
tel. 831.56278

€-€€€, AIC
www.gruit.it

Il Botteghino
C.so Roma, 35

pizzeria
tel. 831.529962

€€, AIC

Penny
Via S. Francesco, 5

restaurant
tel. 0831563013

€€€€, AIC

CAGNANO VARANO

Villaggio 5 Stelle-Garga no Club   resort
C.da Pagliai dei Comb.ti, km 34.500 tel. 884.917583

AIC

CANOSA DI PUGLIA

Twins
Via Lavello, 42

restaurant, pizzeria
tel. 883.6621

AIC

CAPRARICA DI LECCE

Masseria Stali
Via Cisterna Vecchia

agritourism
tel. 349.7439463

AIC

CARMIANO

Salento
Via Veglie, 16

pizzeria
tel. 327.3367745

AIC

CAROSINO

Osteria del Pero
Via Roma

osteria
tel. 99.5925371

€€, AIC

CAROVIGNO

Il Timone
Via dei Tamerici s.n

hotel, restaurant
tel. 0831987900

€€€€, AIC
www.hoteltimone.it

Isola Verde
C.da Morandi, 9

hotel, restaurant, pizzeria
tel. 0831990140

€€, AIC

Riva Marina Resort
Via della Pineta loc. Specchiolla

village, restaurant
tel. 0831095700

€€€-€€€€, AIC
www.rivamarinaresort.it

Drying Clothes (M. Roglieri)

CARPIGNANO SALENTINO

Hotel Le Muse hotel, restaurant AIC
Pr.le 212 Carpignano S.-Cursi tel. 836.580001

CASAMASSIMA

Rossopomod oro c/o Centro Comm. Auchan pizzeria €€, AIC
Via Noicattaro tel. 80.4578335

CASARANO

Araknos pizzeria €€, AIC
Via Nardò, 22 tel. 320.8439913

CASSANO DELLE MURGE

Come una Volta restaurant, pizzeria €-€€€, AIC
Via Mellitto c.da Parete tel. 3296571959
Notes: Closed Mondays, and Tuesdays at lunch.

CASTELLANA GROTTE

Il Piatto Fumante restaurant, pizzeria €€-€€€, AIC
SS.237 per Monopoli, km.11 tel. 0804965630 www.ilpiattofumante.it
Notes: Closed Tuesdays.

Park Hotel La Grave hotel, restaurant, reception hall €€€-€€€€, AIC
S.C. Ferrone, 6 tel. 0804965443
Notes: Closed Mondays.

Villa Angela B&B AIC
Via Vecchia Conversano, 14 tel. 0804967421

CASTELLANETA MARINA

Alborea resort AIC
S.S. 106 Km 466 tel. 99.8201

Bar Europa pizzeria(€, AIC) Via Mare dei Vapori, 1

Calanè S.S. 106 Km 466	resort tel. 99.8201	AIC
Il Valentino S.S. 106 Km 466	resort tel. 99.8201	AIC
Kalidria S.S. 106 Km 466	resort tel. 99.8201	AIC
Ticho's Lungomare Eroi del Mare	hotel, restaurant tel. 99.8430815	AIC

CASTRO

Antico Murisciu Via Luigi Schifano, 78	B&B tel. 349.0879332	AIC

CASTRO MARINA

Panoramico Via Panoramica, 100	hotel, restaurant, reception hall tel. 0836943007	€€€-€€€€, AIC

CEGLIE MESSAPICA

Caelia C.da Circiello	B&B tel. 0831380977	AIC
Montevicoli V.le Aldo Moro, 64	restaurant, pizzeria tel. 0831381323	€€, AIC www.montevicoli.it
Tre Trulli C.da Montevicoli, 115	hotel, restaurant tel. 831.381311	AIC

CELLAMARE

L'Antico Arco C.so Roma, 31	pizzeria tel. 80.465628	€-€€, AIC

CERIGNOLA

Al Caminetto Contrada Quarto, 5	restaurant, pizzeria tel. 0885418488	€-€€, AIC
Hotel Il Quadrifoglio S.P. 143 Km 0.600	hotel, restaurant tel. 885.424154	AIC www.ilquadrifogliohotel.it
Villa Demetra S.S. 16, 18	B&B tel. 885.418988	AIC www.villademetra.it

CISTERNINO

Désirée C.da Sisto, 18	restaurant, pizzeria tel. 0804317760	€€€, AIC www.ristorantedesiree.com
Gluten Free Shop P.zza Marconi, 9	bar, tavola calda tel. 80.4446857	€-€€, AIC
Lo Smeraldo C.da Don Peppe Sole, 7	hotel, restaurant tel. 80.4448044	AIC www.hotellosmeraldo.com

CONVERSANO

Dalis Pizza & Wine Via Palmiro Togliatti, 47	pizzeria tel. 0804950228	€, AIC
Il Sapore Perfetto Via Machiavelli, 27	pizzeria/restaurant tel. 0804956353	€, AIC www.ilsaporeperfetto.it
Savì Via S. Giacomo, 26/28	crêperie tel. 0804957140	€, AIC www.savicreperia.it

CORATO

Caffè Duomo — gelato (€, AIC) — Via Duomo, 107

New Palace Sempione
Via Ruvo, 101
restaurant, pizzeria
tel. 360.931217
AIC
www.newpalacesempione.it

Parco Serrone
Via S. Magno, 4
hotel
tel. 0808984441
AIC
www.hotelparcoserrone.com

CORIGLIANO D'OTRANTO

Pappa & Ciccia
Via Roma, 35
pizzeria
tel. 0836320545
€, AIC

CRISPIANO

Al Borgo Antico
Via Paisiello, 34
B&B, restaurant
tel. 099611460
AIC

Saracino
C.so Umberto, 207
restaurant/pizzeria
tel. 099611455
€ - €€, AIC

Tutto Buono
Via Monte Calvario, 89
pizzeria
tel. 340.3666203
€ - €€, AIC
www.tuttobuono.it

CURSI

Alogne
Via Alogne, 4
restaurant
tel. 836.332975
AIC

Central Bar — gelato (€, AIC) — P.zza Pio XII, 13

CUTROFIANO

Sangiorgio Resort
Via prov.le Noha-Collepasso
hotel, restaurant
tel. 0836542848
€€€€, AIC
www.sangiorgioresort.it

ERCHIE

Antica Osteria
Via Oria
restaurant, pizzeria
tel. 3477075097
€€, AIC

Da Lucio (sede invernale)
Via Roma, 36
pizzeria
tel. 3457956628
€, AIC

FOGGIA

Al Celone
Via S. Severo Km 4
agritourism
tel. 881.206903
€€-€€€, AIC
www.alcelone.it

Al Primo Piano
Via P. Scrocco, 27
restaurant
tel. 0881708672
€€-€€€, AIC

Alta Marea
Via Napoli, Km.28,00
restaurant, reception hall
tel. 0881310477
€€€€, AIC

Corte Corona
Via degli Aviatori km.3
restaurant
tel. 0881612378
€-€€€€, AIC

Funghi e Tartufi della Puglia
Via Monfalcone, 8/12
restaurant
tel. 0881776183
€€€€, AIC

La Locanda di Hansel
Via A.Ricci,59
restaurant
tel. 0881773871
€€, AIC

Le Due Palme
V.le Fortore, 69
pizzeria
tel. 0881725716
€, AIC

Lo Scrigno
Via XXV Aprile, 22
restaurant
tel. 881.708404
AIC

Le amiche a cena (M. Roglieri)

Osteria La Giara Via Saverio Altamura, 34	osteria tel. 881.20692	AIC
Pino Giorgio Via Delli Carri, 17/21	restaurant, pizzeria tel. 0881709890	€, AIC
Pizzeria del Parco Via Rovelli, 2	pizzeria tel. 328.2752967	€-€€, AIC
Villa dei Gourmets Trav.Viale Virgilio	hotel, restaurant, pizzeria tel. 0881632815	€€€-€€€€, AIC
Gabrielino Gelaterie Artigiane	gelato (€-€€, AIC)	C.so Garibaldi, 119
Gelateria Gabrielino	gelato (€-€€, AIC)	P.zza Umberto Giordano, 65
Gelateria Naturale	gelato (€-€€, AIC)	P.zza Italia, 7

FRANCAVILLA FONTANA

La Buona Luna Via Vittorio Alfieri, 23	restaurant, pizzeria tel. 3936732455	AIC

GAGLIANO DEL CAPO

Il Carpaccio P.zza Falcone e Borsellino s.n.	pizzeria tel. 0833547174	€, AIC

GALATINA

Gelateria Eros	gelato (€-€€, AIC)	P.zza S. Pietro, 9
Il Covo della Taranta C.so Garibaldi, 13	pizzeria tel. 3299842820	€, AIC
La Campina te Don Paulu Via Carlo Alberto dalla Chiesa	agritourism tel. 3805065970	€€, AIC
Malibu' Via Largo Tevere, 24	pizzeria tel. 3341596819	€, AIC
Sole e Luna Via Roma,11	trattoria tel. 836.567268	AIC

GALLIPOLI

Eskada
Via Filomarini, 7
pizzeria
tel. 3479105669
€, AIC
www.eskada.it

Il Buongustaio
Via Isabella d'Aragona, 32
trattoria
tel. 833.266343
AIC
www.facebook.com/pages/Il-Buongustaio-Trattoria-Gallipoli-LE/114917535190257

Venti e Mari
P.zza Fontana Greca, 3
B&B
tel. 3496222139
AIC
www.ventiemari.it

GINOSA

Biffy
Via Montescaglioso sn
restaurant, pizzeria
tel. 3470878277
€€, AIC

Valle Rita
C.da Girifalco
agritourism
tel. 0998271824
€€€-€€€€, AIC

GINOSA MARINA

Mille Pini
V.le Mille Pini, 1
hotel
tel. 99.8277001
AIC
www.millepinihotel.it

GIOIA DEL COLLE

Gioia di Pizza
Via Rossellini, 1
pizzeria
tel. 80.3483698
€€€, AIC
www.gioiadipizza.it

GIOVINAZZO

Al Cantagallo
Via Molfetta 18-20
pizzeria
tel. 0803941104
€, AIC

Al Porticciolo
Via L.re Marina Italiana, 1
Notes: Closed Tuesdays.
restaurant
tel. 0803948289
€€€, AIC

Fondaco de' Guelfi
S.S.16 - C.da Torre S.Matteo
agritourism
tel. 0803948008
€€€, AIC

Gran Bar Pugliese
P.zza Vitt. Emanuele, 62
gelato
tel. 080.3942056
€, AIC
www.granbarpugliese.com

Ice Cream Planet
gelato (€-€€, AIC)   P.zza Garibaldi (chiosco Villa C.le)

Riva del Sole
Via Devitofrancesco, 31/C
hotel, restaurant, pizzeria
tel. 0803943166
€€€, AIC

GRAVINA IN PUGLIA

Bar Le Rose
gelato (€-€€, AIC)
Via Potenza, 9

La Lanterna
Viale Orsini, 19
restaurant, pizzeria
tel. 0803264394
€, AIC

GROTTAGLIE

La Piccola Rudie
Via Aldo Moro, 21
restaurant, pizzeria
tel. 0995622823
€€, AIC

Pizza Fast
Via Calò, 49
pizzeria
tel. 0995639902
€, AIC

LECCE

Estia Banqueting
Via Leuca, 90
restaurant
tel. 0832289652
€€, AIC

Fiori di Zucca   trattoria   €€, AIC
Via Forlanini, 26   tel. 0832230313   www.trattoriafioridizucca.it

Grand Hotel Tiziano e Dei Congressi hotel, restaurant   AIC
Viale Porta D'Europa   tel. 832.272111   www.grandhoteltiziano.it

La Pagghiara   restaurant, pizzeria   AIC
Via Taranto, 64   tel. 832.240659   lapagghiara@libero.it

Osteria della Divina Provvidenza   restaurant   €€€, AIC
Via Rubichi, 4   tel. 08321792078

Ramses II   pizzeria   €€, AIC
Via Di Vaste, 80   tel. 832.305955   www.ristoranteramsesii.it

Sottozero   gelato (€-€€, AIC)
Via G. Giusti, 21   www.gelateriasottozero.com

Tentazioni   gelato (€-€€, AIC)   Viale Leopardi, 56

Volo Restaurant   restaurant   €€€, AIC
V.co della Saponea, 15   tel. 0832246815   www.volorestaurant.it

LESINA MARINA-GARGANO

Acapulco 2   restaurant, pizzeria   €-€€€, AIC
V.le Centrale, 49   tel. 0882995079

LEUCA

Osteria del Pardo   osteria   €€, AIC
Via Doppia Croce   tel. 0833758603   www.hosteriadelpardo.com
Notes: Closed at lunch.

LEVERANO

Stuzzicami Vero Salentino   restaurant, pizzeria   €€, AIC
Via Ancona s.n.   tel. 08321790143

LUCERA

Palazzo D'Auria Secondo   restaurant, pizzeria, B&B   €-€€€, AIC
P.zza Oberdan, 3   tel. 0881530446   www.palazzodauriasecondo.it

MAGLIE

Il Viandante   B&B   AIC
Via Dante Alighieri, 9   tel. 366.4350443   www.ilviandantebeb.it

Il Visitatore   B&B   AIC
Via Cav. Di Vitt. Veneto, 6   tel. 836.312672   www.ilvisitatore.it

La Cascina   restaurant, pizzeria   €€, AIC
Via S. Antonio Abate, 41   tel. 0836424712
Notes: Closed Mondays and at lunch.

MANDURIA

Gelateria Miola   gelato (€, AIC)   Via per Maruggio, 96

Lanternella Pub   restaurant, pizzeria   €-€€€€, AIC
Corte Paradiso, 2   tel. 0999711354   www.lanternellapub.it

Relais Reggia Domizia   restaurant   AIC
SS 7 Manduria-Sava c.da Pozzo Capo   tel. 0999745111

MANFREDONIA

Da Tommasino   gelato (€, AIC)   V.le dell'Arcangelo

Regio Hotel Manfredi
S.P. 58 Km.12

hotel
tel. 0884530122

AIC
www.regiohotel.it

MARGHERITA DI SAVOIA

Canneto Beach 2
Via Amoroso, 11

restaurant, pizzeria, wine bar, B&B   €€€€, AIC
tel. 883.651091   www.ristorantecannetobeach2.com

Grande Hotel Terme
C.so Garibaldi, 1

hotel, restaurant
tel. 0883656888

€€€€, AIC

MARTINA FRANCA

Al Focolare
Via Pergolesi, 66

pizzeria
tel. 0804838762

€, AIC

La Rotonda
Villa Comunale Garibaldi

restaurant/pizzeria
tel. 0804807052

€€ - €€€€, AIC

Villa Carmine
Villa Carmine s.n.

restaurant, pizzeria
tel. 0804838910

€-€€€€, AIC

MASSAFRA

L'Orsa Maggiore
Via Cirillo, 19

restaurant, pizzeria
tel. 0998801229

€€, AIC

MATINO

Lu Riale
Via San Michele, 7

pizzeria
tel. 3382857252

€, AIC

MATTINATA

Gabrielino
Via Garibaldi, 3

gelato
tel. 884.559444

€, AIC
www.gabrielino.it

Hotel Ristorante Apeneste
P.zza Turati, 3

hotel, restaurant
tel. 884.550743

AIC
www.hotelapeneste.it

MINERVINO

Masseria Barbera
S.P.le 230 km. 5,850

agritourism
tel. 8'083692095

€€€€, AIC
www.masseriabarbera.it

MINERVINO MURGE

La Tradizione Cucina Casalinga
Via Imbriani, 11/13

restaurant
tel. 0883691690

€€€, AIC
www.osterialatradizione.net

MODUGNO

De Amicis
P.zza De Amicis

restaurant, pizzeria
tel. 0804037930

€-€€€€, AIC

De Gustibus
Via Sanremo, 14

pizzeria
tel. 80.5320676

€, AIC

MOLA DI BARI

Dolcevoglia

gelato (€, AIC)

Via C. Colombo, 42

Le Case di Sottovento
Via di Vagno, 63-69

B&B
tel. 0804741886

AIC
www.lecasedisottovento.it

MOLFETTA

Antica Gelat. Cipriani

gelato (€, AIC)

Banchina S. Domenic, 55

Notes: They also have crêpes. Closed Thursdays.

Bufi
Via Vitt. Emanuele,15-17

restaurant
tel. 0803971597

€€€€, AIC

Dentro le Mura C.so Dante, 42	pizzera, trattoria tel. 80.3349989	€€€-€€€€, AIC www.dentrolemura.com
I Monelli Via Madonna dei Martiri, 108	pizzeria tel. 0809648792	€, AIC www.pizzeriaimonelli.it
Il Vecchio Gazebo Via Marconi, 18	restaurant, pizzeria tel. 0803344877	€-€€€, AIC
Melficta P.zza G. Garibaldi, 49	pizzeria/restaurant tel. 0803358191	€, AIC
Mezzopieno C.so Dante, 106	restaurant, pizzeria tel. 80.334109	€-€€, AIC

MONOPOLI

A Crepétt Via Caporale Contento, 2/f	sandwich shop tel. 0802470353	€, AIC
Bar della Stazione L.go Stazione	pizzeria, bar tel. 80.9306032	€-€€, AIC
Delicatesse Via Marina del Mondo	restaurant, pizzeria tel. 0804107238	€, AIC
Hakuna Matata (ex Upendi) Via Rocco Scotellaro, 8/10 Notes: Closed Tuesdays.	osteria, pizzeria tel. 0802373911	€, AIC
Il Guazzetto Via dell'Erba 39/41	restaurant tel. 0804107175	€€€, AIC
L'Abbraccio di Morfeo Via Lepanto, 101	B&B tel. 080'08872867	AIC
Oltremare via Fracanzano,1	restaurant, pizzeria tel. 80.937186	AIC
San Domenico Via San Domenico	trattoria tel. 080937192	€€-€€€, AIC
Victorian Pub C.da Vagone, 345	restaurant, pizzeria tel. 0806901838	€, AIC
Yogomania Notes: They also have crêpes.	gelato (€, AIC)	Via Rattazzi, 1

MONTERONI DI LECCE

Lo Scacciapensieri Via A. De Gasperi	hotel, restaurant tel. 0832321884	€€, AIC

MOTTOLA

Pizza Taxi Via F.lli Bandiera, 65	pizzeria tel. 99.886301	€€, AIC
Villa Petruscio Via S. Allende,158	reception hall tel. 0998866214	€€€€, AIC

NOCI

Miramonte Party Str. Prov.le per Castellaneta, km 1 Notes: Closed Mondays.	restaurant tel. 0804978005	€€€€, AIC www.miramonteparty.com

Luigi the Pizza Guy Makes the Best GF Pizza

NOICATTARO

Cremeria L'Arca
gelato (€, AIC)
Via P. Nenni, 16/5

ORSARA DI PUGLIA

Nuova Sala Paradiso
Via Piano Paradiso, s.n.
restaurant
tel. 0881964763
€€€€, AIC

ORTANOVA

Hotel Novelli
S.S.16 Km 695+132
restaurant, pizzeria, bar
tel. 885.787432
AIC
www.hotelresortnovelli.com

OSTUNI

Cremeria alla Scala
Piaz.ta don Elio Antelmi, 17
gelato
tel. 338.8221451
€, AIC
www.cremeriaallascala.com

Hostaria San Filippo
C.so Vitt. Emanuele, 218
restaurant
tel. 0831334546
€€-€€€, AIC

La Dolce Vita
gelato (€, AIC)
Via Cav. Di Vitt. Veneto, 15

Piccolo Hotel Villa Rosa
Via per Martina Franca, km.1
B&B
tel. 0831332615
AIC
www.villarosaostuni.it

OSTUNI MARINA

Masseria S. Lucia
S.S. 379 Km. 23,5
hotel, restaurant
tel. 08313560
€€€€, AIC

PALESE

Mychef Aeroporto Civile di Bari Palese mychef
tel. 80.5308201
www.mychef.it
€, AIC

PALMARIGGI

Sciarabba'
Via Roma, 45
restaurant, pizzeria
tel. 0836354497
€-€€€, AIC

PARABITA

Allo Scrigno
Via Salentina, 113

B&B
tel. 0833509947

AIC
www.salentiamoci.it

Bakayokò
Via Isonzo, 2

pizzeria pub
tel. 08331828283

€€, AIC
www.bakayoko.it

Le Veneri
Via Coltura, 70

restaurant
tel. 3453363901

€€-€€€, AIC

Lo Sturno
Via Immacolata, 2

trattoria
tel. 0833593477

€€, AIC

Prima o poi
Via G.ni Vinci, 62

B&B, restaurant, pizzeria
tel. 0833595006

€, AIC

PATÙ

Aquilino
Vico Galliani, 15a

B&B
tel. 3489288087

AIC
www.aquilino.it

PESCHICI

Club Village Maritalia
Baia di Peschici
Notes: Closed October-April.

hotel
tel. 0884963399

€-€€, AIC

Gelateria Pinagel

gelato (€, AIC)

C.so umberto I, 7

Gusmay Resort
Loc. Manacore

hotel
tel. 0884911016

€-€€, AIC

PIETRA MONTECORVINO

Casa Salcone
Via Canalicchio, 28

restaurant/pizzeria
tel. 0881555743

€ - €€, AIC
www.casalcone.com

Marsavè

gelato (€, AIC)

P.zza Martiri del Terrorismo, 16

POLIGNANO A MARE

Casa Dorsi
Via Porto, 58

B&B
tel. 0804251168

AIC
www.casadorsi.com

Donna Gina
Via Cala Porto, 7/9

restaurant
tel. 0804240914

€€€€, AIC
www.donnagina.it

Irvi's Caffè

gelato (€, AIC)

Via Martiri di Dogali, 62

L'Arciere
Via Cosimo Basile, 18

bar
tel. 338.9742217

€, AIC

Petali Rosa
P.zza S. Antonio

B&B
tel. 80.4249478

AIC
www.bebpetalirosa.it

Specchia Sant'Oronzo
Contrada Fratta
Notes: Closed Wednesdays.

restaurant, pizzeria
tel. 0804240386

AIC
www.specchiasantoronzo.it

Villa degli Aranci
Via Caduti di tutte le Guerre, 5/7

restaurant, pizzeria
tel. 0804249161

AIC

Vingtsept Relais & Suite
Via G. Matteotti, 29

B&B
tel. 80.4241361

AIC
www.vingt-sept.it

PORTO CESAREO

Isola Lo Scoglio
P.zza N. Sauro

restaurant
tel. 833.569079

AIC
www.isolaloscoglio.it

PRESICCE

Antico Borgo
P.zza del Popolo, 32
Notes: Closed Tuesdays.
pizzeria
tel. 0833722124
€-€€, AIC

Corte Sant'Andrea
Via Matteotti, 9/I
B&B
tel. 3498321729
AIC
www.corteterrasignura.it

Corte Terra Signura
Via Matteotti, 68
B&B
tel. 3283731355
AIC
www.corteterrasignura.it

PULSANO

Il Grillo
V.le dei Micenei - Lit. Salentina
hotel, restaurant
tel. 0995333925
€€€€, AIC

Le Arcate
Via Paisiello, 31
pizzera, trattoria
tel. 99.5338265
€€, AIC

PUTIGNANO

Agribiotrulli
C.da Madonna del Rosario, 58
agritourism
tel. 3206918541
€€, AIC
www.agribiotrulli.it

Caffè Verdi
gelato (€, AIC)
Via Giuseppe Verdi, 11

Dimora Lama d'Inferno
Sc. Lama d'Inferno, 13
B&B
tel. 80.4031635
AIC
www.dimoralamadinferno.it

Premiata Pizzeria
Via Carlo Rosselli, 32
restaurant, pizzeria
tel. 0804058523
€€, AIC

RODI GARGANICO

Park H. Villa Americana
Via Grossi, 23
hotel, restaurant
tel. 884.96639
AIC
www.villaamericana.it

RUFFANO

Bar Cardigliano
gelato (€, AIC)
Via De Gasperi, 1

RUTIGLIANO

Il Mulino
Via Carlo Rosselli, 32
pizzeria
tel. 0804769029
€, AIC
www.ilmulinopizzeria.it

Lama San Giorgio
Str. Prov.le 84 Rutigliano/Adelfia
agritourism, restaurant, hotel
tel. 0804761609
€€€, AIC
www.lamasangiorgio.it

L'Arte del Gelo
gelato (€, AIC)
C.so Mazzini, 5

RUVO DI PUGLIA

Crem. American Bar
gelato (€, AIC)
P.zza Bovio, 15

U.p.e.p.i.d.d.e.
Vico S.Agnese, 2
restaurant
tel. 0803613879
€€€, AIC

S. CATERINA DI NARDÒ

Desideria
gelato (€, AIC)
Via Mastro Gioffreda

S. FERDINANDO DI PUGLIA

San Cassano
Via Papa Giovanni XXIII, 15
pizzeria
tel. 883.766178
€-€€, AIC

S.GIOVANNI ROTONDO

Hotel Corona
Via Anna Freud, 5
hotel, restaurant
tel. 882.457873
AIC
www.hotelcorona.fg.it

Hotel le Cese C.da Matine	hotel, restaurant tel. 0882450972	€€€€, AIC
Hotel Sollievo Via S. Gennaro, 4	hotel, restaurant tel. 0882456134	€€, AIC www.hotelsollievo.it
Villa Xenia Via Luigi Pinto,1	B&B tel. 882.454981	AIC www.hotelxenia.com

S.GIORGIO JONICO

Da Boe   sandwich shop   €, AIC
Via Principe di Piemonte, 180   tel. 99.4008363
www.facebook.com/pages/Da-Boe-PucciaPizza/1481614212081335?hc_location=timeline

| **Villaggio S.Giovanni**
Contrada S. Giovanni | hotel, restaurant, reception hall
tel. 0995900606 | €€€€, AIC |

S.SEVERO

| **Il Carbonaio**
Via Santa Lucia, 68 | restaurant, pizzeria
tel. 0882331415 | €-€€€, AIC |

SAN DONACI

| **da Peppino**
Via Pastrengo, 23 | restaurant, pizzeria
tel. 831.634084 | €€, AIC
www.dapeppino.vpsite.it |
| **Gargantù**
Via Giulio Cesare, 4 | pizzeria
tel. 3286815776 | €, AIC |

SAN PIETRO IN LAMA

| **Cantina Don Carlo**
Via S. Antonio, 10 | restaurant, pizzeria
tel. 08322632'099 | €€€, AIC |

S. PIETRO IN BEVAGNA-MANDURIA

| **Hotel dei Bizantini**
Via Borraco, 224 | hotel, restaurant
tel. 0999729823 | €€€-€€€€, AIC |

S. SEVERO

| **Ristore**
Via Togliatti, 54 | restaurant/pizzeria
tel. 0882228280 | €€€, AIC |

S. VITO DEI NORMANNI

Cheer's Pub Cafè Via Isonzo, 6	pub tel. 3383295901	€, AIC
Hotel Resort dei Normanni SS. 16 Km 2,7	hotel, restaurant tel. 0831951884	AIC www.hoteldeinormanni.it
Il Vulcano Via Carovigno, 49	pizzeria tel. 333.9792436	€-€€, AIC www.ristoranteilvulcano.com

SANTA MARIA AL BAGNO

Il Covo degli Orsini   gelato (€, AIC)   P.zza Nardò, 21

SANTERAMO IN COLLE

| **Green Elf**
Via Fausto Coppi, 16 | pizzeria pub
tel. 3387019661 | €, AIC |

SAVELLETRI DI FASANO

| **Il Veliero**
P.zza del Porto, 1
Notes: Closed Tuesdays. | restaurant
tel. 0804820022 | €€€-€€€€, AIC |

SELVA DI FASANO

Poggio del Sole restaurant €€€€, AIC
V.le del Minareto, 51 tel. 0804331386

SOLETO

Caffetteria Orsini gelato €, AIC
Via Orsini, 1 tel. 836.663802 www.caffetteriaorsini.it

SQUINZANO

Delizie gelato (€, AIC) Via A. Diaz, 167

SUPERSANO

La Mezzaluna pizzeria €-€€, AIC
Via Vittorio Veneto, 27
Notes: Closed Monday-Wednesday. tel. 0833631687

TALSANO

H.Bel Sit/R.La Nuova Mandragora hotel, restaurant €€€, AIC
Via Mediterraneo, 111/a tel. 0997716362 www.lanuovamandragoraebelsit.com

L'Angolo Nascosto restaurant, pizzeria €€, AIC
C.so Vitt. Emanuele tel. 0997712220

Victory House Coffee gelato (€, AIC) V.le Europa, 121

TARANTO

Al Canale restaurant €€€€, AIC
Discesa Vasto tel. 0994764201

Al Faro hotel, restaurant €€€€, AIC
Via della Pineta 3/5 tel. 0994714444

Bar Pasticc. Principe gelato (€, AIC) Via De Cesare, 38
Gelateria del Ponte gelato (€, AIC) Via D'Aquino, 110

Marc'Aurelio restaurant, pizzeria €-€€€, AIC
Via Cavour, 17 tel. 0994527893

Pandoro L'angelo senza glutine e non pizzeria €€, AIC
Via Japigia, 25 a/b tel. 0997362440

TAVIANO

Irene Marchese B&B AIC
Via M. D'Azeglio, 14 tel. 833.911477 www.irenemarchese.it

Santa Lucia restaurant €€-€€€, AIC
Via Castelforte, 118 tel. 0833911388

TERLIZZI

Alighieri Eventi restaurant €€-€€€, AIC
C.so Dante Alighieri, 15 tel. 80.3514887 www.alighierieventi.it

TORRE A MARE

Miramare gelato (€, AIC) Via G. Leopardi, 54

TORRE CANNE DI FASANO

Villa Imperiale restaurant €€-€€€, AIC
C.da la Cordara-via del Procaccio tel. 3338643215

TORRE COLIMENA

Da Lucio (Sede estiva) pizzeria €€, AIC
Via dei Dentici tel. 0999718793

TORRE SAN GIOVANNI

L'Approdo
C.so Annibale, 68
restaurant, pizzeria
tel. 0833931872
€-€€, AIC
www.approdotrattoria.it

TORREMAGGIORE

La Tana
Via della Costituente, 140
pizzeria
tel. 0882381064
€, AIC

TRANI

Amadeus
Via Statuti Marittimi, 32/34
restaurant, pizzeria
tel. 0883956358
€€, AIC

Bar Gelat. Commercio
gelato (€, AIC)
C.so Vitt. Emanuele, 140

Bodeguita
Via Zanardelli, 27
pizzeria
tel. 0883954303
€, AIC

Donna Rosa
C.so Vitt. Emanuele, 138
pizzeria
tel. 0883764958
€, AIC

Il Melograno
Via Giovanni Bovio, 185
restaurant
tel. 0883486966
€€€€, AIC

Il Paese del Gelato
gelato (€, AIC)
Via S.Giorgio, 5

TREPUZZI

Tre Pozzi
Via P. Giovanni XXIII, 170
B&B
tel. 832.757375
AIC
www.bnbtrepozzi.it

TRICASE

I Fornelli di Teresa
Via Giuseppe Tartini, 34
pizzeria
tel. 833.770312
€-€€, AIC
www.ifornelliditeresa.it

TRIGGIANO

Beverly Hills
Via G. Fortunato, 21/a
pizzeria
tel. 0804688637
€, AIC

TROIA

Fattoria Giuntoli Azienda Agrituristica agritourism
C.da Cisternino
tel. 881.970154
AIC
www.fattoriagiuntoli.it

TUGLIE

Museo della Civiltà Contadina
Via Venturi, 30/32 -P.zzo Ducale
agritourism
€, AIC

TURI

Pizza e Crêpe Desirèe
Via Torino
pizzeria
tel. 80.4512933
€, AIC

VEGLIE

Labor. del Gelato Artigianale-Roxy gelato(€, AIC)
Trav. Di Via Isonzo s.n.

VIESTE

Bar Ruggieri
gelato (€, AIC)
C.so L. Fazzini, 89

Borgo Antico
Via Cesare Battisti, 11
restaurant, pizzeria
tel. 0884701377
€-€€, AIC

Box 19
Via S. Maria di Merino, 13
restaurant
tel. 0884705229
€€, AIC

Hotel degli Aranci
P.zza S. Maria delle Grazie, 10
hotel, restaurant
tel. 0884708557
€€€-€€€€, AIC

I Melograni e Vill. Baia degli Aranci hotel, restaurant   €€€-€€€€, AIC
Lungomare Europa, 48   tel. 0884701088

Le Diomedee   restaurant, pizzeria   €-€€, AIC
Loc. Pantano   tel. 0884706472
Notes: Closed October-April.

Maggiore D.A.   gelato (€, AIC)   Via S. Maria di Merino, 40

Spiaggia Lunga   village, restaurant   €€-€€€, AIC
Litoranea Vieste Peschici km. 7   tel. 0884706171
Notes: Closed October-April.

Villa Carla   B&B   AIC
C.da Intresiglio, 47   tel. 884.702783   www.villacarla.it

VILLA CASTELLI

Pazzi Per Pizza   pizzeria   €-€€, AIC
Via Ceglie, 130   tel. 3358009503

I Trulli

Agrigento (J. Kelly)

SICILIA
(AIC = participates in the Associazione Italiana Celiachia program)

ACI SANT'ANTONIO

Ke Bontà — bakery — €, AIC
Via Fleming C.da Colle del Gelsomino   tel. 095.2969488   www.kebonta.it

ACICASTELLO

Acido Lattico — pizzeria — €, AIC
Via Stazione, 32   tel. 0957111001

Il Timo/Sheraton Catania Hotel — hotel, restaurant — AIC
Via A. da Messina, 45   tel. 095.7114111   www.sheratoncatania.com

La Scogliera — restaurant — €€-€€€, AIC
Via A. Musco, 13/a   tel. 095494634

ACIREALE

Briciole Senza Glutine — bakery, gastropub, rotisserie — €, AIC
Via delle Terme, 7   tel. 339.7791357/342.7258216

La Caverna del Mastro Birraio — restaurant/pub — €€, AIC
Via Cristoforo Colombo, sn   tel. 0958035019   www.lacavernadelmastrobirraio.it

Le Quattro Stagioni — pizzeria — €, AIC
Via Marchese di S. Giuliano, 53/57   tel. 0957634196

ACITREZZA

Pellegrino — pizzeria — €-€€, AIC
P.zza Verga, 6-7   tel. 095276060

ACQUEDOLCI

La Cascina — restaurant, pizzeria — €€, AIC
C.da Oliveto   tel. 0941726193   www.ristorantelacascina.net

AGIRA

Fud Sud Group c/o Sicily Outlet Vill. restaurant/pizzeria   €€€ - €€€€, AIC
C.da Mandre Bianche   tel. 0935594044   www.fudsud.it

AGRIGENTO

Le Caprice   restaurant, pizzeria   €€€, AIC
Via Cavaleri Magazzeni   tel. 0922411364

Terra & Mare   trattoria   €€, AIC
P.zza Lena, 7   tel. 092225413

ALCAMO

G.F.D. di Impellizzeri (Gulliver)   restaurant, pizzeria   €€, AIC
C.da S. Gaetano, 1/a   tel. 092424012

AUGUSTA

Red Lions   pizzeria   €-€€, AIC
Lungomare Rossini   tel. 0931994086

AVOLA

La Scogliera   restaurant, pizzeria   AIC
Via Aldo Moro, 121   tel. 348.1494956   www.ristorantelascoglieradiavola.it

BAGHERIA

Dolce Gelato   gelato   €, AIC
Via Alcide De Gasperi, 61   tel. 334.3383808
www.gelateriapasticceriadolcegelato.blogspot.com

BARCELLONA POZZO DI GOTTO

Casa del Dolce   gelato, bar (€, AIC)   Via On. Giacomo Martino, 1

Napoli Mania   pizzeria   €€, AIC
Via Tenente Genovese, 47   tel. 90.9701301

BELPASSO

Feudo Delizia   restaurant   €€, AIC
C.da Segreta   tel. 095918950   www.ristorantefeudodelizia.it

BUONFORNELLO

Ron e Salvo   restaurant, pizzeria   AIC
S.S. 113 km 207   tel. 0918140159

CACCAMO

A' Castellana   restaurant, pizzeria   €€, AIC
P.zza dei Caduti, 2/3/4   tel. 0918148667   www.castellana.it

CALTAGIRONE

I Marchesi di S. Barbara   restaurant   €€€-€€€€, AIC
Via S. Bonaventura, 22   tel. 093322406

La Piazzetta   restaurant, pizzeria   AIC
Via Vespri, 20/a   tel. 093324178

CALTANISSETTA

Al Rustico   pizzeria   €€, AIC
Via Ten. Lilly Bennardo, 11   tel. 934.2335   www.pizzeriaalrustico.com

Al Vecchio Olmo   B&B   AIC
P.zza Marconi, 6   tel. 934.25376   www.bedebreakfastalvecchioolmo.com

Az. di Turismo Rur. Belvedere   agritourism   AIC
C.da Canicassè snc   tel. 0934568166

Il Bignè	gelato (€, AIC)	Via Calabria, 64/66
Le Fontanelle	agritourism, restaurant	€€, AIC
C.da Fontanelle	tel. 934.592437	
www.agriturismo.8k.com/cl/lefontanelle.htm		

M.B.	gelato (€, AIC)	Via E. Vassallo, 67/69
Panineria Calà	sandwich shop	€, AIC
P.zza Repubblica s.n	tel. 0934591278	
Totò e Peppino	restaurant, pizzeria	€, AIC
Via Piero Leone s.n.	tel. 0934555037	

CAMMARATA

S. Martino de Kamerata	restaurant, pizzeria	€€, AIC
Ugo La Malfa, 10	tel. 0922905572	www.ristorantesanmartino.it

CAMPOBELLO DI LICATA

La Madonnina	restaurant/pizzeria	€€, AIC
Via Edison, 162	tel. 0922870177	www.ristorantelamadonnina.com

CANICATTÌ

Pasticceria Termini	bar, tavola calda	€-€€, AIC
Via Pirandello, 24, 28, 30	tel. 0922851519	

CAPO D'ORLANDO

Il Torrente	restaurant, pizzeria	€, AIC
Via Torrente Forno, 54	tel. 0941901970	

CARLENTINI

Al Punto Giusto	bar	€-€€, AIC
S.S. 194 KM 18+830 dir. Ragusa	tel. 95.94467	

CASA SANTA - ERICE

F.lli Virzì	gelato, bakery	€, AIC
Via Madonna di Fatima, 181	tel. 923.566133	
L'Acquolina in Bocca	sandwich shop	€, AIC
Via Cosenza, 143	tel. 09231893633	

CASTELBUONO

Antico Baglio	restaurant, pizzeria	€, AIC
P.zza Ten. Schicchi, 3	tel. 0921679512	www.anticobaglio.it

Notes: DS pizza point. Closed Mondays and Tuesdays.

CASTELLAMMARE DEL GOLFO

Cozzeria Solemare	restaurant	AIC
Via Don Luigi Zangara,5	tel. 3924570282	www.ristorantecozzeria.it

CATANIA

Biscottissimi e Cannolissimi	bakery	€, AIC
P.zza Michelang elo Buonarroti, 21	tel. 348.9938446	
Catania City Center	B&B	AIC
Via Naumachia, 103	tel. 0957232924	www.cataniacitycenter.com
Delizie Libere	bakery, gastropub, rotisserie	€, AIC
Via Guzzardi, 6/a	tel. 95.432172	www.liberedelizie.it
La Smorfia	pizzeria, sandwich shop	€, AIC
Via Landolina, 50	tel. 95.2180605	www.lasmorfiapizzeria.it

Occhio al Glutine	bakery, rotisserie	€, AIC
Via Barriera del Bosco, 349/a	tel. 347.8818226	www.occhioalglutine.it
Primopiano	restaurant, pizzeria	€€-€€€, AIC
Via A. Decurtis, 8	tel. 095531028	
Stecco Natura	gelato (€, AIC)	Via Etnea, 105

CEFALÙ

Via Roma Vecchia	restaurant, pizzeria	€€, AIC
Via Carlo Ortolani Bordonaro, 76	tel. 921.820143	www.ristorante-viaromavecchia.it

COLLESANO

Casale Drinzi	restaurant, pizzeria	€€-€€€, AIC
C.da Drinzi	tel. 0921.664027	www.casaledrinzi.it

COMISO

Punto Caldo	bakery, rotisserie, gastropub	€, AIC
Via R. Livatino, 21	tel. 0932.721196	www.puntocaldo.it

ENNA

Bar Di Maggio	tavola calda	€, AIC
P.zza A. da Messina, 2/4	tel. 093529343	
Cucaracha	pub	€, AIC
Via G. Marconi, 16/18	tel. 3475179254	
Delizia Bar	bar, tavola calda	€, AIC
P.zza Duomo, 5/6	tel. 0935500549	

ENNA BASSA

Netser	restaurant, pizzeria	AIC
C.da Gentilomo	tel. 093520418	

ERICE

Ulisse	restaurant, pizzeria	€-€€€€, AIC
Via Chiaramonte, 45	tel. 0923869333	www.sitodiulisse
Notes: Closed Thursdays.		
Ulisse Camere	B&B	AIC
Via Santa Lucia, 2	tel. 0923860155	www.sitodiulisse.it

FAVARA

Gluten Bon	bakery, rotisserie	€, AIC
Via Francesco Crispi, 64	tel. 0922.31031	www.facebook.com/glutenbon.favara
Oneiratos	B&B	AIC
Via Soldato Schifano, 5	tel. 922.420163	www.oneiratos.it

FORZA D'AGRÒ

Agostiniana Hotel	hotel/restaurant	€€€€, AIC
Via A. De Gasperi, 54	tel. 0942721608	www.agostinianahotel.com

FURCI SICULO

Fragolina	B&B	AIC
Via 4 Novembre, 3	tel. 0942792951	www.bbfragolina.it

GALATI MAMERTINO

Fattoria Fabio	restaurant	€€, AIC
C.da Sciara	tel. 0941434042	

GIARRE

Le Cisterne
Via S. d'Acquisto, 10

restaurant, pizzeria
tel. 095965093

AIC

GRAVINA DI CATANIA

Al Nord Est
Piazza della Regione, 1

restaurant, pizzeria
tel. 095394797

€, AIC

GUARRATO

Agrit. Baglio Vultaggio
Via Federico dei Roberto

agritourism
tel. 0923864261

AIC

ITALA

Le Giare
Via S. Caterina, 17

hotel, restaurant
tel. 0909595006

€€-€€€, AIC
www.legiare.org

ITALA MARINA

Da Natale
Trav Prov.le, 15

restaurant, pizzeria
tel. 090953144

€, AIC

Gli Infiniti Sapori del Gluten Free bakery, gastropub
Via Roma, 82

tel. 090.8969412

€, AIC

LENTINI

Sicilia Nostra
Via Etnea

restaurant/pizzeria
tel. 0957038582

€ - €€, AIC
www.sicilianostra.it

MARAUSA

Villa Speranza
Via E. Rinaldi, 191

restaurant, pizzeria, B&B
tel. 0923843162

AIC
www.villasperanza.net

MARINA DI RAGUSA

Caffè delle Rose

gelato (€, AIC)

P.zza Duca degli Abruzzi, 25/26

L'Abbuffata
C.da Gaddimeli

restaurant, pizzeria
tel. 932.239521

AIC

MARSALA

Armony
C.da Ciappola, SS 115

restaurant, pizzeria
tel. 0923966551

AIC

Peppizza
C.da Strasatti, 921

restaurant, pizzeria
tel. 0923741403

€, AIC
www.peppizza.it

Sir Damian
Corso Gramsci 143

restaurant, pizzeria
tel. 092371168

€, AIC

MAZARA DEL VALLO

Baby Luna
Via Punica, 1

restaurant, pizzeria
tel. 0923948622

€-€€€, AIC

La Conchiglia
Via S. Quasimodo, 11
Notes: Closed Mondays.

restaurant, pizzeria
tel. 0923945333

AIC

Ariston Caffè

gelato (€, AIC)

C.so Vitt. Emanuele, 161

Casa Canalotto
Via La Loggia, 4

agritourism
tel. 09341900766

€€-€€€, AIC
www.casacanalotto.it

MAZZARINO

Pizzeria Ciancio   pizzeria   €, AIC
V.le della Resistenza, 17/a   tel. 3389991558

MERÌ

L'Arancin o D'oro   tavola calda   €, AIC
Via Dante, 182   tel. 90.9763233

MESSINA

Autogrill Tremestie ri Ovest   autogrill   €, AIC
A20 Messina - Palermo   tel. 90.730269

Gli Antenati   pizzeria/pub   €, AIC
C.so Cavour, 109   tel. 090672430   www.gliantenatipub.it

Le Altre Farine del Mulino   bakery, gastropub, rotisserie   €-€€, AIC
Via I° Settembre, 66   tel. 090.9431962

L'Ossidiana   restaurant   €€€€, AIC
Via dei Verdi, 7/11   tel. 090675899   www.gliantenatipub.it

Number One   restaurant, pizzeria   AIC
Via XXVII Luglio, 79   tel. 090774495   www.numberonemessina.it

Pizza Sprint   pizzeria   €, AIC
Via S. Licandro Piazza XXV Aprile   tel. 09059607

Rossopo modoro   pizzeria   €-€€, AIC
Via S.S. 114 km 4,700 vill. Pistunina   tel. 90.632831

MILAZZO
Sapori di Pane e Più   breads, sandwiches   €, AIC
Via Umberto I, 41 / Via Orsa Maggiore, 16   tel. 340.2494284/324.8286647

MILENA
Le Delizie   gelato (€, AIC)   Via Nazionale, 21/25

MIRABELLA IMBACCARI
Al Canale   bar, tavola calda   €, AIC
Via Roma, 122   tel. 933.991441

La Rondine   restaurant   AIC
C.da Gatta   tel. 933.991139   www.larondineristorante.com

MISILMERI
Alla Botte   pizzeria   €€€€, AIC
Via Mariano Scaduto, 14   tel. 91.873357   www.ristolaveranda.it

MISTERBIANCO
Funny Island c/o Parco Giochi   pizzeria   €, AIC
via Sonnino   tel. 095483676   www.funny-island.com

MODICA
Bye Spike   bakery, rotisserie   €, AIC
Via Fosso Tantillo Pirato, 1   tel. 0932.905525   www.byespike.it

Pietre Nere Resort   hotel, restaurant   AIC
Via Pietre Nere, 142   tel. 932.753051   www.pietrenereresort.it

MONREALE
Il Gelato della Piazzetta   gelato (€, AIC)   Via Roma, 91

Punto ICS Via Etnea, 93/95	## NICOLOSI restaurant, pizzeria tel. 95.7910362	€€, AIC www.pizzeriapuntoics.it
I Giardini di Noto C.da Fiumara	## NOTO restaurant, pizzeria tel. 0931839730	€, AIC
Donna Rosa Via Roma, 27	## OLIVERI restaurant, pizzeria tel. 941.314074	€-€€, AIC www.ristorantedonnarosa.it
Baglio Cantello Via Cantello, 2	## PACECO agritourism tel. 923.526529	AIC www.bagliocantello.it
La Corte di Eolo Via Antonino Uccello, 1	## PALAZZOLO ACREIDE restaurant tel. 0931883185	€€, AIC
Al Gelatone	## PALERMO gelato (€, AIC)	Via Autonom. Siciliana, 98
Aromatico Zero Glutine Via dell'Orsa Minore, 268 Via Trinacria, 40/42	bakery, rotisserie tel. 91.2511603 tel. 91.8873028	€, AIC
Don Rice via Giuseppe Pagano, 13	tavola calda tel. 91.507297	€, AIC
Duetto V.le Regione Siciliana, 710	restaurant, pizzeria tel. 091.590180/328.3342755	AIC
Extrò Cafè Via Terrasanta, 87	bar, pizzeria tel. 91.9801904	€, AIC www.extrocafe.com
Gabibbo Via Oreto, 351	restaurant, pizzeria tel. 0916476195	€, AIC www.pizzeriagabibbo.it
Gelateria Azzurra Via Messina Marine, 627	gelato tel. 91.6221182	€, AIC www.gelateriaazzurra.com
Gelato 2	gelato (€, AIC)	Via Alcide De Gasperi, 215
Il Fedino Via Mongerbin o, 13	restaurant, pizzeria www.ristorantepizzeriailfedino.it	AIC
Il Gelatiere	gelato(€, AIC)	Via C. Scobar, 47/49
Il Genio dei Sapori Via Gen. C. A. Dalla Chiesa	restaurant/pizzeria tel. 0917219260	€€, AIC
Il Marchese del Gatto Via Vincenzo di Marco, 3/a	bakery tel. 91.5081525	€, AIC www.ilmarchesedelgatto.com
King Via Briuccia, 24	trattoria, pizzeria tel. 091511098	€€, AIC
La Dolce Vita Via Giuseppe Giusti,17	restaurant, pizzeria tel. 91.300074	€€, AIC www.ladolcevitapalermo.it
La Gatta Mangiona Via Danimarca, 21/23	restaurant, pizzeria tel. 091.519188	€€€-€€€€, AIC www.lagattamangiona.net

L'Arte Bianca Via Giacinto Carini, 22/24	pizzeria tel. 91.670308	€€, AIC www.pizzerialartebianca.it
L'Aurora del Buon Gelato	gelato (€, AIC)	P.zza Tommaso Natale, 66
Naif Via Vann'Antò, 21	restaurant tel. 091346525	€, AIC www.ristorantenaif.it
Piccola Sicilia Via Tenente Giovanni Ingrao, 2	B&B tel. 091.320335	AIC www.piccolasicilia.it
Sesto Canto Via S. Oliva, 26	restaurant tel. 091324543	€€€-€€€€, AIC
Stancampiano Sabrina	gelato (€, AIC)	Via Aquileia, 60/62
Stecco Natura	gelato (€, AIC)	P.zza Castelnuo vo, 14
Trinkhaus Via S. Isidoro, 23/B	pizzeria tel. 0916731010	€-€€, AIC
Villa Costanza Via Pietro Bonanno, 42	restaurant, pizzeria tel. 91.547027	€-€€, AIC www.villacostanza.com
Zero Via Palmerino, 54/a	bakery, rotisserie, gastropub tel. 91.421221	€, AIC

PARTINICO

Villa Teresa C.da Garofalo	restaurant, pizzeria tel. 091908134	€, AIC

PATERNÒ

Antico Forno Verona Corso Italia, 42	bakery, rotisserie tel. 095.843343	€, AIC www.anticofornoverona.com
Capricci di Gola Piazzale Diritti Umani, 6/7	pizzeria tel. 3407296029	€, AIC

PEDARA

La Tettoia Corso Ara di Giove, 129	restaurant, pizzeria tel. 0957800988	€, AIC

PERGUSA-ENNA

Riviera Hotel Villaggio Pergusa	hotel, restaurant, pizzeria tel. 0935541267	€€, AIC www.hotelrivieraenna.it

PIRAINO

Borgo Murauto C.da Salinà Via Murauto	restaurant (vegan, vegetarian) tel. 0941.581235	€€, AIC www.borgomurauto.it

POLIZZI GENEROSA

U Funnacu Largo Regina Elisabetta, 31	pizzeria tel. 921.688119	€€, AIC www.ufunnacu.it

PORTO EMPEDOCLE

Talia Zucchero e Sale Via Malato, 11	creperie, sandwich shop tel. 366.9833938	€, AIC

POZZALLO

Mastro Pizza V.le Europa	pizzeria tel. 932.956763	€€, AIC www.pizzeriamastropiero.com

RAGUSA

Barbecue   restaurant   €€, AIC
Via Fanfulla da Lodi, 5   tel. 0'0932644963   www.cremiapasticceria.it

Borgo Monachella   B&B   AIC
C.da Monachella   tel. 333.4338523   www.borgomonachella.it

Cuccagna In...   restaurant, pizzeria   €, AIC
Via M. Rumor, 8   tel. 0932255469
Notes: Closed Mondays and month of August.

L'Abbuffata   restaurant, pizzeria   €€-€€€, AIC
C.da Gaddimeli   tel. 0932239521

Limoni di Sicilia (J. Kelly)

RODÌ MILICI

Da Tonino   restaurant, pizzeria   €€, AIC
Via Vittorio Emanuele Orlando, 114 tel. 090.9741358   www.ristorantedatonino.net

ROSOLINI

Rostipan   bakery, rotisserie   €, AIC
Via Manzoni, 184   tel. 0931.1883094   www.rostipan.it

Squillo da Vitaliano e Rosanna   pizzeria   €, AIC
Via Aldo Moro, 8   tel. 0931859994

S. PIER NICETO MARINA

Eurialo e Niso   restaurant, pizzeria   €€, AIC
C.da S. Biagio, 22   tel. 90.9910777   www.eurialoeniso.it

S. TERESA DI RIVA

Le Terrazze   restaurant/pizzeria   €€, AIC
Via Lungomare, 87   tel. 0942792981

S. VITO LO CAPO

Gardenia   hotel   AIC
Via Dante Alighieri, 3   tel. 0923972188

Le Plus Bon Miceli	gelato (€, AIC)	Via Savoia, 72
S. Vito Via S. Vito, 26	B&B tel. 0923.972215	AIC
Stecco Natura Via Savoia, 25	gelato tel. 923.972622	€, AIC www.stecconatura.it
Thaam Via Duca degli Abruzzi, 32 www.sanvitoweb.com/thaam/ristorante.htm	restaurant, B&B tel. 0923972836	€€€, AIC
Vento del Sud Via Duca degli Abruzzi, 183	hotel tel. 0923.621450	AIC www.hotelventodelsud.it

S.GIOVANNI GALERMO

Pizzeria Da Nunzio Via S. Giovanni Battista, 74/76	pizzeria tel. 95.420339	€€, AIC www.pizzeriadanunzio.altervista.org

S.GIOVANNI LA PUNTA FRAZ.TRAPP ETO

Bottega Gastrono mica Via Madonna delle Lacrime, 29	pizzeria, tavola calda tel. 95.8188962	€€, AIC

S.ALFIO

Case Perrotta Via Andronico, 2	restaurant, agri+G2961tourism, B&B tel. 095968928	€€€, AIC www.caseperrotta.it

SAN CATALDO

Mediterranea V.le Italia, 73	pizzeria tel. 0934571045	€, AIC

SANTA CATERINA VILLARMOSA

La Variante Via Aldisio, 52	pizzeria tel. 934.679843	€€, AIC

SANTA NINFA

Due Palme S.S. 119 Km.42,700	restaurant, pizzeria tel. 092461044	€€, AIC
Vecchio Casale Via Di Stefano Perez	pizzeria tel. 3476274967	€-€€, AIC
Pizzeria Diamante Via Nazionale, 103	tavola calda, pizzeria tel. 090.332768/346.3224249	€, AIC

SAPONARA MARITTIMA

SCIACCA

Hostaria del Vicolo Vicolo Sammaritano, 10	osteria tel. 092523071	€€€€, AIC

SCORDIA

Punto Zero Glutine Via Garibaldi, 161	bakery, rotisserie tel. 340.8284351	€, AIC

SELINUNTE DI CASTELVETRANO

Gelateria Mozart	gelato (€, AIC)	Zona Artigianale C.da Strasatto

SICULIANA

Sole Mediterraneo Millennium SNC Via Principe di Piemonte, 1	restaurant/pizzeria, resort tel. 0922815210	€€€, AIC www.solemediterraneo.it

SIRACUSA

Algilà
Via Vitt. Veneto, 93
hotel/restaurant
tel. 0931465186
€€€€, AIC
www.algila.it

Bar Milano
Via Giuseppe Di Natale, 16
pizzeria bar
tel. 093122457
€€, AIC

Celifree
Via Pietro Novelli, 55
bakery, rotisserie
tel. 931.442076
€, AIC

Don Chisciotte
Viale Teocrito, 69/A
pizzeria
tel. 093164324
€€, AIC

Gran Caffè del Duomo
Piazza Duomo, 18/19
restaurant, pizzeria
tel. 931.21544
€€, AIC

Mentirosa
Viale Scala Greca, 409
restaurant, pizzeria
tel. 931.75922
€€, AIC
www.facebook.com/PizzeriaPizzoleriaMentirosa

Neapolis
V.le Scala Greca, 67/h
B&B
tel. 393.5728619
AIC
www.neapolisbb.wix.com

Pizza d'Autore
Via Polibio, 84
pizzeria
tel. 09311852566
€, AIC

Pizzoleria Tica
Viale Tica, 96
pizzeria
tel. 931.413977
€, AIC

Stecco Natura
gelato (€, AIC)
Via Roma, 41

SORTINO

Nabila
Via Santa Sofia, 19
restaurant, pizzeria
tel. 093195395
AIC

TAORMINA

Licchio's Bar
P.zza S. Caterina, 7
bar, pizzeria
tel. 0942.625607
€€€€, AIC

Stecco Natura
gelato (€, AIC)
C.so Umberto, 229

TRABIA

La Tonnara
Largo Tonnara
hotel, restaurant, pizzeria
tel. 91.8146865
€€€, AIC
www.grandhotellatonnara.it

TRAPANI

C'è Pizza per Te
Via Vespri, 194/196
restaurant/pizzeria/sandwich shop
tel. 092328810
€, AIC
www.cepizzaperte.com

Che Pizza!
Via Riccardo Passaneto, 64
pizzeria
tel. 0923.26633/380.4731476
€, AIC

Da Peppe
P.zza Ciaccio Montaldo, 4
pizzeria
tel. 096899300
€, AIC

Duca di Castelmonte
Via Motisi, 3
agritourism
tel. 0923526139
AIC

Gelateria Gino
gelato (€, AIC)
P.zza Gen. Dalla Chiesa, 1

Gelatissimo
gelato (€, AIC)
Via Conte A. Pepoli, 172

Le Plus Bon Miceli
gelato (€, AIC)
Via Giuseppe Garibaldi , 35

TRECASTAGNI

Villa Carmen
Via Madonna dell'Indiriz zo, 64

B&B
tel. 95.7800587

AIC
www.bebvillacarmen.it

VALDINA

Poggio...del Tempo Perduto
Contrada S. Antonino

restaurant, pizzeria
tel. 0909977009

€, AIC

VILLABATE

Magie di Forno
Corso Vittorio Emanuele, 614

sandwich shop, rotisserie, bakery   €, AIC
tel. 327.3091541 www.facebook.com/MagieDiForno

VILLAGRAZIA DI CARINI

Don Guto 1975
Via Nazionale, 149

restaurant (Brazilian)
tel. 091.8674257/345.4240674

€€€, AIC

VILLASETA

La Trizzera
Via Fosse Ardeatine, 59

restaurant, pizzeria
tel. 0922512415

€, AIC

ZAFFERANA ETNEA

Aria dell'Etna
Via Nipitelli, 10

B&B
tel. 349.3162268

AIC
www.bebariadelletna.it

Esperia Palace Hotel
Via delle Ginestre, 27/d

hotel
tel. 95.7082335

AIC
www.esperiapalace.com

La Ginestra dell'Etna
Via delle Ginestre, 27/d

B&B
tel. 0957081302

AIC
www.ginestradelletna.it

Parco dei Principi
restaurant   €€€€, AIC
Via delle Ginestre, 1
tel. 0957082335
www.ristoranteparcodeiprincipi.it

Villa Mirador
restaurant   AIC
Via Zafferrana - Milo, 23
tel. 0957082890

Fish Market (J. Kelly)

Lovers (J.Kelly)

SARDINIA

ALGHERO

Aragon
Via Gramsci, 8
restaurant, pizzeria
tel. 0799731001
AIC

ARZACHENA

Corbezzolo
Piazzetta Fontana - Loc. Baja Sardinia
restaurant, pizzeria
tel. 078999893
€€-€€€, AIC
www.ristorantecorbezzolo.it

Hotel Citti
V.le Costa Smeralda, 197
hotel
tel. 078982662
€, AIC
www.hotelcitti.com

La Rocca
Loc. Pulicinu, box 1392
restaurant
tel. 789.933011
AIC
www.laroccaresort.com

ASSEMINI

Sapore Antico
Via Cagliari, 213
pizzeria
tel. 070940437
€, AIC

BADESI

Resort Le Dune
Loc.tà Li Junchi, snc
hotel
tel. 079610200
AIC

BORTIGIADAS

Golden Gate
SS 127 Km. 53
hotel, restaurant
tel. 079627174
€€, AIC
www.ristorantegoldegate.ory.it

BUDONI

La Volpe
Via Agamennone, 9 fraz. Taunanella

restaurant, pizzeria
tel. 0784837388

€-€€€, AIC

CAGLIARI

Antico Caffe
P.za Costituzione, 10
Notes: Notes: closed Tuesday.

restaurant
tel. 070658206

www.charmingsardinia.com

B&B Le Tartarughe
Via Marconi 41/A, Sinnai

B&B
tel. 070766253

www.letartarughe.net

Caesar's Hotel
Via S. Freud, 5

inn, reception hall
tel. 070340750

€€€€, AIC

da Rita
Via Palestrina, 94
Notes: Closed Mondays and at lunch.

pizzeria
tel. 0704980444

€, AIC

Dal Corsaro
Viale Regina Margherita 28

restaurant
tel. 070664318

€€€-€€€€
www.dalcorsaro.com

Notes: GF pasta with advance notice. English spoken. Reservations necessary.

Flora
Via Sassari, 45

restaurant, pizzeria
tel. 070664735

€€€, AIC
www.florasrl.com

Notes: Closed Sundays and the month of August.

Galleria 18
Viale La Playa, 18

pizzeria
tel. 070680377

€-€€, AIC

Notes: Closed Saturday at lunch and all day Sunday.

Su Gologone
Loc Su Gologone

hotel, restaurant
tel. 0784287512

€€€-€€€€
www.sugologone.it

Notes: Special celiac menu. GF breakfast. Reservations preferred.

Tore
Piazza Belly, 4

restaurant, pizzeria
tel. 3400092174

€, AIC

CANNIGIONE

Hotel Cala di Falco
Loc. Cala di Falco
www.hotelcaladifalco.com/sardinia/camere-2.html

hotel
tel. 0789899200

AIC

CASTELSARDO

Rocca'ja
Via Sedini

restaurant, pizzeria
tel. 079470164

AIC

CASTIADAS

Araxi 'e Mari
Località San Pietro snc

restaurant
tel. 70.995144

€€€-€€€€, AIC
www.araxiemari.it

Pizza Folle
Loc. Olia Speciosa

pizzeria
tel. 0'0709949091

€, AIC
www.pizza-folle.it

DORGALI

Il Querceto
Via La Marmora, 4

hotel/restaurant
tel. 078496509

€€€ - €€€€, AIC
www.ilquerceto.com

S'Adde
Via Concordia, 38

hotel, restaurant, pizzeria
tel. 078494412

€€, AIC
www.hotelsadde.it

IGLESIAS

Baddy's — pizzeria — €, AIC
Via Cappuccini, 16 — tel. 0781255029 — www.ristorantebaddys.it

LA CALETTA

L'Aragosta — hotel, restaurant — €€€-€€€€, AIC
Via Ciusa, 33 — tel. 0784810046 — www.laragostahotel.com

MAMOIADA

Da Mommo — pizzeria — €, AIC
C.so V. Emanuele, 82/a — tel. 078456444

MURAVERA

Vera Club Costa Rei — resort — AIC
Via delle Tuie snc — www.veratour.it

Vera Club Suneva — resort — AIC
Strada per Capo Ferrato sn — www.veratour.it

NUORO

Canne al Vento — restaurant — €€€-€€€€, AIC
Via Biasi, 159 — tel. 0784201762

Il Rifugio — restaurant — €€€, AIC
Via A. Mereu, 28/36 — tel. 0784232355 — www.trattoriarifugio.com

Tamatta — pizzeria — €-€€, AIC
c/o Centro Com.le Pratosardo — tel. 0784294147

OLBIA

Barbagia — restaurant
Via Galvani, 94 — tel. 078951640 — www.ristorantebarbagia.com
Notes: GF pasta. English spoken. Closed Wednesdays.

Caffetteria della Nonna — hotel, restaurant, bar — €€€€, AIC
Via Nazionale, 33 - Loc. Murta Maria — tel. 0789379025 — www.speraesole.it

Gallura — restaurant — €€€€
C.so Umberto, 145 — tel. 078924648

H. Mercure Olbia Hermaea — hotel/restaurant — €€€€
Via Puglie, snc — tel. 07891890067 — www.mercure.com

ORISTANO

Cocco e Dessi — restaurant — €-€€€
Via Tirso, 31 — tel. 0783300720 — www.coccoedessi.it
Notes: English spoken. Reservations essential.

Mariano IV palace hotel — hotel
Piazza Mariano, 50 — tel. 0783360101 — www.m4ph.isarose.net
Notes: GF breakfast. GF pasta. English spoken.

Trattoria Gino — restaurant — €€€-€€€€
Via Tirso, 13 — tel. 078371428

OROTELLI

S'Arzola — pizzeria — €, AIC
C.so Vittorio Emanuele, 82 — tel. 078479303 — www.pizzeriasarzola.com

ORTACESUS

Time's Café — pizzeria — €, AIC
Via Roma, 33 — tel. 0709804306

OZIERI

Terradoro hotel, restaurant, pizzeria AIC
Localitá Chilivani tel. 079758904 www.albergoristoranteterradoro.it
Notes: GFM.

PALAU

H. Cala di Lepre-Delphina Hotels hotel €€€, AIC
Loc. Cala di Lepre tel. 0789702142 www.delphinahotel.it
Notes: Closed October-April.

H. Capo d'Orso-Delphina Hotels hotel €€€€, AIC
Loc. Cala Capra tel. 0789902000 www.hotelcapodorso.com
Notes: Closed October-May. No GF pizza.

Hotel Altura hotel, restaurant €€€-€€€€
Porto Raphael www.hotelaltura.it
Notes: GF upon request.

Il Paguro restaurant €€€€, AIC
Loc. Cala Capra tel. 0789702036 www.delphina.it
Notes: Closed October-April.

PORTO CERVO

Cervo H. Costa Smeralda Resort hotel, restaurant, pizzeria €€€€, AIC
Piazzetta di Porto Cervo tel. 0789931111 www.sheraton.com/cervo

PORTO TORRES

Piazza Garibaldi restaurant, pizzeria AIC
Piazza Garibaldi, 13 tel. 079501570 www.piazzagaribaldiportotorres.it

PULA

Baia di Nora hotel, restaurant AIC
Loc. Su Gunventeddu tel. 0709245551 www.hotelbaiadinora.com
Notes: Closed November-March.

QUARTU SANT'ELENA

Colombo pizzeria €, AIC
Viale Colombo, 264 tel. 070820608
Notes: Closed Wednesdays.

S. TEODORO

Al Faro hotel, restaurant, pizzeria €€-€€€€, AIC
Via del Tirreno Spiaggia La Cinta tel. 0784865665 www.hotelalfaro.com

S. TERESA DI GALLURA

Resort Valle dell'Erica hotel/resort €€€€, AIC
Loc. Valle dell'Erica tel. 0789750020 www.hotelvalledellerica.com

SASSARI

Andreini restaurant €€€€
Via Arduino 45 tel. 079982098 www.ristoranteandreini.it
Notes: GF pasta. Reservations essential. English spoken.

Fainè Da Carlo pizzeria €, AIC
SP Sassari Argentiera, 193/A Loc. Bancali tel. 079309773

I 3 Leoni pizzeria €-€€, AIC
Loc. Bancal, 218 tel. 079308041

Tiffany restaurant, pizzeria €€-€€€, AIC
Via Carlo Felice, 33 tel. 079272434 www.ristorantetiffany.it

SIAMAGGIORE

Da Renzo restaurant €€€€, AIC
SS. 131 Km.99 tel. 078333685
Notes: Closed Sunday evenings and Mondays.

TEMPIO PAUSANIA

Bonvicino restaurant, pizzeria AIC
Loc. Bonvicini Ss127 Km 39, 900

Museum restaurant bar €, AIC
P.zza Gallura, 27 tel. 079671083
Notes: Closed Sundays.

Pausania Inn hotel, restaurant €€, AIC
S.S. 133 Km.1 tel. 079634037 www.hotelpausaniainn.com
Notes: Closed Tuesdays and at lunch.

TORPÈ

Sa Inza agritourism, B&B €€-€€€, AIC
Loc. Santeddu - via Milano, 5 tel. 3282579271 www.agriturismosainza.it

TRINITÀ D'AGULTU

Hotel Marinedda Thalasso & SPA hotel €€€€, AIC
Loc. Isola Rossa tel. 079694185 www.delphina.it

Hotel Relax Torreruja - Delphina Hotels hotel €€€€, AIC
Loc. Isola Rossa tel. 079694155 www.delphina.it

VILLASIMIUS

Chiccheria gelato €, AIC
Via Vittorio Emanuele II 2 tel. 331.5694256 www.chiccheria.com

Gli uccelli (D. Kraushaar)

TORINO, PIEDMONT, AND VALLE D'AOSTA
(AIC = participates in the Associazione Italiana Celiachia program)

TORINO

Al Grassi restaurant €€€€, AIC
Via Beaumont, 32/c corner of Via Grassi   tel. 0114345430   www.algrassi.it

Alma Latina restaurant €€-€€€, AIC
Via Baretti, 8/bis tel. 11.6692554 www.almalatina.to.it
Notes: Latin, Spanish cuisine.

Antica Trattoria con Calma restaurant €€€, AIC
Strada Comunale del Cartman, 59 tel. 0118980229

B&B Lingotto B&B AIC
Via Rocca de Baldi, 23 tel. 0116638878

Bar Myosotis bar €, AIC
Via L. Spallanzani, 1/b tel. 393.8355486

Cafè & Patisserie bar €, AIC
Via Filadelfia, 113/b tel. 11.19506672 www.facebook.com/cafeepatisserie

Caffetteria Lo Spuntino bar €, AIC
Via L. Cibrario, 57 tel. 338.3853491

Casa Firmino B&B AIC
Str. alla Funicolare, 23/4 tel. 0118987517 www.casafirmino.it

Circolo La Toga C.so Casale, 287	restaurant tel. 333.7953679	AIC
Cravero Str. Cimitero Sassi, 6/A	bakery tel. 11.8980034	€, AIC www.pasticceriacravero.com
Crazy pizza Via Vandalino, 56/GH	pizzeria tel. 0117732317	€, AIC www.crazypizzatorino.it
Curryzone Via Gioberti, 4	restaurant tel. 0114546875	€€, AIC
Dolcesalato Senza Glutine Via De Sanctis, 111/a	bakery tel. 11.768131	€, AIC www.dolcesalatosenzaglutinetorino.it
Duca 102 C.so Duca degli Abruzzi, 102	restaurant, pizzeria tel. 0115817273	€€€, AIC
Glutì Nostress Caffè Via dei Mille, 32	bar tel. 11.763353	€, AIC www.gluti.it
Gran Caffè Vittoria Via Genova, 6	bar-cafe tel. 0116964448	€, AIC
Hotel Cairo Via la Loggia, 6	hotel tel. 11.3171555	AIC www.hotelcairo.it
Il Gusto di Carmilla Via San Donato, 29	tavola calda tel. 11.4274001	€, AIC www.ilgustodicarmilla.it
Il Vicolo Via Melchiorre Gioia, 3/D	restaurant tel. 011535233	€-€€, AIC
Kipling Restaurant Via Mazzini, 10	restaurant tel. 0118172616	€€€ - €€€€, AIC www.kiplingrestaurant.com
La Barrique C.so Dante, 53/a	restaurant tel. 011657900	€€€€, AIC www.labarriqueristorante.it
La Birba/Il Briccone Via Barbaroux, 25	restaurant tel. 011533376	€€€, AIC
La Medusa P.zza Pasini, 3	restaurant, pizzeria tel. 0118980371	€-€€, AIC www.ristorantelamedusa.com
La Pasta Fresca P.zza Fontanesi, 4	bakery tel. 11.884357	€, AIC www.pastafrescatorino.it
La Strambata Via Ugo Foscolo, 20	restaurant, pizzeria tel. 0116692681	€, AIC www.ristorantelastrambata.com
Las Rosas Via Bellezia, 15/f	restaurant (Mexican) tel. 0115213907	€, AIC www.lasrosas.it
Locanda del Pentegallo Via Alessandro Volta, 3	pizzeria, restaurant tel. 0117640344	€, AIC www.locandadelpentegallo.it
M**Bun (2 locations) C.so Siccardi 8/a Via Rattazzi, 4	sandwich shop tel. 0115617097 tel. 01119704606	€, AIC www.mbun.it www.mbun.it
Maison del Celiaco Via Avet 8 (Zona P.zza Statuto)	bakery, sandwich shop www.maisondelceliaco.it	€
Mescè	shakes and crepes	€, AIC

Via S. Dalmazzo, 4	tel. 11.5824479	www.walkingfood.it/IWF
Noè	restaurant, pizzeria	€, AIC
Via Guala, 120	tel. 0113174520	
Novotel Torino/Novotelcafé	hotel, restaurant	€€€€, AIC
C.so Giulio Cesare 338/34	tel. 0112601211	www.novotel.com
Panperfocaccia	restaurant, pizzeria	€-€€€€, AIC
Via Conte verde, 7/a	tel. 3468520279	www.panxfocaccia.com
Piero's	pizzeria	€, AIC
Via Principe Amedeo, 25	tel. 0118172254	
Pizzeria da Michi	restaurant, pizzeria	€€, AIC
Via S. Donato, 38	tel. 11.4732408	
Pizzeria Pratico	pizzeria	€€, AIC
Via Madonna di Campagna,9	tel. 11.2768409	www.pizzeriapratico.it
Pizzeria Ristoro Qeendici	pizzeria/restaurant	€, AIC
P.zza Peyron, 15/b	tel. 0114370150	
Rist. La Campana/H. Chelsea	restaurant hotel	€€-€€€, AIC
Via XX Settembre, 79/c/e	tel. 0115214011	www.hotelchelsea.it
Ristorante Massimo Hotel il Convento restaurant, hotel		€€€€, AIC
Via Hermada, 3/A	tel. 161.805181	
www.ilconventoditrino.com/?page_id=51&lang=en		
Sapordivino	restaurant	€€, AIC
Via Borgo Dora, 25/h	tel. 0514365104	www.sapordivino.net
Silvano	gelato	€, AIC
Via Nizza, 142	tel. 11.6677262	www.gelateriasilvano.it
Soup & Go	restaurant	€, AIC
Via S. Dalmazzo, 8/a	tel. 0110712763	www.soupandgo.it
Statuto da Carmen	restaurant, pizzeria	€€, AIC
Via Manzoni, 0/f	tel. 051537363	
Notes: Closed Mondays.		
Tratt. Raffaello 5	trattoria	€€, AIC
C.so Raffaello, 5	tel. 0516694723	www.raffaello5.com
Yogurteria Creperia Fyò	gelato, crepes	€, AIC
P.zza Palazzo di Città, 6/d		
Yogurteria Fyò	gelato, crepes	€, AIC
Via Accademia delle Scienze, 2/e		
Grom	gelato (AIC)	P.zza Paleopaca, 1/d
Grom	gelato (AIC)	Via Accademia delle Scienze, 4
Grom	gelato (AIC)	P.zza S. Rita da Cascia, 6/a
Grom	gelato (AIC)	Via Cernaia, 18
La Gelateria da Bobo	gelato (AIC)	C.so Traiano, 2/c
L'Apegaia	gelato (AIC)	Str. S. Mauro, 180/e
Gelateria Nicola	gelato (AIC)	C.so Vittorio Emanuele II, 199/c
Il Gelato Amico	gelato (AIC)	Via S. Massimo, 34

Auchan
supermarket
Corso Romania 160

Carrefour
supermarket
Corso Grosseto 330

Celi@Chia-Food
supermarkets
Via Somalia 30
Piazza Sofia 28/A
Via Crissolo 23
Pam
supermarkets
Corso Cosenza 46/B
Via Salbertrand 67
Corso Traiano 58
Via Nizza 230
Corso Svizzera 52

Turingel
supermarkets
Corso Sebastopoli 147
Via S. Secondo 48
Corso Vercelli 78

Ave Maria (C. Caneparo)

THE REST OF PIEDMONTE

ACQUI TERME

Vineria Angolo Divino	restaurant	€€, AIC
Via alla Bollente, 44	tel. 0144321005	
Notes: Closed Tuesdays.		
Spigallegra	bakery	€, AIC
Via Rodi, 1/a	tel. 0121.376759	www.spigallegra.it

ALBA

Al Setaccio	restaurant, pizzeria, bakery	€-€€, AIC
Via Crispi, 4	tel. 173.592577	www.al-setaccio.webnode.it
Bar Roma	bar, gelato	€, AIC
Via Alberione, 3/b	tel. 173.442127	
Hotel i Castelli	hotel, restaurant	AIC
C.so Torino, 14/1	tel. 173.361978	www.hotel-icastelli.com
Panetteria Giacosa	bakery	€, AIC
C.so Langhe, 68/a	tel. 173.44058	www.panetteriagiacosa.net

ALBUGNANO

Le Tre Colline	agritourism	€€, AIC
Via Serra, 4	tel. 0119922038	www.letrecolline.com
Ristorante Al Gottardo	restaurant, wine bar	€€€€, AIC
Loc. Vezzolano, 1/bis	tel. 11.9922014	www.ristorantealgottardo.it

Sunset on Lago Maggiore (D. Impastato)

Terra e Gente
Loc. S. Emiliano, 45

agritourism €€€€, AIC
tel. 11.9920841 www.terraegente.it

ALESSANDRIA

Arcimboldo
Via Legnano, 2

restaurant €€€€, AIC
tel. 013152022 www.ristorantearcimboldo.it

Gelat. Soban

gelato (€, AIC) Via S. Lorenzo, 99

Grom

gelato (€, AIC) Via Milano, 1

Il Forno di Madama Caterina
C.so IV Novembre, 13

bakery, sandwich shop, cupcake shop €, AIC
tel. 333.3286158

Il Girone dei Golosi
Via Vinzaglio, 67

restaurant €€-€€€, AIC
tel. 131.22371 www.gironedeigolosi.com

ALFIANO NATTA

Agriturismo Crealto
Str.da Crealto, 6

agritourism AIC
tel. 345.5686278 www.crealto.it

ALICE CASTELLO

Ranch
Via Cavaglià, 20

restaurant €€, AIC
tel. 161.9091

ALMESE

Nonsolovino
Via Avigliana, 107

restaurant €€€, AIC
tel. 0119359774 www.ristorantenonsolovino.it

ALPETTE CANAVESE

Hosteria Alpina
Via Paganini, 5

hotel, restaurant €€, AIC
tel. 0124809143

ALPIGNANO

Farenheit 451
Via Cavour, 46

restaurant, pizzeria €€, AIC
tel. 0119787379

Oasi dello Chef restaurant €€, AIC
Viale Vittoria, 18 tel. 393.2141194 www.oasidellochef.altervista.org

ANGROGNA

Rifugio Jumarre restaurant €€-€€€, AIC
Loc. Vaccera, 266 tel. 0121.944233 www.rifugiojumarre.it

ARONA

Yogorino di Bonetti Giovanna gelato (€, AIC) Corso Cavour, 82

ASTI

Agriturismo il Buon Seme agritourism €€€, AIC
Frazione Sessant, 240 tel. 333.2233491 www.ilbuonseme.it

Al Sangiovanni restaurant €€€€, AIC
Via Guttuari, 12 tel. 141.231317 www.alsangiovanni.it

Campanarò restaurant €€€, AIC
Via Secondo Arò, 30 tel. 014133252 www.campanaro.it

Casa del Ventiniere B&B AIC
Fr. Variglie,81 tel. 348.3934263

Grom gelato €, AIC
P.zza San Secondo, 11 www.grom.it

La Piola restaurant, pizzeria €-€€, AIC
C.so Alessandria, 150 tel. 141.219892 www.pizzeriaristorantelapiola.com

BAGNOLO P.TE

Il Provenzale restaurant, pizzeria €€, AIC
Via Cave, 305 tel. 0175391510 www.ristoranteilprovenzale.it

BALME

La Masinà agritourism €€€, AIC
Loc. Pian della Mussa tel. 3474439384 www.agrimasina.com

BARDONECCHIA

Etable restaurant €€€€, AIC
Via Medail, 82 tel. 012296973

La Pigna hotel, restaurant €€, AIC
Fraz. Melezet, 119 tel. 0122880303 www.hotel-lapigna.it

BARGE

Bar Gazebo bar-cafe AIC
Piazzetta della Madonna s.n. tel. 03487030509

BEINASCO

Mychef Beinasco Nord mychef €, AIC
Progr. km 2,670 diramaz. x Pinerolo della Tang. Sud di Torino tel. 11.3496314
www.mychef.it

BIELLA

Al Buon Ricordo restaurant €€€-€€€€, AIC
Viale Matteotti, 17 tel. 01523831
Notes: Closed Monday-Wednesday.

Alice gelato (€, AIC) Via Italia, 12

Caffè del Chiostro restaurant €-€€, AIC
Via Q. Sella-Museo del Territorio tel. 0152523112

Caffetteria del Corso   bar, tavola calda   €, AIC
Via Italia, 50   tel. 01522345

Fra Le Nuvole   bakery   €, AIC
Via S. Filippo, 17   tel. 015.3700947   www.fralenuvolebiella.com

Giordano   pizzeria   €, AIC
Via Delleani, 33   tel. 015405306

Ristorante Palazzo Boglietti   restaurant   €€€-€€€€, AIC
Via Piacenza, 1   tel. 15.8497995   www.ristorantepalazzoboglietti.it

BORGARO TORINESE

Hotel Atlantic - Rist. Il Rubino   hotel, restaurant   €€€€, AIC
Via Lanzo, 163/165   tel. 0114500055   www.hotelatlantic.com

Mondo Bio   tavola calda   €-€€, AIC
Via Lanzo, 107   tel. 11.4543424   www.spesamondobio.it

BORGO TICINO

Cascina Cesarina   agritourism, B&B   €€, AIC
Via dei Cesari, 32   tel. 032190491   www.cascinacesarina.com

BRANDIZZO

Sòrbole   restaurant, pizzeria   €€-€€€€, AIC
Via Torino, 396   tel. 11.9137498   www.sorbole.it

BRONDELLO

La Torre   restaurant   €€, AIC
Via Villa, 35/a   tel. 017576198   www.ristorantelatorrebrondello.com

BUBBIO

Agriturismo Mondoaranci o   agritourism   AIC
Reg. Stropeta, 100   tel. 331.4467918   www.agriturismomondoarancio.it

BUTTIGLIERA D'ASTI

La Gallina Bionda   pizzera, trattoria   €€, AIC
Via Villanova, 62 - Fr.Crivelle   tel. 11.9921314

CALAMANDRANA

La Corte   hotel, restaurant   AIC
Fr. Quartino, 6   tel. 141.769109   www.agrilacorte.com

CALTIGNAGA

Trattoria Risorgimento   restaurant   €€€, AIC
Via Risorgimento, 26   tel. 0321.652125   www.trattoriarisorgimento.it

CAMINO

Agriturismo Ca' San Sebastiano agritourism   €€€, AIC
Via Ombra, 10/12   tel. 142.9459   www.casansebastiano.it

Billy Bau   restaurant   €€, AIC
Via Rocca, 75- Fraz. Rocca   tel. 142.469014   www.billybau.com

CAMPIGLIONE FENILE

Locanda del Terzo Tempo   trattoria, bar   €€€, AIC
Via Edmondo de Amicis, 13/C   tel. 329.949807

CANALE

La Siesta   pizzeria   €, AIC
P.zza Europa, 5   tel. 3318962126

CANOSIO

Lou Lindal
Frazione Preit, 1
inn, restaurant
tel. 0171998301
€-€€, AIC

CAPREZZO

Villa Pepa
Via Vico, 13
B&B
tel. 0323559039
AIC
www.villapepa.it

CARBONARA SCRIVIA

La Rocca dei vecchi e nuovi sapori
Vicolo del castello, 7/a
pizzeria
tel. 131.89218
€€, AIC

CARIGNANO

Il Canonico
Strada Castagnole, 29
restaurant
tel. 0119692388
€€€, AIC
www.ilcanonico.it

CARMAGNOLA

Trattoria del Porto
Via del Porto, 158
trattoria
tel. 11.9717937
€€, AIC

CASALE MONFERRATO

Mondo Pizza
C.so Valentino, 38/40
pizzeria
tel. 142.74838
€€, AIC
www.mondopizzacasale.com

CASELLE TORINESE

Il Ventaglio
Via Martiri della Libertà, 33
bakery, gelato, bar
tel. 11.9975676
€, AIC

CASSINE

LA.TI.MI.DA.
Str. Ricaldone di Sotto, 28
agritourism
tel. 0144715371
€€, AIC
www.agriturismolatimida.it

CASSINE FRAZ. S. ANDREA

Agriturismo Surì
Via della Chiesa, 3
agritourism
tel. 0144767079
€€, AIC
www.suri.it

CASTAGNITO

Nero Seppia
Via Alba, 12/e Loc. baraccone
restaurant
tel. 0173212025
€€€€, AIC
www.nero-seppia.it

CASTAGNOLE PIEMONTE

B&B Cascina Motette
Via Cascina Motette, 46
B&B
tel. 0119862621
AIC
www.cascinamotette.it

B&B Edera
Via Garibaldi, 27
B&B
tel. 0119862106
AIC
www.edera.net

CASTELLAMONTE

Equin'ozio
Fraz. Filia, 70
restaurant
tel. 124.513635
€€€, AIC
www.equin-ozio.it

Il Valentino
Strada Castelnuovo Nigra, 21
restaurant
tel. 124.515476
€€€, AIC
www.ristoranteilvalentino.it

Trattoria San Giovanni
Via Centrale, 53 Fraz.S.Giovanni
restaurant
tel. 124.513287
€€-€€€, AIC
www.trattoriasangiovanni.it

CASTELLAR

Il Nido di Bacco
Via Pro.le 12
B&B
tel. 017546603
€€€€, AIC

CASTELLERO

Casale Gentile agritourism €€€, AIC
Via Vernetto, 18 tel. 0141669715 www.casalegentile.com

CASTELLO DI ANNONE

Mychef Crocetta Nord mychef €, AIC
A21Torino/Alessa ndria/Piacenz a km 48+225 tel. 141.401162 www.mychef.it

CASTIGLIONE TINELLA

Campagna Verde restaurant €-€€€, AIC
Via Balbi, 22 tel. 0141855108

CERES

Valli di Lanzo restaurant, hotel €€€-€€€€, AIC
Via Roma, 11 tel. 012353397 www.ristorantevallidilanzo.it

CERESETO

Monferrato Resort restaurant, agritourism AIC
Fr. Cascine Franchi tel. 142.940127

CERRETTO LANGHE

Trattoria del Bivio restaurant €€€-€€€€, AIC
Località Cavallotti, 9 tel. 0173520383 www.trattoriadelbivio.it

CERRIONE

Il Tiglio agritourism €€€, AIC
Cascina Ronco tel. 03348592883 www.iltiglio.it

CERVERE

Primi Dolci restaurant €€-€€€, AIC
P.zza S. Sebastiano, 30 tel. 0172474471 www.primidolci.it

CESSOLE

Tenuta Antica S.S. agritourism AIC
Reg. Busdone, 2 tel. 144.80113

CHERASCO

Flyfood bar, tavola calda €, AIC
Via del Lavoro,13 tel. 172.474003

Locanda Pane e Vino restaurant €€-€€€, AIC
Via Moglia, 12 tel. 0172489108

CHIALAMBERTO

La Muanda agritourism €€€, AIC
Fraz. Vonzo, 23 tel. 3498490840 www.lamuanda.com

CHIERI

Dolci & Dolci bakery €, AIC
Via Orfane,5 tel. 11.9413695

Grom gelato €, AIC
Via Vittorio Emanuele, 59 www.grom.it

Il Faro di Mara Cirmia bar €, AIC
Via Andezeno, 6 tel. 11.4276536

Sayuri Sushi Bar restaurant AIC
P.zza Mazzini, 6 tel. 11.9421197

Ristorante Boschetto
Via S.Anna, 26 _ Fraz. Boschetto

CHIVASSO
restaurant
tel. 11.9195948

AIC

CINZANO
Pizza Konnection
Via Statale, 39

pizzeria/restaurant
tel. 0172479073

€ - €€, AIC

CIRIÈ
Il Capriccio di Tiziana
Via Torino,53

bar, restaurant
tel. 331.536585

AIC

La Smorfia
Via Robassomero, 70

pizzeria
tel. 11.9205044

AIC

L'Isola che Non C'è
Località Ghe, 1

agritourism
tel. 0119205669

€€, AIC
www.agriturismolisolachenonce.it

COLLEGNO
Dolci Idee
V.le XXIVMaggio, 5

gelato
tel. 11.4152524

€, AIC
www.gelateriadolciidee.it

Pizzeria del Viale
V.le Antonio Gramsci, 4

restaurant, pizzeria
tel. 011786390

€, AIC

Sapori di Casa
V.le Gramsci, 4/C

gastropub, pizzeria, bakery
tel. 11.7910735

AIC
www.gastronomiasenzaglutine.it

COSSATO
La Bussola
Via Mazzini, 42

restaurant, pizzeria
tel. 015921702

€-€€€, AIC

Panta Rei
Via Mazzini, 42

restaurant
tel. 015921084

€€€-€€€€, AIC
www.ristorantepantarei.com

COSTIGLIOLE D'ASTI
Enoteca Caffè Roma
P.zza Umberto I

wine bar
tel. 0141966544

€€, AIC

CRODO
Belvedere Resort
Fraz. Mozzio, 24

hotel, restaurant
tel. 032461055

€€€, AIC
www.belvederemozzio.it

CUCCARO MONF.TO
La Cantina in Collina
Via Marconi,9

agritourism
tel. 0131771111

€€-€€€, AIC

CUNEO
Alpigrill
Via Bra, 1

restaurant
tel. 0171413249

€€-€€€, AIC

Grom

gelato (€, AIC)

P.zza Galimberti, 2

Les Gourmands
Via Statuto, 3

restaurant
tel. 03357548416

€€-€€€€, AIC
www.lesgourmands.it

Mario Senza Glutine
Via Porta Rossa, 3/b

cupcake shop, bakery
tel. 171.613464

€, AIC
www.mariosenzaglutineglutenfree.eu

DESANA
Agriturismo Oryza
P.zza Castello, 8

agritourism
tel. 0161318565

€-€€, AIC
www.oryzariso.it

Tenuta Larenzania
Borgata Piandeltroglio, 16

DOGLIANI
hotel, restaurant   €€, AIC
tel. 017371086   www.larenzania.it

Il Tiglio
Via Deseno, 3/5

DOMODOSSOLA
B&B   AIC
tel. 0324249306   www.bb-tiglio.com

La Gelattica

DORMELLETTO
gelato (€, AIC)   C.so Cavour, 94

Dalla Padella alla Brace
Via Volta, 31/a

DRUENTO
restaurant, pizzeria, wine bar   €€, AIC
tel. 011994262   www.ristorantedallapadellaallabrace.net

Gli Amici
C.so Matteotti, 25

FAVRIA CANAVESE
hotel, restaurant, pizzeria   €, AIC
tel. 0124360798

Pracatinat
Località Pra Catinat

FENESTRELLE
inn   AIC
tel. 0121884884   www.pracatinat.it

Cascina Monticone
Collina S. Giuseppe, 71

FERRERE
agritourism   AIC
tel. 328.7431747

Amici Miei
S.R. 229, 5

FONTANETO D'AGOGNA
restaurant, pizzeria, Gel   €€, AIC
tel. 322.890053   www.ristorantepizzeriaamicimiei.it

Bastian
Str. Stazione, 13

FONTANILE
agritourism   AIC
tel. 0141774475   www.agriturismobastian.it

Dolcelatte

FOSSANO
gelato (€, AIC)   Via Cesare Battisti, 11

Il Drago e la Fata
Via Marconi, 1

hot dogs, pizza, vegetarian   €, AIC
tel. 392.2920327

Bar di Sotto
C.so Aldo Porro, 22

FUBINE
restaurant, bar   €, AIC
tel. 131.798972

La Rustica
Via Madonna , 69

GATTICO
restaurant, pizzeria   €€, AIC
tel. 0322838781

L'Artigiana del Gelato

GATTINARA
gelato (€, AIC)   C.so Garibaldi, 76

Al Gufo Nero
Via Novara, 162

GHEMME
restaurant   €€-€€€, AIC
tel. 0163840251

Cre' Seren
Fraz. S. Rocco, 10

GIAGLIONE
agritourism   €€, AIC
tel. 0122629264   www.agriturismogiaglione.it

Orchidea
Via Pontepietra, 34

restaurant
tel. 0119363936

€€€, AIC
www.ristorantepizzeriaorchidea.it

Ristorante Novarello
Via D. Graziosi, 1

restaurant
tel. 338.5835902

AIC

Bargiglio Rosso
Via Garibaldi, 157

restaurant, pizzeria
tel. 173.262115

€€-€€€, AIC

La Salinera
Via IV Novembre, 19

restaurant
tel. 0173262915

€-€€, AIC

La Tagliata
Via IV Novembre, 45

restaurant
tel. 173.262692

€€-€€€, AIC
www.latagliata.it

Locanda Vecchio Novecento
Via Corio, 8/a

restaurant
tel. 0119268614

€-€€, AIC
www.vecchionovecento.it

Coop. Agricola del Duc
Strada del Portone, 197

agritourism
tel. 0113149929

€€, AIC
www.cascinaduc.it

Grom

gelato (€, AIC)   Via Crea, 10 C/O Le Gru primo piano

Il Sagittario
P.zza Papa Giovanni XXIII, 15

restaurant/pizzeria
tel. 011701687

€€, AIC

Io e Luna
Fraz. Montebello, 1

restaurant
tel. 0173611724

€€€€, AIC
www.ioeluna.com

Ristorante Pizzeria Eporediese
C.so Vercelli, 132

restaurant, pizzeria
tel. 125.251038

€€-€€€, AIC

Ristorante Campana
Via Torino, 33

restaurant
tel. 011.9842946

€€, AIC
www.ilristorantecampana.it

Bar Ristorante Pizzeria da Frankino restaurant, pizzeria, bar
Loc. Quartino, 5

tel. 144.83536

€€, AIC
www.frankino.it

Roma
P.zza Martiri, 8

pizzeria
tel. 0321469033

€€, AIC
www.trattoriapizzeriaroma.com

La Vecchia Fornace
Via Fornaci, 25

agritourism
tel. 0322870086

€€, AIC

I Sapori
Strada Statale, 193

restaurant, pizzeria
tel. 0175289538

€-€€, AIC

Il Baco da Seta
Via S. Leone, 5

agritourism
tel. 0175289352

€€, AIC
www.ilbacodaseta.com

MANTA DI SALUZZO

Il Pithosforo
S.S. Laghi di Avigliana, 171

restaurant, pizzeria
tel. 017588174

€-€€, AIC
www.hotelcicerone.it

MATHI

Il Forno di Nonna Ada
Via Martiri della Libertà, 15

bakery
tel. 11.0561884

€, AIC

MATTIE

Il Mulino di Chalier
Via Giordani, 52

hotel, restaurant
tel. 0122.238132

AIC
www.mulinomattie.it

MONASTERO BORMIDA

Per i Golosi
Via Monteverde, 2

bakery, gelato
tel. 144.88089

€, AIC

MONASTERO DI LANZO

Il Giardino Pensile
Piazzetta della Parrocchia, 12

restaurant
tel. 01234217

€ - €€€, AIC

MONASTERO DI VASCO

Nuova Gandolfi
Via Gandolfi, 1

restaurant, pizzeria
tel. 0174689628

€€€, AIC

MONCALIERI

Lievito Madre e Puro Latte
Via Garibaldi, 4

restaurant, ice cream shop
tel. 011642673

€€, AIC
www.lievitomadrepurolatte.it

Tosa Restaurant House
Str. Genova, 200

restaurant
tel. 0116474971

€€€€, AIC
www.tosaristorante.it

MONCUCCO TORINESE

Trattoria del Freisa
Via Mosso, 6

restaurant
tel. 0119874765

€€-€€€, AIC
www.trattoriadelfreisa.it

MONDOVI

La Borsarella
Via del Crhist, 2

restaurant
tel. 017442999

€€€, AIC
www.laborsarella.it

MONFORTE D'ALBA

Cascina Pian Borga
Località S.Giuseppe, 11
Notes: Closed Monday-Thursday.

agritourism
tel. 0173789212

€€, AIC

Enoteca Caffè Rocca Costantino
P.zza Umberto I, 20

restaurant, wine bar
tel. 0173707156

€€, AIC

MONTÀ D'ALBA

Belvedere
Vicolo San Giovanni, 3

inn, restaurant
tel. 0173976156

€€€-€€€€, AIC
www.albergobelvedere.com

MONTEU ROERO

Cascina Vrona
Fraz. Sant'Anna, 6

agritourism, B&B
tel. 017390629

€€, AIC

MORNESE

La Fenice
Via Roma, 38
Notes: Great reviews.

restaurant, pizzeria
tel. 342.005852

€€, AIC
www.ristorantepizzerialafenice.eu

Will
Via IV Novembre, 43

NETRO
B&B
tel. 338.8921152

AIC

NICHELINO

da Zio
Via Superga, 18

restaurant, pizzeria
tel. 03484207447

€€€, AIC
www.pizzeriadazio.com

Il Giardino dei Sapori
Via Buffa, 79

restaurant, gelato, pizzeria
tel. 11.6807816

€-€€€€, AIC
www.ilgiardinodeisapori.eu

NIZZA MONFERRATO

La Romantica
Str.da Alessandria, 13

restaurant, pizzeria
tel. 141.701129

€€, AIC

Ristorantino Tantì
Via Pio Corsi, 18

restaurant
tel. 141.727338

€€, AIC
www.tanti.it

NONE

L'Orologio
Via Roma, 71

restaurant
tel. 0119904296

€€€, AIC

NOVALESA

C'era una Volta
Fr. S. Pietro, 1

agritourism
tel. 335.7883741

€, AIC
www.corbusier.it

NOVARA

20 Regioni - Bar Cucina Shop
Via Magnani Ricotti, 14/b

restaurant, bar
tel. 0321331504   www.20r.it

€€, AIC

Autogrill Autostrada A4
Torino - Milano

autogrill
tel. 321.691144

€, AIC

Grom
C.so Italia, 13

gelato
www.grom.it

€, AIC

La Piramide
C.so XXIII Marzo, 314

pizzeria, trattoria
tel. 0321402900

€€€, AIC
www.pizzeriaristorantepiramide.com

Pontida
Via Pontida, 6/a

trattoria
tel. 032135045

€€-€€€, AIC

Rist. Sushi bar Long Jin di Yunana restaurant
C.so Torino, 52/d

tel. 0321031277

€€, AIC
www.longjin.it

Trattoria Cavallino Bianco
Via Vicolo Dell'Arco, 2/A

restaurant
tel. 032139308

€€€, AIC

NOVI LIGURE

La Terrazza
Via Garibaldi, 91

restaurant, pizzeria
tel. 014376688

€€-€€€, AIC

L'ultima Spiaggia c/o Aquarium
Via F.lli Rosselli, 2

restaurant, pizzeria
tel. 0143743789

€, AIC

Mychef Marengo Nord
A26 Genova Voltri Gravellona Toce Km 9.700   tel. 143.417967 www.mychef.it

mychef

€, AIC

OLEGGIO

Az. Agr. Cascine Bellini
Via Cascine Bellini

agritourism
tel. 0321995193

€€€, AIC

Dinamo
Via Paganini, 5

restaurant, pizzeria
tel. 0321998333

€, AIC

OROPA

Croce Bianca
Via Santuario Oropa, 480

hotel, restaurant
tel. 0152455923

€-€€€€, AIC

OROPA SANTUARIO

Ristoralp Croce Bianca
Via Santuario Oropa, 480

hotel, restaurant
tel. 15.2455923

€€-€€€, AIC
www.ristorantecrocebianca.it

ORTA S. GIULIO

S. Rocco
Via Gippini, 11

hotel
tel. 0322911977

€€€€, AIC

OSASCO

La Siepe
Via Rovina, 10

B&B
tel. 0121541552

AIC

www.bed-and-breakfast.it/en/pagina.cfm?id=22296&idregione=12

PARODI LIGURE

Al Ghiottone
Via Cadegualchi, 1
Notes: Closed Monday-Wednesday.

agritourism
tel. 0143681213

€€€-€€€€, AIC

PAVAROLO

Ristorante del Castello
Via Maestra, 7

restaurant
tel. 0119408042

AIC
www.ristorantedelcastello.com

PECETTO TORINESE

L'Escalier
Via Circonvallazione, 22

restaurant, pizzeria
tel. 0118609845

€-€€€, AIC
www.granclasse.com

PEROSA ARGENTINA

Clara's Lodge
Via Monte Grappa, 7

B&B
tel. 0121804009

AIC

PERRERO

Il Girasole
Borgata Moliera, 3 fraz. Riclaretto

B&B
tel. 0121808962

AIC

PIANEZZA

La Fattoria del Gelato

gelato (€, AIC)

Via Grange, 44

La Muradora
ViaGrage, 47

agritourism
tel. 340.0829526

AIC
www.lamuradora.it

Osteria del Musicante
Via Caduti per la Libertà, 26/A

osteria
tel. 0119661249

€-€€€, AIC
www.osteriadelmusicante.com

Severino - Delizie Senza Glutine
Via Mombello, 26

sandwich shop, bakery
tel. 348.0444859

€, AIC
www.deliziesenzaglutine.it

PIEA

Pian Dij Babi
Via Vallunga, 1

agritourism, B&B
tel. 320.1792756

AIC
www.piandijbabi.it

PINASCA

Bella Baita
Serre Marchetto, 1

B&B
tel. 3479842945

AIC

PINEROLO

B&B Casa Carla
Via Costagrande, 51
B&B
tel. 0121322195
AIC

Charlie Bar
P.zza V. Veneto, 7
bar-cafe
tel. 012177331
AIC

Perbacco
P.zza S. Donato, 8
restaurant
tel. 0121397487
€€, AIC

PINO TORINESE

Pinocchio
Via Roma, 3
restaurant
tel. 011842451
€€-€€€, AIC

PIOBESI D'ALBA

Tenuta Carretta
Località Carretta, 2
restaurant
tel. 0173619261
€€€€, AIC
www.tenutacarretta.com

PIOBESI TORINESE

Caffè Ristorante Albergo Stazione bar, hotel, restaurant
P.zza Paracleto, 2
tel. 11.9657372
AIC

Ristorante Hotel Celestino
C.so Italia, 10
restaurant, hotel
tel. 11.9650343
AIC
www.hotelristorantecelestino.it

POIRINO

Trau Brusà
C.so Fiume, 79/bis
pizzeria
tel. 0119450368
€, AIC
www.pizzeriatraubrusa.it

POLLONE

Il Faggio
Via Oremo, 54
restaurant
tel. 01561252
€€€€, AIC
www.ristoranteilfaggio.it

POLONGHERA

La Via del Sale
Via Dellera, 4
trattoria
tel. 011974413
€€, AIC
www.trattorialaviadelsale.com

PONZONE

Malò
P.zza Garibaldi, 1
hotel, restaurant
tel. 014478075
€€-€€€, AIC
www.albergomalo.com

POZZOLO FORMIGARO

La Locanda dei Narcisi
Str. Barbotti, 1 fraz. Bettolle
restaurant
tel. 0143319822
€€€€, AIC
www.lalocandadeinarcisi.it

PRAGELATO

Villaggio Gofree Camping
Via Nazionale, 2/a fraz. Ruà
restaurant, village
tel. 012270045
€, AIC
www.villaggiogofree.com

PRAGELATO LOC.PLAN

La Greppia
Via del Beth, 9
restaurant
tel. 012278409
€€€, AIC

PRALORMO

Ristorante Pizzeria dell'Olmo
Via Alba, 67
restaurant, pizzeria
tel. 11.9481851
€€€ - €€€€, AIC
www.ristorantepizzeriadellolmo.com

Lago Maggiore (A. Komorowski)

PRATO SESIA

Lo Scoglio   restaurant, pizzeria   €-€€€€, AIC
Via Paganini, 5   tel. 0163850581

REVELLO

La Virginia   agritourism   €€€ - €€€€, AIC
Via Valle Po, 77   tel. 0175259026   www.lavirginia.it

RIVALTA DI TORINO

Tomato Pizza Rivalta   pizzeria, restaurant   €, AIC
Via Giaveno, 18 C/O Carrefour   tel. 0119005595   www.tomatopizza.org

RIVAROLO CANAVESE

Amaranto   restaurant, gastropub   €€, AIC
Via Farina ,3   tel. 124.42585   www.amarantofood.it

Crema & Cioccolato   bar   €€, AIC
C.so Indipendenza, 74 c/o Urban Center   tel. 124.428079   www.rivarolourbancenter.it

Oggi Pizza c/o Urban Center   pizzeria   €, AIC
C.so Indipendenza, 74   tel. 0124420113

RIVOLI

2uepuntozero   restaurant   €, AIC
Via Piave, 20   tel. 0119589556   www.2uepuntozero.it

Biogelateria Rivoli   gelato (€, AIC)   Via Stura, 22

M**Bun   fast food   €, AIC
C.so Susa, 22   tel. 11.9534062   www.mbun.it

Pastepartout   bakery   €, AIC
Via Cavalieri Vittorio Veneto, 27   tel. 333.9795996   www.pastepartout.com

ROBILANTE

Pizzeria Brasserie Un'Altra Volta restaurant, pizzeria   €, AIC
Via Vittorio Veneto, 109   tel. 017178197   www.pizzeriaunaltravolta.com

ROLETTO

La Rosa dei Venti restaurant, pizzeria €€, AIC
Via Torino, 6/8 tel. 121.54219 www.larosadeiventiroletto.it

S. MARIA DI LA MORRA

Eremo della Gasprina restaurant €€€, AIC
Borgata Cappallotti, 2 tel. 017350498

S. SALVATORE MONFERRATO

Stella restaurant, pizzeria €€, AIC
Via Prevignano, 7 tel. 0131233107

S.GIACOMO DI ROBURENT

Ristorante Albergo Nazionale hotel, restaurant €€-€€€, AIC
Via Sant'Anna, 111 tel. 174.227127 www.albergonazionale.cn.it

SAGLIANO MICCA

Az. Agrit. Ca' d'Andrei agritourism €€, AIC
Via Trento, 2 tel. 0152475013

SALUSSOLA

Fattoria delle Rose trattoria, agritourism €€, AIC
Cascina Emilia, 1 tel. 0161999955 www.fattoriadellerose.com

SALUZZO

Le Quattro Stagioni d'Italia restaurant, pizzeria €€, AIC
Via Volta, 21 tel. 017547470

Piazza Grande trattoria, self-service €-€€, AIC
V.le Tramvie, 3 tel. 175.290675 www.piazzagrandesaluzzo.it

SAN GILLIO

Profumo di Lillà B&B AIC
Via San Pancrazio, 8 tel. 3496052520

SANTENA

L'Antico Pioppo La Carolina agritourism AIC
Via Badini, 28 tel. 11.9454467 www.anticopioppo.it/agriluogo.html

SAVIGLIANO

Gran Baita hotel, restaurant €€, AIC
Via Cuneo, 23 tel. 0172712060 www.granbaitahotel.it

La Sirenetta pizzeria €, AIC
Via Solerette, 9/a tel. 0172377193

SCARNAFIGI

Nuovo Monarca restaurant €€-€€€€, AIC
Strada Tetti Olio, 2 tel. 017574420

SCURZOLENGO

La Raviola Galante restaurant €€€, AIC
Via Maiocco, 4 tel. 0141203015 www.laraviolagalante.it

SERRALUNGA D'ALBA

La Rosa dei Vini restaurant, B&B €€, AIC
Loc. Parafada, 4 tel. 0173613219 www.larosadeivini.com

SERRALUNGA DI CREA

Ristorante Crea bar, restaurant €€-€€€€, AIC
P.zza Santuario, 7 tel. 142.940108 www.ristorantedicrea.it

SETTIMO VITTONE

La Marenda Sinoira
Fr. Cesnola, 74 Reg.Cornaley
restaurant
tel. 125.65847
€€, AIC
www.marendasinoira.it

SOMERARO DI STRESA

Al Rustico
Via degli Alpini, 16
restaurant
tel. 32832172
€€€-€€€€, AIC

SOMMARIVA PERNO

Ristopizza Nuovi Sapori
Loc. Piano, 56
restaurant, pizzeria
tel. 017246405
AIC

SORDEVOLO

Antico Ca' d'Gamba
Via B. Bona, 78
restaurant
tel. 0152568813
€€€, AIC

SOZZAGO

Al Pum Rus
Via Cerano, 1
agritourism
tel. 321.70178
€€-€€€€, AIC
www.alpumrus.it

STRESA

G.H. Des Iles Borromees
C.so Umberto I, 67
hotel
tel. 323938938
€€€€, AIC
www.borromees.it

La Palma
C.so Umberto I, 33
hotel
tel. 032332401
AIC
www.hlapalma.it

Regina Hotel
C.so Umberto I, 29
hotel
tel. 323936936
AIC
www.regina-palace.com

Il Pianeta 2000
Via Circonvallazione, 29
restaurant/pizzeria
tel. 0171931858
€€, AIC
www.ilpianeta2000.com

TARANTASCA

Il Melograno
P.zza Vitt. Emanuele III, 9
restaurant
tel. 0142401531
€€€, AIC
www.osteriailmelograno.com

TERRUGGIA

La Civetta
P.zza Pietro Micca, 4
restaurant
tel. 3336741005
€€, AIC

TORRE PELLICE

Mediterraneo
Via Arzani 10/d
restaurant, pizzeria
tel. 0131814782
€, AIC
www.ristorantemediterraneo.net

TORTONA

Gelat. Soban
gelato (€, AIC)
P.zza Gramsci, 23

VALENZA

Fungo Reale
Fraz. Airale, 11
hotel, restaurant
tel. 0171717039
€, AIC

VALLORIATE

Geoffrey's
Via S. Marchese, 38
restaurant, pizzeria
tel. 11.4591646
€-€€, AIC
www.ristorantegeoffreys.com

VENARIA

La Smorfia
Via Verga, 14
pizzeria
tel. 0114246595
€, AIC

VENARIA REALE

Al Binario 20
Viale Roma, 20

restaurant, pizzeria
tel. 11.459808

€-€€€, AIC
www.albinario20venaria.it

VENASCA

Trattoria la Terrazza
P.zza Martiri, 4

restaurant, trattoria
tel. 175.567167

€€€, AIC
www.trattorialaterrazza.it

VERBANIA

Edenatura
P.zza Mercato, 25

restaurant, bar
tel. 323404314

AIC
www.edenatura.it

Hotel Ancora
C.so Mameli, 65

B&B
tel. 32353951

AIC
www.hotelancora.it

VERCELLI

di-Lab
Via Vittorio Veneto, 3

sandwich shop, gluten-free products
tel. 161.214887

€, AIC
www.di-lab.it

Grom

gelato (€, AIC)

C.so Libertà, 4

I Due Forni
Via Thaon de Revel, 41

restaurant, pizzeria
tel. 161.302354

€€€, AIC

Ristorante Vecchia Brenta
Via Morosone, 6

restaurant
tel. 161.25123

€€€, AIC
www.ristorantevecchiabrenta.it

VERCELLI - CASCINE STRÁ

Da Pasquale
Via Torino 12

restaurant, pizzeria
tel. 161.313164 www.facebook.com/pasquale.dapasquale

€€, AIC

VERDUNO

Due Lanterne
Borgata Molino, 15

restaurant
tel. 172470127

€€, AIC
www.ristoranteduelanterne.it

La Cascata
Zona Gurej, 1

restaurant
tel. 0172470126

€€-€€€, AIC
www.lacascata.com

VICOFORTE

La Tavola del Chiostro
P.zza Carlo Emanuele I, 4

hotel, restaurant
tel. 17565300

€, AIC
www.santuariodivicoforte.com

VIGNALE MONFERRATO

Ristorante Pizzeria Laura
Via Trento, 3/5

restaurant, pizzeria
tel. 339.8287447

€€€, AIC

VIGNONE

Monte Cimolo
Via Bèe, 1

restaurant, pizzeria
tel. 323551403

€, AIC

VILLADOSSOLA

La Tavernetta
C.so Italia, 4

restaurant
tel. 3396511980

€€€, AIC
www.tavernettaristorante.com

VILLANOVA D'ASTI

Il Valdichiesa da Enzo
Strada per Chieri, 92

restaurant, pizzeria
tel. 3333444941

€€, AIC

La Stella Polare
Strada Cappello, 29

agritourism
tel. 0141946245

€€, AIC

VILLANOVA SOLARO

Castello dei Solaro
Via Vitale, 4

restaurant €€€€, AIC
tel. 017299365 www.castellodeisolaro.it

VILLASTELLONE

La Cascinetta
Via Tetti Mauritti, 26

agritourism AIC
tel. 342.5548652 www.lacascinetta.wix.com/villastellone

VINOVO

Antica Piazza delle Grida
Via Cottolengo, 109
Notes: Closed Mondays.

restaurant €€, AIC
tel. 0119623036

VISTRORIO

Fior di Zucca
Regione Selva, 30

agritourism €€, AIC
tel. 012576405

VOLPIANO

La Lenza
Regione Selva, 30

restaurant €€, AIC
tel. 0119882385 www.lalenza.it

VALLE D'AOSTA
ANTEY SAINT-ANDRÈ

Au Jardin Fleuri
Fraz. Bourg, 7

agritourism AIC
tel. 348.4818426 www.agriturismoantey.com

AOSTA

Grom

gelato (€, AIC) Via Jean Baptiste de Tillier

BREUIL-CERVINIA

Hotel Edelweiss
Via Guido Rey, 18

hotel, restaurant AIC
tel. 166.949078

BRUSSON

Hotel Laghetto
Rue Trois Villages, 291

hotel, restaurant, bar AIC
tel. 125.300179 www.hotellaghetto.it

CHAMPOLUC

Hotel Cré Forné
Loc. Cré Forné

hotel AIC
tel. 125.307197 www.champoluc.it

CHATILLON

Mychef Chatillon Nord

mychef (€, AIC) Autostrad a Torino – Aosta

COGNE

Les Pertzes
Via Dr. Grappein, 93

restaurant, bar €€€, AIC
tel. 165.749227 www.nigritelles.com

COURMAYEUR

Auberge de la Maison
Via Passerin d'Entreves 16

hotel, restaurant
tel. 165869811 www.aubergemaison.it
Notes: English spoken. GF breakfast and pasta with advanced notice.

Cadron Solaire
Via Roma 122

restaurant
tel. 165844609
Notes: Reservations essential. English spoken.

Hotel Aigle
Strada la Palud, 5 fraz.Entréves

hotel, restaurant AIC
tel. 165.8697

Maison de Filippo   restaurant
Fraz. Entreves   tel. 165869797   www.lamaison.com
Notes: Very popular restaurant. Reservations essential. English spoken.

Villa Novecento   hotel, restaurant
Viale Monte Bianco 64   tel. 165843000   www.villanovecento.it
Notes: English spoken. GF with advance notice.

GRESSAN

Le Bon Plat   restaurant   €€, AIC
Fraz. Borettaz, 7   tel. 165.251621
www.facebook.com/pages/LE-BON-PLAT/138059293068653

GRESSONEY LA TRINITÉ

Chalet du Lys   restaurant, hotel restaurant, hotelres   AIC
Loc. Staffal, 14   tel. 0125.366806   www.chaletdulys.it

Romantik Hotel Jolanda Sport   hotel, restaurant   AIC
Loc. Edelbode n Sup. , 31   tel. 125.36614   www.hoteljolandasport.com

GRESSONEY SAINT JEAN

Lyshaus- Carducci   hotel, restaurant   AIC
Loc.tà Tschoard e, 1   tel. 125.356643   www.lyshaus.com

LILLIANES

Maison Vallomy   B&B   AIC
Loc. Vers Chessun, 8   tel. 347.3866874

SAINT MARCEL

Chambre d'Hotes Le Coffret   B&B   AIC
Loc. Jayer, 32   tel. 0165.778751   www.lecoffret.it/en/le-coffre

SAINT VINCENT

Il Ritrovo   restaurant   €-€€€€, AIC
Via Roma, 42   tel. 166.510098   www.ilritrovo-restaurant.it

Oasi   restaurant, pizzeria   €€€€, AIC
Via Cretier, 4   tel. 0166.511577   www.ristorantepizzeriaoasi.eu/en/index.htm

SARRE

Il Pirata   restaurant, pizzeria   €€-€€€, AIC
Fraz. Arensod, 39   tel. 165.257988   www.dalpirata.it

VALTOURNENCHE

Au Vicariat   B&B   AIC
Loc. Capoluog o   tel. 166.92348   www.vicariat.it

Lo Baracon Dou Téne   restaurant   €€€€, AIC
Località Cime Bianche   tel. 0166.93023   www.baracon.blogspot.com

Rifugio Perucca Vuillermo z   B&B   AIC
Vallone di Cignana   tel. 166.969747   www.rifugioperuccavuillermoz.it

VILLENEUVE

Hotel Valdotain   restaurant, hotel   AIC
P.zza Assunzion e, 6/7   tel. 0165-95032   www.valdotain.it

Bellezza (D. Kraushaar)

ALTO ADIGE, TRENTINTO, AND THE DOLOMITES

ALTO ADIGE
(AIC = participates in the Associazione Italiana Celiachia program)

BRESSANONE

Harpf
Loc. La Mara, 107
restaurant, pizzeria
tel. 0472851047
€€, AIC
www.harpf.net

CALDARO

Pensione Christl
Via S. Antonio, 23
inn
tel. 0471963173
AIC
www.pension-christl.it

CAMPO TURES

Alphotel Stocker
Via Wiesenhof, 39/41
hotel
tel. 0474678113
AIC
www.hotelstocker.com

Hotel Drumlerhof
Via Municipio, 6
hotel, restaurant
tel. 0474678068
€-€€€€, AIC
www.drumlerhof.com

LAIVES

Grill Raif
Via Kennedy, 258
restaurant, pizzeria
tel. 0471590681
€€, AIC

MAREBBE

Ucia Picio Prè
La Plì, 29
restaurant
tel. 3381406452
€€-€€€, AIC
www.piciopre.it

MELTINA

Pensione Schlaneiderhof
Località Salonetto, 7
inn
tel. 0471668147
AIC
www.schlaneiderhof.com

MOLINI DI TURES

Schofflmair
Via Tures, 23
hotel, pizzeria
tel. 0474678126
€€-€€€, AIC
www.schoefflmair.com

ORTISEI

Hartmann
Via Rezia, 308
hotel
tel. 0471774444
AIC
www.hotel-hartmann.com

PARCINES

Hotel Weiss
Via Venosta, 38
hotel
tel. 0473967067
AIC
www.hotelweiss.it

POSTAL

Happy
Via Roma, 44
restaurant, pizzeria
tel. 0473290057
€€, AIC

S. SIGISMONDO CHIENES

Petra
Via Pusteria, 16
restaurant, pizzeria
tel. 0474569600
€€, AIC
www.pizzeriapetra.it

SELVA DI VAL GARDENA

Acadia Beauty & Relax
Via Puez, 24
hotel
tel. 0471774444
€€€€, AIC
www.acadia.it

SESTO-SEXTEN

Family Resort Rainer
Via S. Giuseppe, 40
hotel, restaurant, pizzeria, catering
tel. 0474710366
AIC
www.hotelrainer.com

SIUSI ALLO SCILIAR

Hotel Villa Madonna
Via Ibsen, 29
hotel
tel. 0471708860
AIC
www.villamadonna.it

TIROLO

Mair am Turm
Via Principale, 3
hotel, restaurant
tel. 0473923307
€€, AIC
www.mairamturm.it

VALLE AURINA

Sporthotel e Resid. Griesfeld
Via St. Johann, 5/6
hotel
tel. 0474671172
AIC

TRENTINO

ALA

Al Giardino
Via Ronchiano 1
pizzeria
tel. 0464671058
€, AIC

ALBA DI CANAZEI

Albergo Villa Adria
Via De Cost, 109
hotel
tel. 462.601291
AIC

ARCO

Ca' Rossa
Via Linfano, 47
restaurant, pizzeria
tel. 464.50642
AIC

BASELGA DI PINÈ

El Filò
Via Miralago, 43
restaurant
tel. 0461553156
€€-€€€, AIC
www.ristoranteelfilo.it

Pasticceria Pinetana Gelateria — gelato (€, AIC) — C.so Roma, 61

BEDOLLO

Hotel Pineta — hotel, restaurant — AIC
Lago delle Piazze — tel. 461.556642

La Laita — B&B — AIC
Via Massenzi 2 — tel. 333.6853285

BELLAMONTE

Hotel Sole — hotel — AIC
Via De L'Or, 8 — tel. 0462576299 — www.hsole.it

BOLZANO

Caffè Edicola Degustibus — bar — €, AIC
Via Rosmini 51 — tel. 471.983373

La Lanterna — restaurant, pizzeria — AIC
Via Rovigo 14 — tel. 471.502107

Walthers' — restaurant, pizzeria, bar — AIC
P.zza Wolther, 6 — tel. 0471/982548 — www.walthers.it

BRENTONICO

La Pineta — B&B, pizzeria — €-€€€€, AIC
Loc. S. Caterina — tel. 464.395258 — www.pizzeriapineta.it

BRESSANONE

Harpf — restaurant, pizzeria — AIC
Loc. La Mara 107 — tel. 472.851047 — www.harpf.net

CALDARO

Hotel Masatsch — hotel, restaurant — AIC
Pianizza di Sopra 30 — tel. 471.669522 — www.masatsch.it

CAMPITELLO DI FASSA

Hotel Relais San Giusto — hotel, restaurant — AIC
Via Roma 1 — tel. 462.750331 — www.san-giusto.it

CAMPO TURES

Alphotel Stocker — hotel — AIC
Via Wiesenhof, 39/41 — tel. 474.678113 — www.hotelstocker.com

Hotel Drumlerhof — hotel, restaurant — AIC
Via Municipio, 6 — tel. 474.678068 — www.drumlerhof.com

CANAZEI

Hotel Astoria - Rist. De Tofi — hotel, restaurant — AIC
Streda Roma, 92 — tel. 462.601302 — www.hotel-astoria.net

CANEZZA DI PERGINE

Osteria Storica Morelli — restaurant — AIC
P.zza Petrini, 10 — tel. 461.509504 — www.osteriastoricamorelli.it

CAVALESE

Bellavista — hotel — AIC
Via Pizzegoda, 5 — tel. 0462340205 — www.hotelbellavista.biz

CAVEDAGO

Fiore Blu — restaurant, pizzeria — AIC
Via de la Viola, 9 — tel. 0461654019

Hotel alle Rose
Via Tomas 12

hotel
tel. 461.654219

AIC

CENTA S. NICOLÒ

Agritur Maso Rauter
Loc.Rauteri 16

B&B
tel. 461.722257

AIC

Martinelli
Fraz. Doss, 4

agritourism
tel. 0461722125

€-€€, AIC

CLES

Il Giardino
Via Pilati, 16

restaurant, pizzeria
tel. 463.422709

AIC

COMANO TERME

Cattoni Hotel Plaza
Via Cesare Battisti, 19

hotel
tel. 0465701442

AIC
www.cattonihotelplaza.com

Don Pedro
Via C. Battisti, 26

pizzeria
www.pizzeriadonpedro.it

€ - €€, AIC

COREDO

Nardis
Via Moncher, 3

pizzeria
tel. 0463538000

€, AIC

COSTA DI FOLGARIA

Nevada
Via Fontanelle, 47

hotel, restaurant
tel. 0464721495

€€, AIC
www.villaggionevada.it

DARÉ

Le Fontane
Via Civico, 115

restaurant, pizzeria
tel. 0465801601

€, AIC

FAI DELLA PAGANELLA

Agostini
P.zza Italia Unita, 16

pizzeria
tel. 0461583301

AIC
www.pizzeriaagostini.it

FOLGARIA

Az. Agr. La Fonte
Loc. Gruim Mezzomonte

agritourism
tel. 0464720041

€€, AIC
www.la-fonte.org

Cogola Ristorante e B&B
Via Pasubio 135 -Serrada

restaurant, B&B
tel. 464.727156

AIC

ISERA

Agritur Maso Carpenè
Loc. Carpenè 1

agritourism
tel. 335.5926227

AIC

Locanda delle Tre Chiavi
Via Vannetti, 8

restaurant
tel. 0464423721

€€€€, AIC
www.locandadelletrechiavi.it

LAIVES

Res.Rest.Lounge bar Alpenrose
Via San Giacomo, 91

restaurant, hotel, bar
tel. 0471252209

€€€€, AIC

LEDRO - BEZZECCA

Albergo Maggiorina
Via XXIV

hotel
tel. 464.591029

AIC

LEVICO TERME

Alla Loggia dell'Imperator e
Via G.Prati, 27

B&B
tel. 461.706261

AIC

LODRONE

Trenti NO glutine
Via XXIV Maggio, 16
bakery
tel. 465.880776
€, AIC

MADONNA DI CAMPIGLIO

Hotel Crozzon
Viale Dolomiti di Brenta, 96
hotel, restaurant
tel. 465.442222
AIC

St. Raphael
Via Torre del Brenta, 1
hotel
tel. 0465441570
€€€, AIC

MEANO

Agriturismo alle Gorghe
Strada alle Gorghe, 17
agritourism
tel. 0461448268   www.facebook.com/agriturallegorghe
€€, AIC

MELTINA

Pensione Schlaneiderhof
Località Salonetto, 7
hotel
tel. 471.668147
www.schlaneiderhof.com
AIC

MERANO

Happy Pomodoro
Via Laurin 8/a
restaurant, pizzeria
tel. 473.222884
www.pizzeriahappy.com
AIC

MEZZO LOMBARDO

Al Castagneto da Giorgio
Loc. ai Piani, 1
restaurant, pizzeria
tel. 0461601359
www.alcastagneto.net
€€€, AIC

MOENA

Faloria
Piaz de Sotegrava, 18
inn, restaurant
tel. 0462573149
www.hotelfaloria.it
AIC

Lo Sfizio
Piazza de Ramon, 32
Notes: Very favorable reviews.
restaurant, pizzeria, creperie
tel. 462.574757
€€, AIC

MOLINI DI TURES

Schofflmair
Via Tures, 23
hotel, pizzeria
tel. 474.678126
www.schoefflmair.com
AIC

MOLVENO

Hotel Des Alpes
Via Nazionale, 7
hotel
tel. 0461586983
www.desalpes.it
AIC

Hotel Excelsior
Via Nazionale, 41
hotel
tel. 0461586921
www.molveno-excelsior.it
€€€€, AIC

MONTAGNAGA DI PINÈ

Comparsa
Via Domenica Targa, 49
pizzeria
tel. 0461557006
€, AIC

MONTEVACCINO-TRENTO

Bosco Incantato
Loc. Montevaccino, 1/d
pizzeria
tel. 0461960826
€-€€, AIC

NAVE SAN FELICE

Alla Nave
Fr.Nave San Felice 29
pizzeria
tel. 461.870111
€-€€, AIC

ORTISEI

Hartmann
Via Rezia, 308
B&B
tel. 471.774444
www.hotel-hartmann.com
AIC

Hotel Grones
VIA Stufan, 110
hotel
tel. 471.79704
AIC

PARCINES
Hotel Weiss
Via Venosta,38
hotel
tel. 473.967067
AIC
www.hotelweiss.it

PEJO FONTI
Hotel Vioz
Via dei Cavai, 10
hotel
tel. 463.753146
AIC
www.hotelvioz.it

Rosa degli Angeli
Via del Fontanino, 2
hotel, restaurant
tel. 0463743031
€, AIC
www.hotelrosadegliangeli.it

PERGINE VALSUGANA
Antiche Contrade
Via al Lago, 11
restaurant, pizzeria bar
tel. 0461538228
€€€, AIC
www.antichecontrade.com

Giropizza Vip
Loc. Valcanover, 13
pizzeria
tel. 0461512282
€ - €€, AIC

PINZOLO
Hotel Corona
Corso Trento, 31
hotel
tel. 465.50103
AIC
www.hotelcoronapinzolo.it

POZZA DI FASSA
Rifugio T. Taramelli (m. 2.046)
Loc. Valle dei Monzoni
restaurant
tel. 360.879719
AIC

Vidor
Strada Ruf de Ruacia, 15
pizzeria
tel. 0462760022
€, AIC
www.campingvidor.it

RISCONE
Hotel Petrus Aichner H. & Co. KG
Reinthalstr. 11
hotel, restaurant
tel. 474.548263
AIC

RIVA DEL GARDA
Agritur Eden Marone
Via Marone, 11
agritourism
tel. 0464521520
€€€, AIC
www.edenmarone.com

Hotel Villa Enrica
Via Brione 1/A
B&B
tel. 464.551254
AIC
www.hotelvillaenrica.com

La Berlera
Loc. Ceole, 8/b
restaurant
tel. 0464521149
€€€-€€€€, AIC
www.laberlera.it

Villa Nicolli
V.le Cattoni, 5
hotel
tel. 0464552589
AIC
www.hotelvillanicolli.com

ROVERETO
Bar Botti
Corso Verona, 76/A
restaurant, pizzeria
tel. 0464432521
€, AIC

Cherry Gelateria Pasticceria
Via Roma 24
gelato, bakery
tel. 335.83425
€, AIC

S. CRISTINA
Smart Hotel Saslong
Via Pallua, 40
B&B
tel. 471.774444
AIC
www.saslong.eu

S.SIGISMONDO CHIENES

Petra — restaurant, pizzeria — AIC
Via Pusteria, 16 — tel. 0474.569600/348.7094907 — www.pizzeriapetra.it

S.ORSOLA TERME

Malga Agritur Cambroncoi — agritourism — AIC
Loc. Cambroncoi — tel. 329.8016326 — www.hotel-malgacambroncoi.it

SAN CANDIDO

Acquafan — restaurant, pizzeria — AIC
Via Hueber, 2 — tel. 474.914102

SAN CRISTOFORO AL LAGO - PERGINE VALSUGANA

La Darsena — restaurant, pizzeria — AIC
Via dei Pescatori, 47 — tel. 328.0364129

SAN LORENZO IN BANALE

Rifugio Silvio Agostini Val D'Ambiez (m. 2.410) restaurant — AIC
Val D'Ambiez — tel. 465.734138

SELVA DI VAL GARDENA

Acadia Beauty & Relax — hotel — AIC
Via Puez, 24 — tel. 471.774444 — www.acadia.it

Boutique Hotel Nives — hotel, restaurant — AIC
Via Nives, 4 — tel. 471.773329 — www.hotel-nives.com

SESTO-SEXTEN

Family Resort Rainer — hotel, restaurant, pizzeria — AIC
Via S. Giuseppe, 40 — tel. 474.710366 — www.familyresort-rainer.com

SIUSI ALLO SCILIAR

Hotel Villa Madonna — hotel, restaurant — AIC
Via Ibsen, 29 — tel. 471.70886 — www.villamadonna.it

SMARANO

Ostaria Del Filò — osteria — €€€, AIC
Viale Merlonga, 48/A — tel. 463.538057 — www.ostariadelfilo.it

SOPRAMONTE

Alpino — pizzeria — €-€€, AIC
Strada di Spineda 6 — tel. 461.866115

SOVER

Maso Sveseri — restaurant — AIC
Loc. Sveseri 22 — tel. 461.698106 — www.maso-sveseri.it

STENICO

Grand Hotel Terme — hotel, restaurant — AIC
Loc. Terme di Comano — tel. 465.701421 — www.ghtcomano.it

TESERO

Agritur Maso Zanon — agritourism — AIC
Via Cerin 15 — tel. 462.814215 — www.agriturdarial.it

Hotel Scoiattolo — hotel, restaurant — AIC
Loc.Pampe ago 1 — tel. 462.813244 — www.scoiattolo.it

La Trattoria — restaurant, pizzeria — €€€-€€€€, AIC
Via Stazione - fraz.Lago — tel. 462.810203

TIROLO

Mair am Turm   hotel, restaurant   AIC
Via Principale, 3   tel. 473.923307   www.mairamturm.it

TONADICO

Hotel Tressane   hotel   AIC
Via Roma, 30   tel. 439.762205   www.brunethotels.it

Park Hotel Iris   hotel   AIC
Via Roma 26   tel. 439.762   www.brunethotels.it

TRAMBILENO

Rifugio Alpe Pozza "Vincenzo Lancia" (m. 1.802) restaurant   AIC
Loc. Alpe Pozza   tel. 464.868068

TRANSACQUA

Il Caminetto   pizzeria   €-€€, AIC
Via Lungo Canali, 29   tel. 439.762088

TRENTO

Agritur al Vigneto   B&B   AIC
Loc.Mader no 16   tel. 461.822322   www.agrituralvigneto.it

America   inn, restaurant   €€, AIC
Via Torre Verde, 50   tel. 0461983010   www.hotelamerica.it

Bouganville   restaurant, pizzeria   €, AIC
Via Petrarca, 1/4   tel. 0461236666

Grom   gelato (€, AIC)   Piazza Duomo, 27

L'Angolo dei 33   pub, restaurant   AIC
Via Santi Cosma e Damiano, 66   tel. 392.0454593

Montana   restaurant, hotel   €€, AIC
Strada di Vason, 70 - Monte Bondone   tel. 0461948200   www.hotelmontana.it

Rebuffo   restaurant, pizzeria   AIC
Via per Fontanasa nta 24   tel. 461.265932

Uva & Menta   pizzeria   €, AIC
Via Dietro le Mura, A35   tel. 04611903162

VALLE AURINA

Sporthotel e Resid.Griesfeld   hotel   AIC
Via St. Johann,5/6   tel. 474.671172   www.sporthotel-griesfeld.com

VARENA

Hotel alla Rocca   hotel   €, AIC
Via Alpini, 10   tel. 0462340321   www.hotelallarocca.biz

VERMIGLIO

Milano   hotel, restaurant   €-€€, AIC
Via Borgonuovo, 44   tel. 0463758124   www.albergomilano-50629.ea29.com

VIGO CAVEDINE

Genzianella   pizzeria   €-€€, AIC
Via Zurlon 1   Fraz.Masi di Vigo   tel. 461.566084

VIGO DI FASSA

Family Hotel La Grotta   hotel   AIC
Strada de Soraporta 8   tel. 462.76445   www.hotellagrotta.it

Rifugio Roda di Vael (m.2.283)   restaurant   AIC
Loc.Sella del Ciampaz   tel. 462.76445

VIPITENO
Sterzingerhof K.G.   restaurant, pizzeria   AIC
Geizkofler, 15   tel. 472.765128

VOLANO
Alle Palme   pizzeria   €-€€, AIC
Via Panizza 56   tel. 464.411201

Statue (D. Kraushaar)

FRIULI VENEZIA-GIULIA
(AIC = participates in the Associazione Italiana
Celiachia program)

AQUILEIA
Pasticceria Mosaico   bakery   €, AIC
P.zza del Capitolo, 17   tel. 431.919592
www.pasticceriamosaico.com

ARIIS DI RIVIGNANO
Principato di Ariis   inn, restaurant
€€-€€€, AIC   Via Chiesa, 2
tel. 0432775008   www.principatodiariis.com

AVIANO
Aviano Inn   restaurant, pizzeria   AIC
Via Sacile, 23   tel. 0434651050

Mychef Porcia Nord   mychef   (€, AIC) A
28 Portogruaro Pordenone Conegliano Veneto

La bella figura (D. Kraushaar)

BUDOIA
Il Rifugio   restaurant   €€€€, AIC
Via S. Tomè, 85   tel. 0434654915   www.ilrifugio.net

CASTELLO DI PORPETTO
Al Vecchio Mulino   restaurant, pizzeria   €, AIC
Via Palmanova, 13/a   tel. 043160498   www.alvechiomulino.net

CASTIONS DI STRADA
Andronute   agritourism   €€€, AIC
Vicolo Cornelio Gallo   tel. 0432768363   www.agriturismoandronute.it

La Rucola   restaurant   €€€€, AIC
Via D. da Tolmezzo   tel. 0432769624   www.larucolaristorante.it

CERVIGNANO DEL FRIULI
Chichibio   restaurant, pizzeria   €-€€€€, AIC
Via Carnia, 2   tel. 043132704   www.ristorantechichibio.it
Notes: Closed Wednesdays and Saturday at lunch.

H. Internazionale/Rist. La Rotonda hotel, restaurant   €€€, AIC
Via Ramazzotti, 2   tel. 043130751   www.hotelinternazionale.it
Notes: Restaurant closed Sunday and Monday.

CIMANO S. DANIELE
Dal Piciul   restaurant   €€-€€€, AIC
Via dei Ponti, 36   tel. 0432957390

CIVIDALE DEL FRIULI
Al Monastero   restaurant   €€€-€€€€, AIC
Via Ristori, 9   tel. 0432700808

Il Giardino 1886   restaurant, pizzeria   €-€€, AIC
Via Doria, 1   tel. 432.73114   www.ilgiardino1886.it

CODROIPO

Ai Gelsi
Via Circonvallazione Ovest, 12

hotel/restaurant
tel. 0432907064

€€€€, AIC
www.gelsi.com

COLLOREDO DI PRATO

Al Cercjeben
Via Udine, 60
Notes: Closed Mondays, and Tuesday night.

trattoria
tel. 0432652527

€€-€€€, AIC
www.alcercjeben.it

CORDENONS

Osteria Al Curtif
Via Del Cristo, 3

osteria
tel. 0434931038

€€€, AIC

FAGAGNA

Agrit. Casale Cjanor
Via Casali Lini, 11

agritourism
tel. 0432801810

€€ - €€€, AIC
www.casalecjanor.com

Al Castello
Via S. Bartolomeo, 18

restaurant
tel. 0432800185

€€€€, AIC
www.ristorantealcastello.com

Per Tutti i Gusti
Via San Giacomo, 5

bakery
tel. 338.9306793

€, AIC
www.pertuttiigusti.me

Road House Blu's
Via Spilimbergo, 184

sandwich shop
tel. 432.800132

€, AIC

FIUMICELLO

La Catapecchia
Via Trieste, 120
www.it-it.facebook.com/events/263918543664988

restaurant, pizzeria
tel. 431.970869

AIC

FORNI AVOLTRI

Vill. Turistico M.no Ge.Tur.
Loc. Piani di Luzza

resort
tel. 043372041

AIC
www.getur.com

FORNI DI SOPRA

Davost
Via Tagliamento, 26

hotel, restaurant
tel. 043388103

€€, AIC
www.hoteldavost.it

GORIZIA

Al Lampione
Via Silvio Pellico, 7

pizzeria
tel. 048132780

€, AIC
www.pizzerialampione.it

GRADISCA D'ISONZO

Al Pellegrino
P.zza G. Marconi, 5

restaurant, pizzeria
tel. 048199918

€-€€€€, AIC

LATISANA

La Fattoria dei Gelsi
Via Lignano Sud, 55

restaurant
tel. 043153100

€€€€, AIC
www.gelsigroup.com

LAUCO

Barbavigi
Via Capoluogo, 146

B&B
tel. 0433747721

AIC
www.barbavigi.it

LIGNANO PINETA

Hotel Bella Venezia Mare
Via Arco del Grecale, 18/a

hotel, restaurant
tel. 0431422184

€€, AIC
www.bellaveneziamare.it

LIGNANO SABBIADORO

Al Mirelia
Via dell'Acquedotto, 6

restaurant
tel. 043173064

€€, AIC
www.alsoreli.com

Al Soreli restaurant €€, AIC
Raggio dell'Ostro, 14 tel. 0431422766

Atlantic hotel, restaurant €€€, AIC
Lungomare Trieste, 160 tel. 043171101 www.hotelatlantic.it

Désirée hotel, restaurant €€, AIC
Via Aquileia, 47 www.hoteldesiree.it

La Pigna hotel, restaurant, wine bar AIC
Via dei Pini, 9 tel. 431.428991 www.hotelapigna.it

Vill. Ge.Tur - Santa Maria del Mare resort AIC
Viale Centrale, 29 tel. 431.409511 www.getur.com

MANZANO

Elliot restaurant €€-€€€€, AIC
Via Orsaria, 50 tel. 0432751383 www.elliotenoteca.com

MORTEGLIANO

Da Nando trattoria, inn €€€€, AIC
Via Divisione Julia , 14 tel. 0432760187 www.danando.it

PALAZZOLO DELLO STELLA

Gelateria Carapina gelato (€, AIC) Via Nazionale 45/1

PORDENONE

Alle Grazie restaurant €€€, AIC
Via Dogana, 11 tel. 0434573197

B&B E.B.Camere in Villa B&B AIC
Via S. Quirino, 60 tel. 345.6089089

B&B Il Vicolo B&B AIC
Vicolo Roggiuzzol e, 5 tel. 345.6089089 www.ilvicolobeb.it

Gelateria Montereale gelato, bar €, AIC
Via Montereale, 23 tel. 434.365107 www.biscottopordenone.it

Il Principato del Gelato gelato (€, AIC) Via San Quirino, 11

Mamey Cafè Pordenone bar €, AIC
Via Udine, 80 tel. 434.28796 www.mamey.it

Ristorante Pizzeria Alla Catina restaurant, pizzeria €-€€, AIC
Piazza Cavour, 3 tel. 434.520358 www.allacatina.it

REMANZACCO

Al Cardinale restaurant, pizzeria €-€€, AIC
S.S. 54,55 tel. 432.649021 www.ristorantealcardinale.it

ROVEREDO IN PIANO

Tepepa Ale House Country Bar bakery €, AIC
Via Brentella 53/5 tel. 328.3986436

S. DANIELE DEL FRIULI

Al Picaron hotel/restaurant €€€€, AIC
Via S. Andrat, 3 tel. 0432940688 www.alpicaron.it

Al Portonat osteria €€, AIC
Piazza Dante Alighieri, 7/9 tel. 0432940880 www.alportonat.it

S. FLORIANO DEL COLLIO

Osteria Gostilna Gorsic
Loc.tà Sovenza, 7

restaurant
tel. 0481884248

€€€€, AIC

S.DANIELE DEL FRIULI

Al Portonat
Piazza Dante Alighieri, 7/9

osteria
tel. 432.94088

€-€€, AIC
www.alportonat.it

Notes: Great prosciutto. Nice restaurant for celiacs.

S.FLORIANO DEL COLLIO

Osteria Gostilna Korsic
Loc.tà Sovenza, 7

restaurant
tel. 481.884248

€€€, AIC
www.korsic.it

S.GIORGIO DI NOGARO

Laguna Blu
Via Marittima 69/B

restaurant, pizzeria
tel. 431.621436

€-€€, AIC

Pizzeria Ristorante Da Alfonso
Via Roma 73

restaurant, pizzeria
tel. 431.65375

€-€€, AIC
www.pizzeriadaalfonso.com

SAN CANZIAN D'ISONZO

Arcimboldo
Via Risiera San Sabba, 17

restaurant
tel. 048176089

€-€€, AIC
www.arcimboldo.go.it

SAVOGNA D'ISONZO

Locanda Devetak
Via Brezici, 22

restaurant
tel. 0481882488

€€€€, AIC
www.devetak.com

SISTIANA MARE

Chiosco Verde
Baia di Sistiana

restaurant
tel. 339.4783591

€-€€€, AIC
www.chioscoverde.com

SPESSA DI CIVIDALE

Agrit. Borgo dei Sapori
Str. di Planez, 60

agritourism
tel. 0432732477

€, AIC
www.borgodeisapori.net

TARCENTO

Costantini
Via Pontebbana, 12

restaurant, inn
tel. 0432792372

€€€€, AIC

TERENZANO

Gelateria Vanillà

gelato (€, AIC)

Piazza Terenzio, 27/c

TERZO DI AQUILEIA

Ristorante Pizzeria All'Anfora
Via Julia Augusta, 3

restaurant, pizzeria
tel. 431.31188

€, AIC
www.allanfora.it

TRICESIMO

Al Glicine

gelato (€, AIC)

P.zza Garibaldi, 3

Da Miculan
P. Libertà, 16

trattoria
tel. 0432851504

AIC
www.trattoriamiculan.com

Moby Dick
Via Michelangelo 30 - loc. Morena

restaurant, pizzeria
tel. 0432851711

€€, AIC

TRIESTE

Ainoa La Cucina delle 4 Stagioni
Via Rossetti, 75

restaurant
tel. 0402601283

€€, AIC
www.ainoa.it

Bora di Trieste B&B AIC
Via della Raffineria, 8 tel. 40.661988 www.boraditrieste.freshcreator.com

Grom gelato (€, AIC) Via S. Nicolò, 18/b

Hotel Savoy Excelsior Palace hotel, restaurant €€€€, AIC
Riva del Mandracchio, 4 tel. 0407794730 www.savoytrieste.it

Pasticceria Rosa bakery €, AIC
Via Giulia 25 tel. 40.573079 www.pasticceriarosa.com
Notes: 100% GF!

Pepenero Pepebianco restaurant €€€€, AIC
Via Rittmeyer, 14/a tel. 0407600716 www.pepeneropepebianco.it

UDINE

Accademia del Gelato gelato (€, AIC) Via Crispi, 13

Alle Due Palme hotel, pizzeria €€-€€€, AIC
Via Leonardo da Vinci 5 tel. 432.481807 www.alleduepalme.it

Ancona 2 restaurant, pizzeria €€, AIC
V.le Tricesimo, 101 tel. 0432545262

Astoria Hotel Italia hotel AIC
Piazza XX Settembre, 24 tel. 432.505091 www.hotelastoria.udine.it

Da Guido restaurant, pizzeria €-€€, AIC
Via Po, 82 tel. 0432282812

Damadolce Senza Glutine bakery, gastropub €, AIC
Via Veneto, 65 -Cussignacco tel. 366.4368479 www.damadolce.it

Gelateria da Nonno Carletto gelato (€, AIC) Piazzale Cella, 20
Gelateria Gusto Antico gelato (€, AIC) Via Cividale 524
Grom gelato (€, AIC) Via Rialto, 12/c

Hotel Friuli hotel AIC
Viale Ledra, 24 tel. 432.234351

Hotel Suite Inn hotel €€€€, AIC
Via F. di Toppo, 25 tel. 0432501683 www.hotelsuiteinn-udine.com

Il Ristorantino da Maria restaurant €€€€, AIC
Via Bertaldia, 25 tel. 432.504545

Vitello d'Oro restaurant €€€€, AIC
Via Valvason, 4 tel. 0432508982 www.vitellodoro.com
Notes: Closed Monday at lunch, Wednesdays.

VILLA VICENTINA

Al Ragno d'Oro inn, restaurant AIC
Via Trieste, 18 tel. 043196058

Scale (D. Kraushaar)

THE MARCHES

(AIC = participates in the Associazione Italiana Celiachia program)

. ACQUAVIVA PICENA

Azzurro Via Fontepezzana, 1	restaurant tel. 0735764175	€€, AIC

ANCONA

Dolce e Amaro Via Piave, 17/b	bar, tavola calda tel. 71.20021	€, AIC polidorigianni@alice.it
Gelateria La Golosa Via delle Grazie, 140	gelato tel. 71.2804218	€, AIC www.gelaterialagolosa.it
Il Lazzaretto Largo Fiera della Pesca Molo Sud	restaurant, pizzeria tel. 71.55368	€€, AIC www.ristoranteillazzaretto.it
La Botte Via Tavernelle, 14 Notes: Closed at lunch.	restaurant, pizzeria tel. 07185325	AIC www.labotte1986.it
Opera Nova della Marca Fr.ne Varano, 127	restaurant tel. 71.2861093	€€-€€€€, AIC www.operanovadellamarca.it
Osteria Teatro Strabacco Via Oberdan, 2	restaurant Ost tel. 07156748	€€€, AIC www.strabacco.it
Rossopomodoro Via P. Filonzi, 4	pizzeria tel. 71.2916363	€€, AIC

ASCOLI PICENO

Al Teatro
Via del Teatro, 1
restaurant, pizzeria
tel. 736.253549
€€-€€€€, AIC
www.ristorantealteatro.com

Bella Napoli
Via Bonaparte, 18/20
Notes: Closed Thursdays.
pizzeria
tel. 0736257030
€, AIC

Il Viaggio
Via Cino del Duca, 10
restaurant
tel. 736.252119
€€, AIC
www.ilviaggioristorante.it

La Cittadella
Via Napoli, 106/112
Notes: Closed Tuesdays.
restaurant, pizzeria
tel. 0736343088
€, AIC
www.lacittadella.it

Mister O.K.
Via G. Spalvieri, 20
restaurant, pizzeria
tel. 073643483
€-€€, AIC

BELFORTE DEL CHIENTI

Chiaroscuro
Via Nazionale, 27
pizzeria
tel. 733.905499
€€, AIC
www.ristorantechiaroscuro.it

CAGLI

Le Fontane
Strada Cagli-Pergola, 126/a
restaurant, pizzeria
tel. 0721790148
€€€-€€€€, AIC

CAMERINO

Etoile
Via Le Mosse, 69
restaurant, pizzeria
tel. 0737630238
€, AIC

CAMPOCAVA LLO DI OSIMO

Il Villino
Via Cagiata, 135
restaurant
tel. 71.717014
€€-€€€, AIC
www.ilvillino-osimo.it

CASTELRAIMONDO

Gelateria Bar Carnevali
gelato (€, AIC)
Corso Italia, 57

CIVITANOVA MARCHE

Bar Caffetteria Romoli
V.le Vittorio Veneto, 187
bar-cafe
tel. 0733771990
€, AIC

Hotel Cosmopolitan
Via Alcide De Gasperi, 2
hotel, restaurant
tel. 733.771682
AIC
www.cosmobusinesshotel.it

Mangia Centro Degustazione
Via Pitignano, 50
agritourism
tel. 0733890053
€€-€€€, AIC

Verde e Azzurro
Via B. Brin
B&B
tel. 0733709397
AIC
www.bbverdeazzurro.it

COLDELCE

La Celletta Country House
Via Serra di Genga, 7
Notes: Closed Mondays and Tuesdays.
restaurant
tel. 0721495130
€€€, AIC

CORRIDONIA

Gelatomania
gelato (€, AIC)
Via Trento, 8

Itaca
Via L. Lotto, 66/68
Notes: Closed Tuesdays.
restaurant, pizzeria
tel. 0733433935
€, AIC

CUPRAMONTANA

Ristorante Gina
Parco E. Amatori

restaurant, pizzeria
tel. 731.780157

AIC

ESANATOGLIA

Sibylla
Loc. Bresciano s.n.c.

restaurant
tel. 0737889140

€, AIC

FABRIANO

Bynice Gelateria Naturale

gelato (€, AIC)

Via Cialdini, 1

Gentile da Fabriano
Via Pontemagno, snc
Notes: Closed Fridays.

hotel, restaurant
tel. 0732627190

€€€, AIC

Marchese del Grillo
Via Rocchetta Bassa,73
Notes: Closed Sunday night and Mondays.

hotel, restaurant
tel. 0732625650

€€€€, AIC
www.marchesedelgrillo.com

FALCONARA

Oasi Paese dei Bimbi
Via Castello di Barcaglione, 10
Notes: Closed Tuesdays.

restaurant
tel. 071910849

€€-€€€, AIC

Ristorante Il Cantuccio
Via dei Mille, 10

restaurant
tel. 71.911596

€, AIC

Strabaccoamare
Via Flaminia, 480 (bagni 13)

restaurant
tel. 71.911037

€€€€, AIC
www.strabacco.it

FANO

Il Barone Rosso
Via E. Mattei, 50

restaurant, bar
tel. 0721865835

€€-€€€, AIC

Kalaverde
Via Fratelli Zuccari, 43

restaurant, pizzeria
tel. 721.84008

€€-€€€, AIC
www.kalaverde.it

Osteria dalla Peppa
Via Vecchia, 8

restaurant
tel. 721.823904

€€-€€€, AIC
www.osteriadallapeppa.it

FERMO

Gelateria Caffetteria Antonini
P.le Azzolino, 21

gelato, bar
tel. 743.221705

€, AIC

FOLIGNANO

Best Western Hotel Villa Pigna
V.le Assisi, 33

hotel, restaurant
tel. 0736491868

€€-€€€, AIC
www.hotelvillapigna.it

FOSSOMBRO NE

Nuovo Giardino
Viale Martiri della Resistenza, 1

restaurant, pizzeria
tel. 721.715198

€€€, AIC
www.nuovogiardino.net

FRAZ. RONCITELLI-SENIGALLIA

Degli Ulivi
Via Gioco del Pallone, 2

restaurant
tel. 0717919670

€€-€€€, AIC

GABICCE MARE

Grand H. Michelacci
P.zza Giardini, 1

hotel, restaurant
tel. 0541954361

AIC
www.michelacci.com

Hotel Alexander
Via Panoramica, 35

hotel
tel. 0541954166

€€€-€€€€, AIC

Hotel Perla
Via Trento, 5

hotel, restaurant
tel. 541.954672

AIC
www.hotel-perla.it

GRADARA

Mastin Vecchio
Via D. Alighieri, 5

restaurant, osteria
tel. 541.964024

€€-€€€, AIC
www.mastinvecchio.com

GROTTAMMARE

Chalet Ciaschì
Via C. Colombo, 18
Notes: Closed Mondays.

restaurant
tel. 0735735570

€€-€€€€, AIC

JESI

Aesis La Dolce Collina
Via Maccarata, 2

B&B
tel. 0731245854

AIC

Bar Il Tasso Alcolico
Via Marche, 14/D

bar
tel. 731.53785

€, AIC

Ciro & Pio Gelato Mio

gelato (€, AIC)

Via Don Sturzo, 7

Federico II
Via Ancona, 100

hotel, restaurant
tel. 0731211079

€€€, AIC

Mezzometro da Ale
Via Leopardi, 1

restaurant, pizzeria
tel. 0731213290

AIC

Paoloni La Brusca
Via Mazzangrugno, 78
Notes: Closed Mondays.

restaurant, pizzeria
tel. 0731246237

€-€€€, AIC
www.labrusca.it

MACERATA

Osteria dei Fiori
Via Lauro Rossi, 61

osteria
tel. 0733260142

€€€, AIC

Tuttogelato

gelato (€, AIC)

Via Spalato, 124 c/d

MARINA DI MONTEMARCIANO

Maison del Celiaco
Via Verga 33

bakery, sandwich shop
www.maisondelceliaco.it

€

Ristorante Delle Rose
Via delle Querce, 1

restaurant
tel. 0719198668

€€€€, AIC
www.ristorantedellerose.it

MARINA MONTEMARCIANO

Il Girasole
Via Media, 11

restaurant, pizzeria
tel. 0719198408

€-€€€, AIC

MAROTTA

La Riva
L.mare Cristoforo Colombo, 180

restaurant, pizzeria
tel. 0721960816

€€€-€€€€, AIC

MERCATELLO SUL METAURO

Ca' Montioni
Loc. Montioni, 23

agritourism, B&B
tel. 072289706

€€€, AIC
www.camontioni.it

MONDAVIO

Maria
Via Cavallara, 3

restaurant
tel. 0721976220

€€€, AIC

MONDOLFO

Chiostro dell'Avis
Via Fermi, 4

restaurant, pizzeria

€€-€€€, AIC

Albergo Vettore
Via Piane Ascolane, 8
Notes: Closed March-November.

MONTEGALLO
inn
tel. 0736806116

€€-€€€, AIC
www.albergovettore.it

MONTEMARCIANO
B&B
tel. 71.9198408

AIC
www.lacasasulsentiero.net

B&B Il Sentiero
Via Media, 11

NUMANA
inn
tel. 0717390170

AIC

Cantarini
Via Litoranea, 90
Notes: Closed October-March.

ORTEZZANO
agritourism
tel. 734.779348

AIC
www.vecchiogelso.com

Agriturismo Vecchio Gelso
C.da Casali,11

OSIMO
restaurant, pizzeria
tel. 071715666

€-€€, AIC

Ada
Via Molino Mensa, 37
Notes: Closed Tuesdays.

PESARO
bar
tel. 721.23391

€, AIC

Bar Le Café
Via Mario del Monaco, 12

Chiccoteca
Via Buozzi, 20

restaurant, pizzeria, bar
tel. 721.34324

AIC

G.H. Vittoria/Rist.Agorà
P.le della Libertà, 2
Notes: Closed Mondays.

hotel, restaurant
tel. 072134343

AIC

Gelateria del Corso

gelato (€, AIC)

C.so 11 Settembre, 168

H. Savoy/Rist. Ariston
V.le della Repubblica, 22

inn, restaurant
tel. 072133133

AIC

Hotel Nautilus
V.le Trieste, 26

hotel, restaurant
tel. 721.30275

AIC
www.nautiluspesaro.edenhotels.it

La Testa del Re
Via delle Galligarie, 22/24

restaurant, pizzeria
tel. 072167609

€, AIC

Lo Squero
Strada delle Marche, 60
Notes: Closed Mondays.

restaurant
tel. 072165405

€-€€€€, AIC
www.ristorantelosquero.it

Polo Pasta e Pizza
V.le Trieste, 231

restaurant
tel. 0721375902

AIC

Ristò Vera
Via Yuri Gagarin, sn
Notes: Closed Sundays.

restaurant
tel. 0383813135

€, AIC

Da Lorenzo
Via Ponte Armellina, 68

PETRIANO
restaurant, pizzeria
tel. 722.52093

AIC

PIETRARUBBIA
restaurant, pizzeria
tel. 722.75387

€-€€€€, AIC
www.ristorantelalocandadeltorrione.it

La Locanda del Torrione
Via Montefeltresca, 193
Notes: Very highly rated.

POLLENZA

La Terrazza del Sole
L.go Giovanni Verga, 15
pizzeria
tel. 0733549948
€, AIC

PONZANO DI FERMO

Artigiangel
gelato (€, AIC)
V.le Trieste, 30

PORTO RECANATI

Gelateria del Corso
gelato (€, AIC)
C.so Matteotti, 269

Giannino
Via C. Colombo, 25
hotel, restaurant
tel. 0719799141
AIC
info@conerohotel.com

PORTO SAN ELPIDIO

Ciak Brasserie dal 1983
Via Canada, 16
restaurant, pizzeria
tel.. 734.99577
€€, AIC
www.pizzeriaciakbrasserie.it

PORTO SAN GIORGIO

Chalet Duilio
L.re Gramsci Sud
restaurant, pizzeria
tel. 0734678731
€€-€€€, AIC
www.chaletduilio.it

Gelateria Pelacani di Giacomozzi A. gelato (€, AIC)
P.zza Mentana, 5

Happy Days
Via Verdi, 24
restaurant, pizzeria
tel. 0734673900
€, AIC
Notes: DS pizza point. Closed Tuesdays.

Vela
L.re Gramsci Nord
restaurant
tel. 734.676482
AIC
www.chaletvela.com

RECANATI

La Cantina di Ale
Via Le Grazie
restaurant, pizzeria
tel. 071977101
€€, AIC

RIPATRANSONE

Az. Agrit. Frattini Laura
Contrada Canali, 33
B&B
tel. 3282732083
AIC
www.agriturismopiceno.com

ROSORA

L'Oasi
Via Clementina, 9
restaurant, pizzeria
tel. 0731814308
AIC
Notes: DS pizza point. Closed Mondays.

S. ANGELO IN VADO

La Vecchia Fattoria
Via Fiorenzuola, 32
pizzeria
tel. 722.88667
€, AIC
www.misterimprese.it

S. BENEDETTO DEL TRONTO

La Sfinge
Via S. Giacomo, 48
hotel
tel. 0735655555
€€€€, AIC
Notes: Closed October-March.

Pizza Leggera Picena
P.za Sacra Famiglia, 1
restaurant, pizzeria
tel. 0735656645
€, AIC
Notes: DS pizza point.

Playa Marconi
Viale Europa, 3
pizzeria bar
tel. 03402206499
€, AIC

S. MARCELLO

Le Stagioni
Via Montelatiere 17/a
restaurant
tel. 731.267926
AIC
www.le-stagioni.it

S. SEVERINO MARCHE

Caffetteria Gelateria Dignani — bar, gelato (€, AIC) — Via Eustachio, 12/14

Il Taccolito — agritourism — €, AIC
Loc. Taccoli, 41 — tel. 0733637257

La Lucciola — restaurant, pizzeria — €€€, AIC
C.da Colleluce, 55 — tel. 733.638777 — www.ristorantelalucciola.com

S.BENEDETTO DEL TRONTO

Dal Gelataio — gelato (€, AIC) — Via Monfalcone, 17

Hotel Canguro — hotel — AIC
Via S. Giacomo, 52 — tel. 735.650977 — www.hotelcanguro.it

S.COSTANZO

Locanda La Cerasa — restaurant — €€€, AIC
Strada Piagge, 1 — tel. 0721935117
Notes: Closed Mondays.

Mary Sierra — restaurant, pizzeria — €€, AIC
Via delle Grazie, 22 — tel. 721.930515 — www.pizzeriamarysierra.it

SAN SEVERINO MARCHE

La Lucciola — restaurant, pizzeria — €, AIC
C.da Colleluce, 55 — tel. 0733638777

SANT'IPPOLITO

Cascina delle Rose — restaurant — €€€, AIC
Via delle Industrie, 9 — tel. 0721728197 — www.cascinadellerose.com

SENIGALLIA

Bano Ristorante — restaurant, pizzeria — €€-€€€, AIC
L.re Leonardo da Vinci — tel. 07160643

Eden — restaurant, pizzeria — €-€€€, AIC
Via Marzi, 4 — tel. 071659165 — www.ristoranteden.it

Gelogiallo — gelato (€, AIC) — Via L. da Vinci, 52

Hotel Sirena — hotel — AIC
L.re Dante Alighieri, 78 — tel. 0717920605 — www.hotelsirena.com
Notes: Closed October-March.

Hotel Trieste — hotel, restaurant — AIC
Via Trieste, 27 — tel. 71.659057 — www.hotelpensionetrieste.com

Il Casale — restaurant — €-€€€, AIC
Str. Prov.le S. Angelo, 20 — tel. 071665003 — www.ilcasaleristorante.it

Michele da Ale — restaurant, pizzeria — €€€, AIC
L.mare L. Da Vinci, 33 — tel. 07160578 — www.micheledaale.it

Universal — hotel — AIC
Lungomare Mameli, 47 — tel. 0717927474 — www.hoteluniversal.it

STAFFOLO

Belvedere — inn restaurant bar — €€€-€€€€, AIC
Via Redipuglia, 1/3 — tel. 0731779261

TAVULLIA

Brezza di Mare — restaurant — €€€-€€€€, AIC
Via Ofanto, 4/a — tel. 721.49175 — www.brezzadimare.it

La Nuova Briciola
P.zza Togliatti, 3
Notes: DS pizza point.

restaurant, pizzeria
tel. 0733974504

€, AIC

San Nicola
Via Flaminia, 6

restaurant, pizzeria
tel. 0733967448

€€, AIC

Antiche Mura
Via Don Minzoni, 11
Notes: Closed Tuesdays.

TREIA
restaurant, pizzeria
tel. 0733217053

€€, AIC

Da Otello
Via S. Lorenzo, 60
Notes: Closed Wednesdays.

restaurant, pizzeria
tel. 0733215710

€€, AIC

Villa Cortese
C.da Sterpare, 32

restaurant
tel. 0733216891

€€€€, AIC
www.villa-cortese.it

Zì Marì
Via Bocca Trabaria ovest, 145

URBINO
pizzeria
tel. 722.57105

€€, AIC
www.zimari.it

La Nuova Fazenda
Via Nazionale Urbinate, 201

VALLEFOGLIA
restaurant, pizzeria
tel. 721.496154

€, AIC
www.lanuovafazenda.it

Locanda Montelippo
Via Canarecchia, 31

agritourism, restaurant, B&B
tel. 721.416735

€€, AIC
www.montelippo.it

A Beautiful Grave (D. Kraushaar)

Vasto Marina (E. DiFabio)

ABRUZZO

(AIC = participates in the Associazione Italiana Celiachia program)

ALBA ADRIATICA

Me Gusta	gelato (€, AIC)	L.re Marconi, 80
Me Gusta Mas	gelato (€, AIC)	Lungomare Marconi 166

ATESSA

Royal Garden restaurant, pizzeria €-€€, AIC
Via Piana La Fara, 157 tel. 0872895301

AVEZZANO

Attacchi di Pane bakery €, AIC
Via Mercato 6 tel. 335.6301244 www.attacchidipane.it/1

Barone Rosso pizzeria €-€€, AIC
Via Don Minzoni, 5 tel. 0863453155
Notes: Closed Mondays.

Cozzolino pizzeria €-€€, AIC
Via Sandro Pertini 116 tel. 863.22199
https://it-it.facebook.com/pages/Ristorante-Pizzeria-Cozzolino/165288806824839

Piadiland restaurant €, AIC
Via Trieste, 15 tel. 3285964047 www.piadiland.com

Umami restaurant 2, AIC
Via Antonio Gramsci 6/B tel. 0863.33372/347.2632555

BUGNARA

H.Sagittario/Rist.Tre Archi hotel, restaurant €-€€€, AIC
Via Nolfese, 2 tel. 086446463

	CASALINCONTRADA	
La taverna di Pop's	pizzera, trattoria	€-€€, AIC
Via Orientale 15	tel. 871.371051	
	CASOLI	
Biocasa Quarto a Monte	B&B	AIC
Via Roma 12	tel. 347.6071674	www.quartoamonte.it
	CASTEL DI SANGRO	
Il Sorriso	restaurant	€, AIC
Via Pontenuovo, 45	tel. 0864840922	www.pizzeriailsorriso.com
	CASTELLANA DI PIANELLA	
La Rustica	agritourism	€€€-€€€€, AIC
C.da Astignano, 13	tel. 0859771650	www.agriturismolarustica.com
Notes: Must reserve in advance.		
	CELANO	
Alle Coste Gluten Free	B&B	AIC
Via Aterno 33	tel. 863.791457	www.allecosteglutenfree.it
Bar Gelateria Castello	gelato (€, AIC)	Via L. Giuliani, 20/22
La Cittadella	trattoria	€-€€, AIC
Via Tiburtina Km.6930	tel. 0863791293	
Le Mirage	pizzeria	€€, AIC
Via Ranelletti, 278-280	tel. 0863790830	
Notes: Closed Tuesdays.		
	CEPAGATTI	
I Due Leoni	trattoria	€€€€, AIC
Via Nazionale, 58/c	tel. 0859772685	
Notes: Closed Mondays, Tuesdays and at lunch.		
	CESE DI PRETURO	
Il Girasole	restaurant, pizzeria	€€, AIC
Via Sant'Anna	tel. 0862461290	
	CHIETI	
Alternativa al Grano	bakery, gelato	€, AIC
Strada per Popoli	tel. 347.896864	www.alternativaalgrano.it
Gelat. Sigismondi	gelato (€, AIC)	P.zza Trento e Trieste, 6/8
Nino	restaurant	€€, AIC
Via P.ssa di Piemonte, 6	tel. 087163781	
	CHIETI SCALO	
Bar Gelat. Ariston	gelato (€, AIC)	Via De Meis, 36
	CITTÀ S. ANGELO	
La Rusticana	restaurant, pizzeria	€-€€€, AIC
C.da Madonna della Pace, 100	tel. 085959434	
Notes: Closed Tuesdays.		
Miramare	hotel, restaurant, pizzeria	€-€€€€, AIC
Via T. De Caesaris, 8	tel. 08595321	www.miramarehotel.it
	COPPITO-L'AQUILA	
L'Isola Che Non C'era	pizzeria	€, AIC
Via Vetoio	tel. 0862319930	

S. Eufemia
Via Aterno, 435
Notes: Closed Fridays.

FARA FILIORUM PETRI
inn, restaurant €€, AIC
tel. 087170154 www.hotelsanteufemia.altervista.org

La Villetta
c/o Villa Comunale

FARA SAN MARTINO
pizzeria €-€€, AIC
tel. 872.980452

La Nave
Viale Kennedy, 2
Notes: Closed Wednesdays.

FRANCAVILLA
restaurant €€€€, AIC
tel. 085817115

Compagnia della Pizza
Via Trieste, 181/183

GIULIANOVA
pizzeria €, AIC
tel. 3205569797 www.compagniadellapizza.com

Gelateria Magrini Ice
Piazza Dalmazia, 8/9
gelato €, AIC
tel. 349.1376404 www.magrinigelati.it

Hotel Clipper
Via Quinto, 5
hotel AIC
tel. 0858028579 www.hotelclipper.com

Evergreen
C.da Iconicella 332

LANCIANO
pizzeria, restaurant €-€€, AIC
tel. 872.43767 www.evergreenristorante.com

Pizzangelo
Via del Pescara, 7/a
Notes: DS pizza point. Closed Tuesdays.
pizzeria €, AIC
tel. 3383151900 www.pizzangelo.it

Ruhental
Via Follani, 138
Notes: Closed Tuesdays and lunch.
pizzeria, trattoria €, AIC
tel. 087244101

Carmine
C.da Remartello, 52

LORETO APRUTINO
restaurant €€€€, AIC
tel. 0858208553 www.ristorantecarmine.it

Le Magnolie
C.da Fiorano, 83
Notes: Closed Wednesdays, Sundays.
agritourism €€-€€€, AIC
tel. 0858289534

Rychot's
gelato (€, AIC) Via Vittorio Veneto, 67

Peter Pan
P.zza Della Repubblica 6

MAGLIANO DE' MARSI
pizzeria €-€€, AIC
tel. 863.515032

B&B La Palma
Via Aremonga, 14

MONTESILVANO
B&B AIC
tel. 3396035640 www.beblapalma.it

Bella Notte
Via Orsini 20/B
B&B AIC
tel. 388.191494 www.bellanottemontesilvano.it

Dolce Capriccio
gelato (€, AIC) V.le Abruzzo, 46

Hotel d'Atri
Via Calabria, 14/1
hotel, restaurant AIC
tel. 0854450112 www.hoteldatri.it

Zelig
Via Vestina, 415

restaurant, pizzeria
tel. 0854680673

€, AIC

MONTORIO AL VOMANO

Hotel Vomano
V.le Risorgimento, 113

hotel, restaurant, pizzeria
tel. 0861598498

€-€€, AIC
www.hotelvomano.it

MOSCIANO S. ANGELO

Borgo Spoltino
Str. Selva Alta
Notes: Closed Mondays, Tuesdays.

restaurant
tel. 0858071021

€€€-€€€€, AIC
www.borgospoltino.it

Via Veneto
Via V.Veneto, 8
Notes: Closed Mondays and at lunch.

pizzeria
tel. 0858062259

€, AIC

NOCCIANO

Le Nostre Radici
C.da Prato S. Lorenzo, 36
Notes: Closed Monday-Thursday

agritourism
tel. 085847644

€€€, AIC

ORTONA

La Magnolia
C.da Cucullo 28
www.bedandbreakfastlamagnolia.com

B&B
tel. 085.9031289/328.6761836

AIC

Novecento

gelato (€, AIC)

C.so Vittorio Emanuele, 94

PESCARA

Bibò

gelato(€, AIC)

Via Pepe, 105

Buffalo Bill
Via T. Da Celano, 22

restaurant, pizzeria
tel. 08563355

€-€€, AIC

Caprice Fabrizio Camplone
P.zza Garibaldi, 29

gelato, bar, bakery
tel. 85.691633

€, AIC
www.fabriziocamplone.com

De Marco
P.zza Duca Deli Abruzzi 63/65

gelato, bar
tel. 393.0736235

€, AIC

Grotta del Marinaio
Via Bardet, 6
Notes: Closed Mondays and at lunch.

restaurant
tel. 085690454

€€-€€€€, AIC

La Scuderia
c/o Parco Sabucchi   tel. 85.4711492

restaurant, pizzeria

€-, AIC
https://it-it.facebook.com/scuderiasabucchi

Maison del Celiaco
Via del Santuario 139 - Zona Gesuiti

bakery, sandwich shop

€
www.maisondelceliaco.it

Parc H. Villa Immacolata
Str. c.le S. Silvestro, 340

hotel
tel. 0854980031

€-€€, AIC

Pipè
V.le della Riviera 249

restaurant, pizzeriaizzeria
tel. 85.75178

€-€€, AIC
www.ristorantepipe.it

PESCASSEROLI

Pagnani
V.le Colli dell'Oro 5

hotel
tel. 349.2338659

AIC
www.hotelpagnani.it

PETTORANO SUL GIZIO

La Quercia
S.S. 17 km.107

restaurant, pizzeria
tel. 086448202

€, AIC

PINETO

La Pineta   hotel   AIC
V.le G.D'Annunzi o 193   tel. 085.9491406/338.8150994 www.hotellapineta.eu/en

RIMINI

Star Bene Senza Glutine   bar, desserts   €
Vicolo del Voltone 2/4   tel. 0541.1736666 www.starbenesenzaglutine.it

ROCCAMONTEPIANO

Brancaleone   restaurant (0)   €€€, AIC
Via Corsi, 36   tel. 087177571   www.ristorantebrancaleone.it

ROCCARASO

La Fattoria   pizzeria   €, AIC
S.S. 17 km.139   tel. 086462980
Notes: DS pizza point. Closed Tuesdays.

ROSETO DEGLI ABRUZZI

Gelat. Mario Magrini   gelato(€, AIC)   L.re Roma, 22

S. DEMETRIO NE' VESTINI

L'Angolo dello Spuntino   pizzeria   €, AIC
Largo Stazione   tel. 0862810200
Notes: DS pizza point. Closed Tuesdays.

Raggio Verde   gelato (€, AIC)   Via Nazionale, 29

S. SALVO MARINA

Cioccolat Gelateria ai 3 Scalini   gelato (€, AIC)   Via Magellano, 287

La Massaia   pizzeria   €-€€, AIC
Via Montegrappa 4   tel. 873.520496

S. VITO CHIETINO

Il Fienile   restaurant, pizzeria   €-€€, AIC
C.da Murata Alta, 50   tel. 0872618288
Notes: DS pizza point. Closed Wednesdays.

S.TER. DI SPOLTORE

Gelateria Franca   gelato (€, AIC)   Via M. Adriatico, 46

SANT'EGIDIO ALLA VIBRATA

O' Sole Mio   restaurant, pizzeria   €-€€, AIC
Via M. Buonarotti 53   tel. 861.842408   www.pizzeriaosolemio.eu

SCERNI

Az Agr. Fontemaggio   restaurant   €€, AIC
C.da Caltrucci, 33   tel. 0873914525

SULMONA

Di Silvio   gelato (€, AIC)   Via Solino, 2

TERAMO

La Tana di Lucifero   restaurant, pizzeria   AIC
Via R. Campana, 6   tel. 086243915

TORNARECCIO

Il Ristoro dei Paladini   restaurant   €€-€€€, AIC
Parco Monte Pallano   tel. 0872866621

TORTORETO LIDO

A Casa di Ludo
gelato (€, AIC)
Via Trieste 141

Rist. Zafferano/H. Aurea
Via Leonardo da Vinci, 46
hotel, restaurant
tel. 0861786430
€€, AIC
www.aureahoteltortoreto.it

Ulivo Mare/H.CIVI
Via Milano, 23, 32
restaurant, pizzeria, hotel
tel. 0861788026
€€€, AIC
www.ristoranteulivomare.it

VACRI

Il Tucano
Via Sterpara, 55
restaurant, pizzeria
tel. 0871720024
€-€€€, AIC

VAL VOMANO

Poemi
Piazza ex Mercato Coperto
restaurant, pizzeria
tel. 389.6815179
AIC
www.pizzeriadeipoemi.it

VASTO

Caffè de Parma
C.so de Parma, 13/15
bar
tel. 873366919
€, AIC

Dolce Brivido
Via S. Caterina da Siena, 16/18
gelato
tel. 348.872193
€, AIC

Il Giardino dei Sogni
Via Colli, 1
B&B
tel. 0873361663
AIC
www.ilgiardinodeisogni.net

Peste e Corna
Via G. Leopardi, 6/8
Notes: Closed Tuesdays.
pizzeria
tel. 0873370808
€, AIC

Terzo Tempo Food & Fun
Via Conti Ricci, 1
sandwich shop, bar
tel. 0873378795
€, AIC

Vecchia Vasto
L.go Siena, 14
B&B, restaurant, pizzeria
tel. 0873363420
€ - €€€, AIC
www.vecchiavasto.com

VILLAMAGNA

Lucky Star
Via Val di Foro SS 263
restaurant
tel. 0871300283
€€€€, AIC
www.ristoranteluckystar.it

The Grapevine (E. DiFabio)

Santa Maria della Grazia (M. Roglieri)

MOLISE

AGNONE
Staffoli Horses agritourism   AIC
S.P. Montesangrin a, km.1
tel. 0865.771775
www.staffoli.it

BOJANO
Da Tonino   restaurant, pizzeria €€, AIC
Via S. Antonio Abate sn
tel. 0874.773031
www.pizzeriadatonino.it

CAMPOBASSO
Al Camaleonte   bar   €, AIC
Via Elena, 8   tel. 339.8917846

da Sasà e Barbara   gastropub, rotisserie   €€, AIC
Via Mazzini, 111   tel. 874.62081

Flower B&B   B&B   AIC
Via Novelli, 3   tel. 338.3030338
www.bed-and-breakfast.it/pagina.cfm?id=32915&idregione=11

Hotel Donguglielmo   hotel, restaurant   AIC
C.da S. Vito, 15/b   tel. 0874.418178   www.donguglielmo.it

Il Capriccio   gelato (€, AIC)   Via XXIV Maggio, 40

La Regina   pizzeria   €€, AIC
Via nicola Neri, 1 9   tel. 0874.1961290   www.pizzerialaregina.it

Ristorante Pizzeria Castello   restaurant, pizzeria   €€, AIC
Via De Pretis, 27/a   tel. 0874.415845

CAPRACOTTA
L'Elfo   restaurant   €€, AIC
Via Campanelli, sn   tel. 0865.949131   www.ristorantelelfo.it

CAROVILLI
La Bacca Rara   restaurant, pizzeria   €€€, AIC
Via Fonte Curelli   tel. 339.3348900   www.labaccarara.it

CASTELMAURO
Parco delle Stelle   hotel, restaurant   €€, AIC
C.da Codarda   tel. 0874.744622   www.ricevimentiparcodellestelle.com

FORNELLI
Il Parco degli Ulivi   restaurant   €€€, AIC
Bivio Fornelli   tel. 0865.956662   www.ilparcodegliulivi.com

Le Terre del Sacramento
C.da Collefalcone

GUARDIALFIERA
agritourism
tel. 0874.1865813

€€€, AIC
www.leterredelsacramento.com

Solelago
C,da Difese delle Camerelle

restaurant, hotel
tel. 0874.840198

€€€, AIC
www.solelago.com

ISERNIA

Grand H. Europa
V.le dei Pentri, 76

hotel, restaurant
tel. 865.2126

€€€, AIC
www.grandhotel-europa.it

Il Forno di Chiara
Via Laurelli, 6

bakery
tel. 339.5703166

€, AIC

L'Affresco
C.so Marcelli

restaurant
tel. 0865.413836

€€€, AIC
www.ristoranteaffresco.com

Pasta & Pizza
Via XXIV Maggio II° Trav. 6

pizzeria
tel. 0865414549

€, AIC

LARINO

Agriturismo La Collinetta
C.da Colle di Lauro, 16

agritourism
tel. 348.9582862

AIC
www.agriturismocollinetta.com

LUCITO

Bar Biferno
C.da Giardini, 8

bar
tel. 340.6851424

€, AIC

MACCHIA D'ISERNIA

Vecchia Taverna
Via G. Marconi

restaurant, pizzeria
tel. 865.5566

€€-€€€, AIC
www.vecchiataverna.eu

MONTAQUILA

Il Giardinetto del Volturno
C.so 25 Archi, 13

restaurant, pizzeria
tel. 865.96504

€€-€€€, AIC

ORATINO

Ristorante Olmicello
Via Regina Margherita, 48

restaurant
tel. 874.38285

€€-€€€, AIC
www.ristoranteolmicello.com

PESCOPENNATARO

Parco Attrezzato l'Abete Bianco
Via Turistica snc

restaurant
tel. 0865.941180

€€, AIC
www.parcoabetebianco.com

POZZILLI

Hotel Dora
S.S. 85 Venafrana, km 24,600

hotel
tel. 0865.908006

AIC
www.hoteldora.it

RIPALIMOSANI

Celiaco.M SRL
c.da Selva, snc

sandwich shop, bakery
tel. 0874.701842

€, AIC

Cinecittà
via Madonna della Neve, 3

restaurant, pizzeria
tel. 328.4990465

AIC

ROCCAMANDOLFI

Masseria La Curea
C.da Curea s.n.

agritourism
tel. 340.0868596

AIC
www.agriturismolacurea.it

Pizzeria Da Paride
Via Cortina, 16

restaurant, pizzeria
tel. 0865.814517

€, AIC

TERMOLI

Basilico
Via Madonna delle Grazie, 48

pizzeria
tel. 3396514595

€, AIC

Il Binario dei Sapori
Via XXIV Maggio, 12

restaurant
tel. 0875.705645

AIC
lucaracano@libero.it

La Corte della Contessa di Porticone agritourism
via del Mare,1
tel. 0875.705248

€-€€, AIC
www.agriturismoporticone.it

La Quercia
Via Elba, 1

pizzeria
tel. 0875.707211

€ - €€€, AIC
www.pizzerialaquercia.it

Sognadoro
Via Mugnano Rocco, 3/a

restaurant/pizzeria
tel. 0875706442

€€ - €€€€, AIC

VASTOGIRARDI

Agrit. S. Mauro
Loc. San Mauro

agritourism
tel. 0865.836744

€€ - €€€€, AIC
www.agriturismosanmauro.it

Rifugio dei Briganti
Via San Felice

B&B
tel. 3343759773

AIC
www.ilrifugiodeibriganti.com

VENAFRO

Al Ghiottone
Via Acluzio Gallo, 3/a

restaurant, pizzeria
tel. 0865.909556

€€-€€€, AIC

Ristorante La Viuzza
Via Duomo, 13 zona laghetto

restaurant
tel. 0865.909190

€€-€€€, AIC

Ovid in Sulmona (D. Frost)

Angel and cross (D. Krauschar)

BASILICATA

(AIC = participates in the Associazione Italiana Celiachia program)

GRUMENTO NOVA

H. Park Grumentum	hotel, restaurant	€€, AIC
Contrada Traversiti	tel. 97565592	www.hotelparkgrumentum.com

MATERA

Alle Fornaci	restaurant	€€, AIC
P.zza Cesare Firrao, 7	tel. 0835335037	www.ristoranteallefornaci.it
Casa Vacanze del Corso	B&B	AIC
Via del Corso, 46	tel. 3934939569	www.bedandbreakfast.it
Sapere e Sapori	restaurant	€€€-€€€€, AIC
Via Dante, 54/56	tel. 0835256548	

MELFI

Sole di Mezzanotte	restaurant, pizzeria	€€, AIC
Via Cittadinanza Attiva	tel. 0972236819	

MONTICCHIO LAGHI

Lago Grande	restaurant, pizzeria	€€, AIC
Via Lago Grande	tel. 0972731181	

MURO LUCANO

Miramonti	hotel, restaurant	€-€€, AIC
C.da Fontanelle	tel. 09762657	

NOVA SIRI

Villaggio Giardini d'Oriente	resort, hotel, restaurant	AIC
Via Luci del Varietà	tel. 835.877684	www.giardinidoriente.com

La Sosta dei Cavalieri C.da Serralta, 12	<u>PICERNO</u> agritourism tel. 0971990035	€€, AIC
Hurricane Contrada Tora, c/o Lago Pantano	<u>PIGNOLA</u> restaurant, pizzeria tel. 0971486204	€, AIC
Il Gazebo C.da Tora, 17/bis	restaurant, pizzeria tel. 0971471471	€€, AIC
Blue Lion C/da Varco d'Izzo snc	<u>POTENZA</u> pizzeria, pub tel. 971.576	€-€€, AIC
Caffetteria Garibaldi C.so Garibaldi, 22	café tel. 3398108051	€€, AIC
Gambero Rosso V.le Dell'Unicef cc Galassia	restaurant, pizzeria tel. 0971470989 www.gamberorosso.apotenza.it	€, AIC
Pasticceria La Delizia Via del Gallitello, 265-267	bar, gelato tel. 971.444209	€, AIC
Pasticceria La Terrazza Via Umberto I°, 143	<u>RIONERO IN VULTURE</u> bakery, bar, gelato tel. 972.724187	€, AIC
Locanda al Giglio D'Oro C.da Serre S. Andrea	<u>RUVO DEL MONTE</u> restaurant tel. 097697516	€€, AIC
Tropical Via Medaglia d'Oro	<u>SAN CHIRICO NUOVO</u> restaurant, pizzeria tel. 0971731472	€, AIC
Agriturismo Tenuta Fortunato Contrada Serra della Pietra	<u>SENISE</u> agritourism tel. 3391825956 www.tenutafortunato.com	AIC

CALABRIA

(AIC = participates in the Associazione
Italiana Celiachia program)

Bistecca (D. Frost)

ACRI

Antico Rustico
V.co I Montessori, 40/42
restaurant, pizzeria
tel. 0984954432
€-€€, AIC

Il Carpaccio
C.da Cocozzello, 197/a
restaurant
tel. 0984949205
€€€, AIC
www.ilcarpaccio.it

Lulù
C.da Duglia, 226
restaurant, pizzeria
tel. 0984950695
€€-€€€, AIC

Panoramik
Via Alcide De Gasperi, 305
restaurant, pizzeria
tel. 0984941809
€€, AIC
www.residencepanoramik.com

AMANTEA

Hotel La Tonnara
Via Tonnara, 13
hotel, restaurant
tel. 0982424272
€€€€, AIC
www.latonnara.it

Il Sombrero
Via Lungomare
restaurant, pizzeria
tel. 0982428469
€€-€€€, AIC
www.ilsombrero.it

Mediterraneo Palace Hotel
Via Stromboli 79
hotel, restaurant
tel. 982.42209
AIC
www.mediterraneohotel.net

BADOLATO

Euro Bar 2000
gelato (€, AIC)
Via Nazionale, 180

BAGNARA CALABRA

Al Vecchio Teatro
Via Nastari 20
pizzeria
tel. 966.37159
€, AIC

G.H. Victoria
P.zza Marconi, 4
hotel
tel. 0966376126
€€€, AIC
www.victoriagrandhotel.it

Le Saie
Corso Garibaldi, 200
hotel
tel. 0966474412
€€€-€€€€, AIC
www.lesaie.it

Gelateria Capotirone

BELVEDERE M.MO
gelato (€, AIC)

Via Capo Tirone, 7

BOCALE SECONDO
B&B Casa Per Ferie da Nonno Ciccillo B&B
Viale Paolo Renosto   tel. 328.3722888

AIC

Baia Del Capo
Via Filippo Turati

BONIFATI
restaurant, pizzeria
tel. 3403722908

€-€€, AIC

Pietrabianca
C.da Sparvasile

restaurant, pizzeria
tel. 098296322

€, AIC
www.ristorantepietrabianca.com

Feudo degli Ulivi
Contrada Fiego

BORGIA
inn, restaurant
tel. 0961956435

€€€, AIC
www.feudodegliulivi.com

La Casa di Botro
Via Zaccagnini, 2

BOTRICELLO
agritourism
tel. 0961966592

€€-€€€, AIC

Gelateria Ficara

BOVA MARINA
gelato, bar (€, AIC)

Via Nazionale 51/53

La Perla Jonica
Loc. S. Pasquale

restaurant, pizzeria
tel. 0965.764366

€€-€€€, AIC

Hotel Tasso
Via Tasso - Camigliatello Silano

CAMIGLIATELLO
hotel
tel. 0984578113

€€, AIC
www.hoteltasso.it

Lido Dello Stretto
Via Risorgimento, 141

CAMPO CALABRO
restaurant, pizzeria
tel. 347.8820260

€€-€€€, AIC

La Principessa
SS 18

CAMPORA S. GIOVANNI
village, reception hall
tel. 098246903

€€, AIC
www.hotellaprincipessa.it

La Fattoria della Piana
Contrada Sovereto

CANDIDONI
agritourism
tel. 3481000710

€, AIC
www.fattoriadellapiana.it

Pedro's
Via S. Patrizi

CARIATI
restaurant, pizzeria
tel. 0983969311

€€, AIC

Blade Runner
Via Papa Giovanni XXIII

CASTROLIBERO
pizzeria
tel. 0984852859

€, AIC

Antica Trattoria
Via Padre Francesco Russo

CASTROVILLARI
restaurant, pizzeria
tel. 981.22604

€-€€, AIC

La Falconara
Via Falconara - contr. Pietà

hotel, restaurant
tel. 098144109

€€-€€€, AIC
www.lafalconarahotel.it

Mordi & Fuggi
Viale Umberto Caldora 23

restaurant, pizzeria
tel. 0981.48001 9

€-€€, AIC

Palm Tavern Pub
P.zza Indipendenza, 8
sandwich shop
tel. 3342626695
€, AIC

Sottosopra/Bar Marilyn
Via Roma, 101
pub, bar
tel. 098121600
€, AIC

CATANZARO

Agriturismo Raffaella
Contrada Comunale di Petrini
agritourism
tel. 0961761747
€€€, AIC
www.agriturismoraffaella.it

Ai Reduci
C.da Sangue di Cristo loc. Siano
agritourism
tel. 0961469771
€€, AIC

Bacchus
V.le dei Normanni, 57
restaurant
tel. 0961753013
€€, AIC

Il Gufo
Via V. Gattoleo, 5 loc. Pitera
sandwich shop
tel. 0961741650
€, AIC

Magic Pub
Via Fiume Busento 130/a
pizzeria
tel. 3397014532
€-€€, AIC

CATANZARO LIDO

Albatros
Via T. Gulli 33
restaurant/pizzeria
tel. 0961738316
€, AIC
www.ristorantealbatros.it

Bausan
gelato (€, AIC)
Via Bausan, 15/17

Happy Pizza
Via Caprera, 395
tavola calda, pizzeria
tel. 380.3641913
€-€€, AIC

Tortuga Pub
Via Lungomare, 289
restaurant, pizzeria sandwich shop
tel. 0961360008
€, AIC

CATONA-REGGIO CALABRIA

Regent Hotel della Cisca
Via Mercato, 9
hotel, restaurant, pizzeria catering
tel. 0965301067
€€, AIC
www.regenthotel.rc.it

CAULONIA

Agriturismo Feudo Gagliardi
C.da Stincuso
agritourism, restaurant
tel. 964.84621
AIC
www.feudogagliardi.it

CETRARO

Voglia di Pizza
Via Lungo Aron
pizzeria
tel. 098291960
€, AIC
www.vogliadipizzaglutenfree.com

CITTANOVA

Il RE Leone
Via Bruzio, 19
pizzeria
tel. 0966.655583
€-€€, AIC

COLOSIMI

Blue Moon
Via Stazione, 1
pizzeria
tel. 0984963198
€, AIC

CORIGLIANO CALABRO

Il Sombrero
Via Berlinguer
restaurant, pizzeria
tel. 3392850724
€, AIC

La Corte
via S. Giovanni Evangelista
restaurant, pizzeria
tel. 0983.887305
€€-€€€, AIC

CORIGLIANO SCALO

Villaggio Airone Resort
Località Scavolino

resort
tel. 0983547140

AIC

COSENZA

A Cannarutia
C.da S. Pietro - Donnici Superiore

restaurant, pizzeria
tel. 0984781856

€€, AIC

Al Vicoletto
Via Simonetta, 7-9-11

restaurant
tel. 0984791609

€-€€€€, AIC

Da Tonino
Via Alimena, 125

tavola calda, catering
tel. 09841811285

€, AIC

Italy srl

gelato (€, AIC)

Via Caloprese 123

CROPANI MARINA

Prima o Poi
L.tà Sena Vill. Mimosa

restaurant, pizzeria
tel. 0961960944

€€€-€€€€, AIC

San Marco
V.le Venezia, sn

restaurant, pizzeria
tel. 0961962127

€€-€€€, AIC

CROTONE

B&B Villa Ermenegilda
Via dei Gelsomini 74

restaurant, B&B
tel. 0962.930209

AIC
www.villaermenegilda.it

Bar - Pizzeria Degli Amici
Via Nazioni Unite, 47

pizzeria bar
tel. 0962962330

€, AIC

Capriccio
Via Mario Nicoletta, 176-178

restaurant, pizzeria
tel. 3289164833

€, AIC

Il Convivio di Hera
Via Capo Colonna, 103

hotel, restaurant
tel. 0962934153

€€€€, AIC
www.conviviodihera.it

Le Lanterne
S.S. 106 Km.247

restaurant, pizzeria
tel. 347.2224840

€-€€, AIC

Lido degli Scogli
V.le Magna Grecia

inn, pizzeria, restaurant
tel. 096228625

€€€€, AIC
www.albergolidodegliscogli.com

Pepe Nero
via Regina Margherita 23/25

restaurant, pizzeria
tel. 962.24847

€-€€, AIC

Zzà Rosì
Via A. Tedeschi, 81

restaurant, pizzeria
tel. 0962900422

€€, AIC

Blob Il Gelato
Ice Cream

gelato (€, AIC)
gelato (€, AIC)

Via Napoli, 30
V.le Gramsci, 96

DECOLLATURA

Cardel
Villaggio Cesariello

hotel, restaurant
tel. 096861334

€€-€€€, AIC
www.hotelcardel.com

La Vecchia Fattoria
Loc. Sorbello

agritourism
tel. 096861815

€€-€€€, AIC
www.agriturismolavecchiafattoria.it

DIAMANTE

Gel. Come Una Volta

gelato (€, AIC)

Via Mazzini

Hotel Cristina
c/da Pietrarossa, 24

hotel, restaurant
tel. 098581210

€€, AIC
www.cristinahotel.com

FALERNA

Hotel Torino
S.S. 18
hotel, restaurant
tel. 096893053
€, AIC
www.hotel-torino.org

Ristorante Hotel Sagapò
Via Vittoria 8
hotel, restaurant
tel. 968.97124
AIC
www.ristorantehotelsagapo.it

FEROLETO ANTICO

Il Casale Osteria Tipica
Contrada Malaspina
restaurant, pizzeria
tel. 0968455023
€€-€€€, AIC

FUSCALDO

L'Etoile
gelato   (€, AIC)
Piazza Marconi, 18

Solero Beach
C.da Valle Santa Maria
pizzeria
tel. 0982618200
€, AIC

GALLICO MARINA

Bar Gardenia Gelateria
gelato   (€, AIC)
Via Quarnaro 1,traversa,Mar ra 17/e

La Madonnina
Via Marina, 37
restaurant, pizzeria
tel. 0965370023
€, AIC

GALLINA R.C.

Royal Garden
Via Provinciale 218
restaurant
tel. 0965682703
€€€-€€€€, AIC
www.royalgarden.it

Windy Hill
P.zza S. Francesco di Sales
restaurant, pizzeria
tel. 0965682656
€-€€€, AIC
www.ristorantewindyhill.it

GASPERINA

Paladina
Via Sandro Pertini
restaurant, pizzeria
tel. 096748094
€, AIC
www.ristorantelapaladina.it

Park H. Mirabeau
C.da Pilinga
hotel, restaurant
tel. 0967577656
€€€, AIC

GIOIA TAURO

L'antica Ciambra
Via Lungomare
restaurant, pizzeria
tel. 3476207978
€, AIC

GIOIOSA JONICA MARINA

Golosia
gelato (€, AIC)
Piazza Zaleuco

GIRIFALCO

Parco Attrez. Monte Covello
Via Montecovello
restaurant, pizzeria
tel. 0968749515
€€€, AIC

Re Artù Pizzeria
Via 3° Vico Fratelli Bandiera 5
pizzeria
tel. 0968.748811
€, AIC

GIZZERIA LIDO

L'Oasi
Contrada Mortella
restaurant
tel. 0968466181
€€€-€€€€, AIC

ISOLA CAPO RIZZUTO

Baia degli Dei
loc. Annunziata Le Castella
hotel
tel. 0962.795235
AIC
www.baiadeglidei.com

LAMETIA TERME

Bram Hotel
Via Del Mare
hotel, restaurant
tel. 968.51598
AIC
www.bramhotel.it

Parva Domus
Via D'Audino 19

B&B
tel. 0968.436352

AIC
www.bebparvadomus.com

Sapori senza glutine
Via Della Vittoria

sandwich shop, bakery
tel. 3895682260

€€, AIC

LAMEZIA TERME

A Ruga
Via S. Giovanni

restaurant
tel. 096825486

€€-€€€, AIC

Associazione Accademia Della Pizza Italiana La Brace restaurant, pizzeria
Via G. Murat

tel. 0968.453610

€€, AIC

LAUROPOLI DI CASSANO

Arnold's
Via Paolino Chidichimo

pizzeria
tel. 3336801558

€ - €€, AIC

LAZZARO

La Cascina Calipso
Via Nazionale Fornaci

restaurant, pizzeria
tel. 0965.676017

€-€€, AIC

L'Antico Casale
S.S. 106, 261

restaurant, pizzeria
tel. 0965714146

€-€€€, AIC

LOCRI

Winter Cactus
C.so Vitt. Emanuele, 87

restaurant, pizzeria
tel. 3384396246

€, AIC

LONGOBARDI

La Collina Verde
S.S.182

restaurant, pizzeria
tel. 348.1225026

€-€€, AIC

MAIDA

La Coccinella

gelato (€, AIC)

Via Nazionale, 8

MAIERATO

Popilia country resort
Località Cutà s.s. 110 km 1

hotel, restaurant
tel. 0963.264252

€€-€€€, AIC
www.popiliaresort.it

MALVITO

La Cambusa
C.da Peiorata 9

pizzeria
tel. 347.7849567

€-€€, AIC

MANDATORICCIO

Castello Flotta
Località Procello

restaurant
tel. 983.90889

€€-€€€, AIC

MARINA DI GIOIOSA JONICA

Gambero Rosso
Via Montezemolo, 65/67

restaurant
tel. 0964415806

€€€€, AIC

MELIA DI S. ROBERTO

La Locanda di Marcello
Via Purgatorio

hotel, restaurant
tel. 0965755407

€€-€€€, AIC
www.lalocandadimarcello.it

MELITO PORTO SALVO

L'Angelo Biondo
Via Madonnuzza, 5

restaurant, pizzeria
tel. 3450661905

€€, AIC

Black Bar Rist. Pizz. Via Spadolini	**MIRTO CROSIA** restaurant, pizzeria tel. 983.42798	€-€€, AIC
Villa Santa Caterina Via Garigliano	**MONTALTO UFFUGO** agritourism, restaurant tel. 0984934433	€€-€€€, AIC www.agriturismovillasantacaterina.it
Costaraba Via delle Mandrelle	**MONTAURO SCALO** restaurant, pizzeria tel. 0961578800	€ - €€, AIC ristorantecostaraba@gmail.com
Lido On The Beach Calalunga	restaurant, pizzeria bar tel. 567577351	€€, AIC
Il Capriccio Via Nazionale, 229	**MONTEPAONE LIDO** restaurant, pizzeria tel. 0967576654	€, AIC
Il Ghiottone Via Mazzini, 38	restaurant, pizzeria tel. 0967576837	€, AIC
Al Convento Via Vincenzo Severini, 1	**MORANO CALABRO** restaurant, pizzeria tel. 09811896138	€, AIC
Chalet Rocco Località Campotenese	B&B tel. 098133992	AIC www.chaletrocco.com
Green House Contrada Barbalonga	B&B tel. 3493536413	AIC www.greenhousebb.it
Hotel Regina C.da Campotenese	hotel, restaurant, pizzeria tel. 098133768	€-€€, AIC www.reginahotel.calabria.it
L'Accademia L.re Cicerone - Lazzaro	**MOTTA SAN GIOVANNI** restaurant tel. 0965714132	€-€€, AIC
Brivido Gelat. Artigianale	**PAOLA** gelato (€, AIC)	C.so Garibaldi, 35
Il Pavone Via della Libertà, 8	pizzeria tel. 0982583661	€, AIC
Pa Pla P.zza del Popolo, 2	sandwich shop tel. 0982611080	€, AIC
Sancho Panza Via Sant'Agata, 38	restaurant, pizzeria tel. 0982612155	€€, AIC
La Collina degli Ulivi Via Martorara, 2	**PELLARO** trattoria tel. 3336292558	€€-€€€, AIC
Mamas Via Quattronari, 14	pizzeria tel. 0965.35838	€, AIC
Tahiti Via Nazionale Trav.H 20	pizzeria, ice cream tel. 0965350342	€, AIC

PIANETTE DI ROVITO

New Number One
Via A. Gramsci 10

pizzeria
tel. 0984.433653

€-€€, AIC

PIZZO CALABRO

Hale Bopp
Via A. Anile, 8

restaurant
tel. 0963532259

€€, AIC

Corallini
Gelateria Enrico
Gelateria Ercole
Il Tartufo Domenico Penna

gelato (€, AIC)
gelato   (€, AIC)
gelato (€, AIC)
gelato (€, AIC)

Via Lung.re C. Colombo
Via Prangi 104 Loc. Marinella
P.zza Della Repubblica, 18
Via S. Sebastiano

POLISTENA

Il Gusto
Via On. Luigi Longo 81

restaurant, pizzeria
tel. 0966932999

€, AIC

Miaglut
Via Perugia 12

bakery, rotisserie
tel. 0966.935210

€, AIC

PRAIA A MARE

Escopocodise ra
Via Leonardo Da Vinci 20

pizzeria
tel. 3406523131

€, AIC

REGGIO CALABRIA

Armacà
contradà armacà

restaurant, pizzeria
tel. 965.48765

€€, AIC

Baylik
Via Vico Leone, 1-3-5

restaurant
tel. 096548624

€€€, AIC

Bridge Lounge Pub
Via Sbarre C.li, 775 (Ponte S. Agata)

pub
tel. 0965025504

€, AIC

Caffetteria Biesse
c/o la Fac. di Archit.-salita Melissari

tavola calda
tel. 0965800213

€, AIC

E' Hotel
Via Giunchi, 6

hotel, restaurant
tel. 0965893000

€€€, AIC
www.ehotelreggiocalabria.it

El Puente
Via Sbarre Centrali, 765

pizzeria
tel. 0965594465

€, AIC

Gelateria Bar Mckenzye   gelato (€, AIC) Via Giudecca 15, 1° tratto Tapis Roulant

Il Rusticone
Via S. Caterina, 29

pizzeria
tel. 096544433

€, AIC

Le Specialità Senza Glutine
Via Antonio Cimino, 54

restaurant, pizzeria
tel. 0965324461

€, AIC

Mamas
Viale Calabria 349

pizzeria
tel. 0965626000

€, AIC
wwwpizzeriamamas.it

Pizza New
Via Guglielmo Pepe 12/a

restaurant, pizzeria
tel. 0965324461

€, AIC

Pizza Roma
Via San Francesco Da Paola 24

pizzeria
tel. 0965.951278

€, AIC

Pizzeria Spaccanapoli
Via Fata Morgana 3/5

pizzeria
tel. 0965.312276

€, AIC

Zero Glut bakery, pizza, rotisserie €, AIC
Via Ipponio 99 tel. 3480127619

RENDE

Giòpasticceria bakery, pizza, rotisserie €, AIC
Via Leonardo Da Vinci 80 tel. 331.9026612

La Cantina del Contadino agritourism €, AIC
Via Rocchi, 3 tel. 0984403679 www.agriturismoquercia.com

La Conca d'Oro gelato (€, AIC) Via Modigliani-S. Agostino

Nonsolopizza pizzeria €, AIC
Via G. Dechirico 121 tel. 0984.466579

Palagarden restaurant, pizzeria €, AIC
C.da Marchesino - Parco Robinson tel. 0984464529

S. Francesco hotel €€, AIC
Via Ungaretti, 2 tel. 0984461721 www.hsf.it

RICADI

Hotel Incoronato hotel, restaurant €€-€€€, AIC
Via Grotticello Loc. S. Nicolò tel. 0963663428 www.hotelgrotticelle.it

Villaggio Hotel Tonicello hotel AIC
Contrada Capo Vaticano tel. 0963663724 wwwtonicello.com

Villaggio Pineta Petto Bianco hotel, restaurant €€, AIC
Contrada Campia tel. 0963665768 www.villaggiopettobianco.it

RIZZICONI

Borgo Cariati bakery €, AIC
Via Risorgimento S.S, 111 tel. 0966.046258

ROCCABERNARDA

Al Favaloro restaurant, pizzeria €€-€€€€, AIC
Via dei Bizantini, 13 tel. 096256551

Fish market (J. Kelly)

ROCCELLA JONICA

La Cascina
S.S. 106

restaurant, pizzeria
tel. 0964866675

€€€, AIC

La Taverna di Bacco
Via Orlando, 5

restaurant, pizzeria
tel. 096485666

€, AIC

L'Angelo Dolce

gelato (€, AIC)

Via Roma, 55

Parco dei Principi
C.da Badessa

hotel
tel. 0964860201   www.parcodeiprincipi-roccella.com

AIC

Ranch Sound
C.da Canne

restaurant, pizzeria
tel. 0964863389

€€, AIC

ROGLIANO

Il Girasole
Viale Stazione 16

B&B
tel. 0984.982025

AIC

ROMBIOLO

Il Casolare
Loc. Romanò str.prov. Nicotera

agritourism
tel. 3401512890

€€-€€€, AIC
www.agriturismo-ilcasolare.com

ROSE

Caravaggio
C/da Petraro

pizzeria, restaurant
tel. 0984993327

€, AIC

ROSSANO SCALO

Il Drago
Via Ippocrate, 24

restaurant, pizzeria
tel. 0983512189

€, AIC

Pascia'
Contrada Cutura

restaurant, pizzeria
tel. 0983565493

€€€, AIC

SALINE JONICHE

Le Agavi
Via Fucidà 2

agritourism, restaurant, pizzeria
tel. 0965782371

€, AIC
www.leagavi.net

Naif
Via Nazionale, 195

restaurant, pizzeria
tel. 0965772968

€, AIC

SAN FERDINANDO

Le Dune Blu
Località Baia dei Pini

resort
tel. 0966.766649

AIC

SAN FILI

Il Carro
Via Gramsci

agritourism
tel. 3492439940

€, AIC
www.agriturismo-ilcarro.it

SAN GIOVANNI IN FIORE

Brillo Parlante
Via Lungo Lago Lorica

restaurant
tel. 984537282

€, AIC

Da Paura
Via Fiume Lese 36

restaurant, pizzeria
tel. 0984.970025

€€, AIC

Hotel Biafora
Contrada Garga, 9

hotel, restaurant
tel. 0984970014

€€-€€€, AIC
www.hotelbiafora.it

Hotel Duchessa Della Sila
Viale della Republica 461

hotel, restaurant, pizzeria
tel. 0984.915522

AIC
www.duchessadellasila.it

La Pirainella restaurant, pizzeria €€, AIC
Via G.A. Lopez tel. 0984.970579

L'angolo Del Gusto pizzeria €, AIC
Via Roma tel. 984913038

SAN LUCIDO

Eat and Drink pizzeria, sandwich shop €, AIC
Corso Umberto, I tel. 098284705

Rist.Dragut/H. La Fortezza hotel, restaurant €€€, AIC
Via Marina Taverna, 22 tel. 0982848784 www.residencelafortezza.it

SAN MARCO ARGENTANO

L'Etoile gelato (€, AIC) P.zza Selvaggi

L'Europa restaurant, pizzeria €, AIC
C.da Iotta tel. 0984522028

SAN NICOLA ARCELLA

Il Furano restaurant €€, AIC
C.da Marinella tel. 0985300644

SAN SOSTENE

Residence Paradise restaurant, pizzeria €€€, AIC
Via delle Magnolie tel. 096771648

SAN VINCENZO LA COSTA

La Locanda del Greco agritourism €€, AIC
C.da Greco Battista, 15 tel. 0984936615

SANGINETO

Sachsenhausen restaurant, pizzeria €€, AIC
S.S. 18 n° 41 tel. 098296378

SAN STEFANO D'ASPROMONTE

B&B Musolino-La Civetta restaurant €, AIC
Via Nazionale Cucullaro tel. 0965740304

Le Fate dei Fiori hotel, restaurant AIC
Via Nazionale, 53 tel. 0965749015 www.lefatedeifiori.it

Rifugio Husky restaurant, pizzeria €€, AIC
Via degli Abeti - Gambarie tel. 3492351243

SANTA CATERINA DELLO JONIO

Excalibur restaurant, pizzeria €€-€€€, AIC
Via delle Serre, 21/23 tel. 096783407

SATRIANO

Fuego pizzeria €, AIC
Viale Europa, 196 tel. 0967620148

La Villa B&B AIC
Via S. Bruno da Colonia tel. 09674059193

SCALEA

Albergo Residence Villa Brazzano hotel, restaurant AIC
Via Foresta 11 tel. 0985.939895 www.forestvillabrazzano.it

Hotel Talao hotel €, AIC
C.so Mediterraneo, 66 tel. 098520444 www.hoteltalao.it

SCILLA

Krataiis
Via G. Oriccioli, 26
restaurant
tel. 0965754022
€€€€, AIC

SETTINGIANO

L'Orso Cattivo
Contrada Gambieri
restaurant, pizzeria
tel. 0961998149
€€, AIC

SIDERNO

Hotel President
S.S. 106
hotel, restaurant
tel. 0964343191
€€, AIC
www.grandhotelpresident.com

La Mimosa
Via Mediterraneo, 78
restaurant, pizzeria
tel. 0964342303
€-€€, AIC

SORBO SAN BASILE

Il Faro
Contrada Cutura
restaurant
tel. 0961921214
€€, AIC

SOVERATO

Al Marinaio
Via Cristoforo Colombo, 16
pizzeria
tel. 096721233
€, AIC

Bar Morè
gelato (€, AIC)
Via Chiarello Poliporto

Braxtor
Via Marina, 24/30
pizzeria
tel. 0967528456
€, AIC

La Tavola di Melusinda
Via della Vittoria, 1/3
restaurant
tel. 3493766493
€€-€€€, AIC

Pizzeria Da Benito
Via F. Cilea 64
pizzeria
tel. 3383959754
€-€€, AIC

SPADOLA

La Fontanella Rist. Pizz.
Località Cannella ss 110
restaurant, pizzeria
tel. 963.70136
€-€€, AIC

SPEZZANO DELLA SILA

La Pignanella
C.da Molarotta- Camigliatello S.no
restaurant
tel. 0984.578443
€€-€€€, AIC

STALETTÌ

Baia dell'Est
Via Caminia
hotel, restaurant
tel. 0961911352
€€€, AIC
www.baiadellest.it

Hotel Club Poseidon
Via Lido di Copanello, 12
hotel, reception hall
tel. 0961911252
€€-€€€, AIC
www.hotelresidenceposeidon.it

Ristorante la baia di Caminia
Via del Mare 2
restaurant, pizzeria
tel. 0961.911093
€€-€€€, AIC

STECCATO DI CUTRO

Villaggio Serenè
Loc. Marinella
resort
tel. 962.77
AIC
www.bluserena.it

TAURIANOVA

La Cucciarda
Contrada Pegara
restaurant, pizzeria
tel. 0966612766
€€, AIC

Metropolis' Pizza
C.da Crocicchia c/o Parco
restaurant, pizzeria
tel. 0966645073
€€, AIC

Scionti Francesco Pasticceria gelato (€, AIC) Via Roma, 55

TAVERNA

Hotel Sila hotel, restaurant €€, AIC
Via Villaggio Mancuso tel. 0961922032

TERRANOVA DA SIBARI

Hostaria Antico Borgo restaurant, pizzeria €€, AIC
Viale Castello 17 tel. 0981955964

TORTORA MARINA

La Locanda del Corso B&B AIC
C.so Aldo Moro, 87/91 tel. 0985766849 info@lalocandadelcorso.it

TREBISACCE

Capraro pizzeria €, AIC
Via 25 Aprile, 36 tel. 098158281

TRENTA

Lucignolo pizzeria €, AIC
Via F. Gullo 60 tel. 0984.439871

TROPEA

Da Nico e Lilly restaurant, pizzeria AIC
Via Orazio Toraldo Di Francia tel. 3930037114 www.ristorantedanicoelillytropea.it

VIBO MARINA

Birreria Tato's restaurant, pizzeria €, AIC
Via Longobardi, 15 tel. 0963571530

La Rada restaurant AIC
Via A. Vespucci tel. 0963.577030 www.ristorantelidolarada.com

VIBO VALENTIA

Glut Word tavola calda €, AIC
Via Dante Alighieri tel. 330982495

Ristorante Pizzeria Terravecchia restaurant, pizzeria €-€€, AIC
Via Terravecchia 184 tel. 3283796701

VILLA S.GIOVANNI

De la Ville hotel, restaurant €€-€€€, AIC
Via Ammiraglio Curzon tel. 0965795600 www.grandhoteldelaville.eu

Il Gallo D'Oro restaurant, pizzeria €€-€€€, AIC
Via Roma, 81 tel. 0965.752258

VILLAPIANA

Orto della Signora restaurant, pizzeria €€, AIC
C.da Orto della Signora tel. 0981505688 www.ortodellasignora.it

ZAMBRONE

Hotel La Praia hotel, restaurant AIC
Via Del Mare tel. 0963.392086 www.lapraia.it

Cioccolati di Pasqua (J.Kelly)

SAN MARINO
(AIC = participates in the Associazione Italiana Celiachia program)

DOGANA

Dell'Angelo   restaurant, pizzeria   €-€€€, AIC
Via 3 Settembre, 65   tel. 0549941292
Notes: Closed Fridays.

DOMAGNANO

Pizza Leggera   pizzeria   €, AIC
Str. Di Paderna, 2   tel. 0549909608
Notes: DS Pizza Point. Closed Mondays.

SAN GIOVANNI-BORGO MAGGIORE

Boschetto   restaurant, pizzeria   €-€€€, AIC
Strada San Gianno, 97   tel. 0549878450
Notes: DS Pizza Point. Closed Mondays.

SAN MARINO

H. La Rocca R. Il Beccafico   hotel, restaurant   €-€€€, AIC
Via Salita alla Rocca, 35   tel. 549991166

Index

Index

Index

Index

Index